A BESTSELLING BOOK
AN ACADEMY AWARD
WINNING FILM
A RIVETING STORY OF
MULTIPLE PERSONALITIES!

"ONCE IN A BLUE MOON A BOOK HITS YOU LIKE THIS ONE. It is the fantastic true story of a young housewife who was three women in one body . . . more fascinating and suspenseful than most novels. AN UNFORGETTABLE EXPERIENCE."
—*Chicago Tribune*

"Engrossing from the first headache to the last shriek."
—*Indianapolis Star*

"Rarely does medical history—or fact of any nature—attain the suspense and interest found in THE THREE FACES OF EVE. No subject can be more fascinating."
—*Kansas City Star*

ABOUT THE AUTHORS

Both Drs. Thigpen and Cleckley are native Georgians and both took their medical degrees at the Medical College of Georgia. Dr. Thigpen is now Associate Clinical Professor of Psychiatry and Neurology at the Medical College of Georgia and a member of the Psychiatric Staff at the University Hospital in Augusta.

Dr. Cleckley is a Diplomate of the American Board of Psychiatry and Neurology and a Fellow of the American Psychiatric Association and of the American College of Physicians. He was Professor of Psychiatry and Neurology at the Medical College of Georgia from 1937 to 1955. He is at present Clinical Professor of Psychiatry and Neurology at the Medical College of Georgia and Chief of the Psychiatric Service at the University Hospital. He is the author of *The Mask of Sanity,* a study of the psychopathic personality.

In 1954 Drs. Thigpen and Cleckley wrote a technical article, "A Case of Multiple Personality," for the *Journal of Abnormal and Social Psychology*. This appeared before they had completed the work on the case. *The Three Faces of Eve* is an extension of that collaboration—a complete account of this extraordinary case which is likely to engage the lay reader's interest as vividly as that of physicians and professional workers in psychology and sociology.

THE 3 FACES OF EVE

CORBETT H. THIGPEN

and

HERVEY M. CLECKLEY

POPULAR LIBRARY • NEW YORK

TO LOUISE MARTIN CLECKLEY

Who was often called into service as psychiatrist to both of us through the bewildering years while we were treating this patient. Often the effort of two men seemed not quite adequate to deal with the three faces of this problem. For the contribution of a woman's understanding to our work and for true collaboration in presenting this study we are immeasurably grateful.

ACKNOWLEDGEMENTS

It is our pleasure to express appreciation to several people who in various capacities generously and ably assisted us in gathering the extensive material on which this study is based, in editing our manuscript, in reading proof, in carrying out technical examinations, and in other ways. Among these are Dr. Fred B. Thigpen, Dr. Allen Turner, Dr. Lester Bowles, Dr. Julius Johnson, Dr. B. F. Moss, Dr. W. P. Robison, Dr. John Manter, Dr. Leopold Winter, Captain Ward Atherton, Mr. Joseph B. Cumming, Mr. B. C. Thigpen, Mr. Edison Marshall, Mrs. Victor E. O'Neill, Mr. James F. Fulghum, Dr. Charles Osgood, Dr. Zella Luria, Mrs. Mary C. Dolan, Mrs. Louise Chambers Thigpen, Mr. Jack Woods, Mr. Lee Barrett, Miss Anne Jamison, Mrs. Jacqueline Williford, Mrs. Cornelia C. Fulghum, and Miss Maud Barragan.

We are particularly grateful to Dr. J. McV. Hunt for the invaluable help and encouragement he has given us in the preparation of this study since its early stages.

FOREWORD

Although multiple personality is a rarity in psychopathology, it poses more dramatically than any other set of phenomena the enormity of the task of conceptualizing personality organization. This challenge emerges, however, only when the behavioral phenomena of multiple personality are made clear.

Clinical observers who can see the nuances of behavioral transformations and describe them with literary skill are as rare as cases of multiple personality. For the first time, the exigencies of chance have brought together these two rarities. In his celebrated Beauchamp case, Morton Prince, founder of the *Journal of Abnormal and Social Psychology*, presented the phenomena of multiple personality in good case reporting and attempted to explain them, after the fact, with mentalistic concepts.* Shepard Ivory Franz did this again in his book.† In *Dr. Jekyll and Mr. Hyde*, Robert Louis Stevenson built a literary classic on this theme, but the phenomena were imaginary. In this book, Dr. Cleckley and Dr. Thigpen do something more than have any of their predecessors. They cast their clinical observations, wonderful in their acuteness, their detail and their connection with theoretical issues, into delightful prose.

In this book, "you are there." You are, in dramatic effect, with Eve White in the consulting room. You apprehend the transformations of facial and bodily expression, gesture, and speech that bring Eve Black "out." Later, you are with Jane. You share the perplexity of Eve's husband experiencing, in alternation, two highly different characters in one wife. You share the perplexity of the nurses and the interns in the hospital when they first witness the phenomenon of the transformation. You share the astonishment and puzzlement of the authors, who are hardheaded clinical observers, as the drama of the case unfolds. You face with them

---

* Prince, M.: *The Disassociation of a Personality*. New York: Longmans, Green, 1906.

† Franz, S. I.: *Persons, One and Three: A Study in Multiple Personalities*. New York and London: McGraw-Hill, Whittlesey House, 1933.

the human, the therapeutic, and the theoretical issues so dramatically posed by the case story. These authors present their clinical experience as would a highly skilled novelist; they neither make a case report nor do they write a novel, for the truth is far more challenging than fiction.

A brief first report of this case came to me as the editor of the *Journal of Abnormal and Social Psychology*, where the Beauchamp case had once appeared.* As was customary, I sent the piece on to a consultant for an independent evaluation. This consultant was Professor Gordon Allport. His response read: "By the shades of Morton Prince, do not let this piece escape the pages of the *Journal*." Needless to say, the piece did not escape.

It was also my privilege to introduce Professor Charles Osgood and his Semantic Differential to Drs. Cleckley and Thigpen. It is theoretically both interesting and important that in a blind analysis this instrument for measuring the meanings that we proverbially "carry around in our heads" clearly brought out the differences among the three "faces of Eve," whereas such customary clinical tools as tests of intelligence and the Rorschach test failed to differentiate them at all.

When neurophysiologists, psychologists, psychiatrists, and sociologists achieve a coherent and connected theory of multiple personality, they shall have gone a long way in understanding personality and its organization. This book poses and dramatizes the issues as nothing else has. It is a high privilege to be permitted to introduce you, the reader, to this most delightful treat in the psychopathological literature of the mid-twentieth century.

J. McV. Hunt
Past President,
American Psychological Association

---

* Prince, M.: Miss Beauchamp—the theory of the psychogeneses of multiple personality. *J. abnorm. Psychol.*, 1920, 15, 82-135.

CHAPTER 1

She did not at first appear to be an unusual or a particularly interesting patient. This neat, colorless young woman was, she said quietly, twenty-five years of age. In a level, slightly monotonous voice she described the severe headaches from which she had suffered now for several months and for which she had been unable to obtain relief. Unlike some patients to whom the elastic term *neurotic* is applied, she did not say that the pain was "unbearable," or that it was "as if an ax were splitting her skull." Nor did she otherwise take a histrionic role in telling her troubles. Without emphasis she described the attacks.

Demure and poised, she sat with her feet close together, speaking clearly but in soft, low tones. Her dark hair and pale blue eyes were distinctly pretty, though she seemed too retiring and inert to utilize, or even to be very clearly aware of, her good features and her potential attractiveness.

Her local physician had sent her from her home in a town approximately a hundred miles away for psychiatric consultation. Ordinary physical examinations, X-ray and laboratory studies, had disclosed no cause of the headaches. This superlatively calm, utterly self-controlled little figure of propriety showed no suggestion of anything that the layman might think of as *nervousness*. Her hands lay still on the arms of her chair as she spoke. Her head and shoulders drooped just a little. So thorough was her quality of gentle formality that it was difficult to believe that her eyes might ever flash in merriment, that she could ever have told a joke, or that even as a child, she could have teased anyone in some spontaneous outburst of feeling.

She spoke of serious problems in her life and without evasion discussed a situation that might cause distress, perplexity, worry, and frustration for any person of normal feelings. Six years ago she had married a young man. He was a faithful and serious member of the Catholic Church. As a Baptist, serious too in her own religion, she had had misgivings about the oath she was required to take, an oath promising that her children would be carefully brought up as Catholics.

9

Despite these misgivings she had so committed herself and had intended to carry out the solemn agreement.

At the first interview she admitted that she could not bring herself to send her little girl, Bonnie, to her husband's church and to tell her that here was to be found the truth and the only truth, about life's final and deepest problems. She wanted Bonnie to go to Sunday school and to have all the benefits of religion, but she feared that her promise of some years ago would force the little girl into something she might not voluntarily accept if she could be given freedom of choice until she attained sufficient age and experience to consider such matters maturely. She had stubbornly refused to have her child baptized in the Catholic Church. Her mother and father took an active part in the contention between husband and wife, repeatedly urging her not to give in. Her husband had argued that if Bonnie went to the Baptist Sunday school she would be similarly indoctrinated in that faith and hence no better prepared to make a truly impartial decision for herself later in life.

Mrs. White discussed this problem not as one who is argumentative or fanatical about religion but with the real perplexity of a meek, conscientious person who is overwhelmed by a distressing dilemma. This young mother's sense of guilt and shame in failing to carry out her vow seemed genuine. Prior to the marriage, despite a deep reluctance, she had been able to promise in all sincerity that any children she might bear would be raised strictly according to the rules of her husband's church. Now, with little Bonnie not a generality but an actual girl of three years, she could not, as she expressed it, turn her only child over to an institution that seemed ever more alien and inhospitable. As time passed she apparently had tended to identify all her husband's faults and all sources of contention between them with his church.

Mrs. White did not spontaneously heap blame upon her husband or hold him alone responsible for the sorrows and difficulties of their marriage. In fact, she took pains to defend him and offered magnanimous explanations for some of his attitudes and actions that had made her suffer considerably. With encouragement and unhurried persuasion she reluctantly gave some details of the quarreling that had become habitual. Her husband, she said, had seldom been able to show affection or even friendliness toward her during the last few months. Often he seemed to her irritable or sarcastic. Sometimes she could not tell what had offended him and she found herself puzzled about the nature of his complaints. She finally admitted that on one occasion, quite unlike himself, he had struck her. Though it was apparently only a light slap administered in exasperation, her feelings had been deeply hurt.

It was almost impossible to imagine this gentle little woman raising her voice in anger or participating aggressively in a personal argument. Her deep and genuine humility seemed to enforce a meekness upon her that one felt might even prove a serious handicap in what lay ahead. Something about her also suggested a few of the admirable qualities implied in the Christian principle of turning the other cheek. This was a woman, it seemed, not lacking in spirit, but who would not be likely to assert herself actively in opposition to another. Surely it must be an unusual man who would lose his temper with this unprovocative, unvengeful woman. What were the grounds for his anger?

"He must have his reasons," she granted thoughtfully. "I am not quite sure what it is I do that aggravates him so." She hesitated, then sadly admitted, "I've never seemed to make him happy."

He had apparently lost most of the sexual interest he had once felt for her. Never, she confessed with regret, had she been able to reach an orgasm or any sort of exciting fulfillment in their marriage relations. This regret did not seem to arise from personal disappointment in something she had counted on as exhilarating and important, but from a feeling that she had in this respect given her husband grounds for disillusionment and vexation. She denied any other sexual experience and seemed almost unaware of passionately erotic impulses. Since the general marital status had become so unpleasant, she found physical contact with her husband distasteful.

The joy this couple must have felt in each other's presence when they planned to marry had, so far as one could tell, disappeared entirely. Little closeness or sharing of interests and personal feelings had grown between them. It was plain that Mrs. White saw no hope of happiness with her husband. It was equally plain that she did not want a divorce. Though she assumed no air of martyrdom, she admitted that she felt strong obligations to continue her marriage. Her failure to have her little girl baptized in the Catholic Church seemed to augment her determination not to break another vow by seeking relief in divorce. Despite all the unpleasantness that

11

had arisen, Mrs. White in many respects showed a convincing loyalty toward her husband. Serious financial obstacles also stood in the way of any solution through divorce. It seemed evident that little Bonnie was the central focus of this woman's feelings and of her being. Fear of what divorce might do to her child convinced her that, no matter how unhappy the marriage might be, she must continue it.

Throughout the long first interview Mrs. White did not raise her voice—nor did she shed a tear. The cadence of her speech varied little. Superficially she seemed at times a dull, colorless person, too bound by propriety and inhibition to manifest herself warmly or adequately. Such an impression was misleading, the examiner soon decided. Behind this restrained expression, this almost stiltedly decorous posture, indications of deeply felt grief, despair and bewilderment, and an almost desperate love for little Bonnie became ever more apparent.

Were the emotional conflicts and stresses described by Mrs. White responsible for the attacks of severe headache which had brought her to her local doctor? If so, what could be done to give her relief? In referring to her headaches the patient sometimes spoke of them as "blinding." It was not easy to tell precisely what she meant by this term. Apparently she did not literally or totally lose her sight, but suffered some of the many visual disturbances often reported in migraine. She also spoke of blackouts which followed the headaches. Though she never seemed deliberately evasive, it was difficult for the examiner to get a clear conception of what occurred during these spells. At times Mrs. White referred to them in such a way as to suggest that she simply fainted; and at times the examiner felt she might be describing more complicated periods of amnesia. Neurologic examination revealed no indication of brain tumor or of any other organic disease that might cause periods of unconsciousness. There was no history of convulsive disorder.

So this is how the patient, Eve White, appeared in her first psychiatric interview. She was not undernourished but seemed somehow very delicate, the reticent, meticulous manner suggesting a physical fragility. This manner also tended to make some of the troubles she described seem inevitable. Her clinical symptoms were not unusual. Her personal problems were complicated and serious, but by no means extraordinary. (Both cancer and schizophrenia are, from a statistical point of view, commonplace disorders.)

12

In this first interview everything about the patient seemed ordinary. Her complaints were ones that might be encountered by almost any physician in the course of a typical day's work. During the second, the third, and the fourth visit she remained the same quiet, unspectacular figure. Her personality seemed to the observer quite free of any strange or vivid features, of any unusual potentialities. Nothing about her suggested that she was capable of manifestations likely to arouse wonder in him who beheld them, to raise questions even in the unspeculative mind about the basis of human entity, or to stir the imagination inexpressibly about matters that still elude comprehension.

There was nothing that led the examiner to suspect that fascinating and bewildering prospects lay ahead. He would have been astonished at any hint of suggestion that from this colorless little person would emerge phenomena so challenging and significant that he would labor to investigate and record them in detail, that eventually her case would be presented as something almost unique at a meeting of the American Psychiatric Association. Like other matters presented at such meetings, accounts of this report were carried by the Associated Press and appeared in many newspapers. The patient's name and all data that might lead to her identification were, of course, omitted in the medical report and consequently from the news items. Comments on the case in the lay press apparently attracted widespread attention.

Perhaps because of the rarity of her disorder, and probably also because of something inherently stimulating to the human imagination in the peculiar situation of our patient, expressions of interest in her plight have come to us from many parts of the world. Though more than three years have passed (at this writing) since the case was presented, communications still come in, offering a great variety of explanations and therapeutic procedures. Many of these are intelligent comments; some authoritatively declare that our patient is suffering from a voodoo spell or some similar type of conjuring. Astrologers have sent us typed single-spaced sheets of material in which the influences of Libra, Taurus, Virgo, Venus, and other planets are elaborately charted, intricate planetary influences discovered for the reported illness, and methods of relief suggested by such means as getting "Capricorn to balance the Bull and Scales, the Bull balancing

13

the Goat and Scales, and the Scales balancing the Goat and Bull."

Many students of the occult confidently inform us that our patient is "obsessed with discarnate spirits." One such corespondent urges that static electricity be applied to her body in order to drive these invaders out. Another announces that "the soul is attached to one's body by the ductless glands. Over a period of years or minutes," he adds, "when these connections become loose..., one's soul quits one's physical body." He goes on to explain how one's ordinary body can be possessed by the astral body of another, "...the...soul is loosed from the ductless glands but connected with his physical body by an ectoplasmic chord. If this chord snaps, the soul is unable to re-enter the physical body." This, according to our adviser, leaves it vulnerable to possession.

A learned man wrote to us from Europe furnishing an extensive exposition of the patient's psychopathology in its fourth-dimensional aspects. Some correspondents, who claimed the personal experience of devil possession, even volunteered to cast out the indwelling fiend they were sure resided in the body of our patient. Another counselor from a suburb of Los Angeles rebuked us for "metaphysical illiteracy." He said:

> Your patient...can easily be relieved of her possessing entities through exorcism by a competent spiritualist, preferably by one who has had experience in this particular field.
> One half the mental patients in our mental institutions suffering from schizophrenia can also be cured. I have studied this subject for many years and know whereof I speak.

To us, as well as to "President Eisenhower, Sir Winston Churchill, Bishop Burgmann (of Canberra), the Jung Institute at Zurich, and the Press" came an open letter from a philosophic observer in Australia pointing out that our case had demonstrated "the link between schizophrenia and the Jungian Mandala, [the] symbol of personality integration [as revealed in] the *Secret of the Golden Flower*." The writer of this open letter maintained that our patient was a reflection of the general state of the world and that, from the "full impact of psychological immortality" upon her, a transcendent creativity would evolve. And from Holland we received an interpretation in terms of "subtranscendental principal figurations."

CHAPTER 2

Over a period of several weeks, during which she returned for a few more interviews, Eve White made gratifying improvement. She still had occasional headaches but they were less severe. She no longer reported blackout spells. From her husband, Ralph White, who accompanied her on one of these visits, the therapist obtained additional information. This man confirmed in general the history as given by the patient. He admitted that at times she showed peculiar changes of mood and that he had occasionally lost his temper with her for a moment. He regarded her, nevertheless, as a patient industrious wife, a devoted mother, and described her general behavior in such terms that one might have suspected her of being an eventual candidate for cannonization.

"It's hard to believe, doctor, that such a sweet, steady woman could ever aggravate anybody. Maybe she is too good. Maybe that is why I lose my temper once in a while. You get accustomed to what she's like and you don't know what to make of . . . of anything different . . . when it comes."

When asked to elaborate, Ralph White spoke of rare occasions when Eve had showed something less than her customary forbearance and calm.

"It must be a sort of little erratic streak that comes out just every now and then," he suggested. He spoke also of occasional forgetfulness that had caused misunderstandings between them.

"I know it's the right thing to try to talk over misunderstandings," he said, "but I can't usually get Eve to go into such things."

In retrospect it seems remarkable how little emphasis Ralph White put on these points, how little detail he gave.

Several weeks passed without news from Mrs. White. In the interviews with her and with her husband the therapist had tried to help them resolve their difficulties. Relations between them were apparently much better. The headaches became only a minor trouble. There seemed little hope that the marriage would ever become really happy or gratifying, but considerable ground had been gained.

Then a discouraging letter from the husband was received. It announced the return of severe headaches and requested an early appointment. Seated in the office Eve White again seemed very tense and dejected. The headaches had recently kept her miserable much of the time. She was in considerable pain at present. She seemed concerned with a dream which she told the therapist had recurred several times.

"I am in a tremendous room," she said. "It's outline seems vague and dim because of its size. Toward the center of this room is a pool of stagnant green water. On the edge of the pool stand my husband and my uncle. I am in the water with Bonnie. I am trying to get her out for we both seem to be drowning, but I must not take her out where she will be near my husband or my uncle. Despite all I can do to the contrary, I put her directly into my husband's hands. Then my uncle, whom I love dearly, tries to push my head under the slimy water. I can remember nothing more."

She seemed unable to relate this dream or any of its details to the events of her life. The therapist suggested that she undergo hypnosis. She agreed to this, apparently without reluctance; and after several brief unsuccessful attempts, hypnosis was induced. The patient was in this state when asked to repeat the dream and told that on awakening she would endeavor to determine what it might reflect of her situation in actual life.

Awake, she stated without hesitation that the room seemed to represent her existence, the stagnant pool her husband's religious affiliation. In the dream, as in reality, she was trying to escape the influence of his church and trying especially to prevent her child from becoming a part of it. The dream showed her husband standing aside, refusing to help her in this struggle. The uncle who stood with him, unlike her parents and other relatives, had encouraged her to fulfill her promise and have her daughter raised as a Catholic.

Though this interpretation of the dream revealed nothing she did not already know quite clearly and consciously, discussing it seemed to help her bring out some of the emotion connected with these problems which during previous interviews she had carefully restrained. The headache, to her surprise, suddenly ceased. She left the office in much improved spirits, more nearly relaxed and cheerful than the therapist had yet seen her.

For almost a year after this the patient got along fairly well. During that period she returned only two or three times to discuss relatively small problems. Then one day came a letter from Eve White. The contents were at first puzzling. She had been involved in a serious quarrel with her husband. She had begun to feel that divorce was unavoidable. There were references to other matters unfamiliar to her physician. On reaching this point he noted that the letter had been written to some relative of the patient though the envelope was addressed to him. He mailed the letter back to Eve White.

Nothing more was heard from her until her husband called to say it was urgent that she return for help. The quarrel mentioned in her letter had apparently caused deep disturbances in the marriage. While visiting the relative for whom the missent letter was intended, a bitter disagreement had developed. After a truly violent scene both husband and wife had, in anger and with finality, announced the end of their relationship. Ralph White had then left at once for home where he waited for his wife to return for her clothes and personal possessions.

When she came he was astonished at her smile, at the gentle tone of her voice. She kissed him lightly on the cheek, then casually began her routine household tasks as if no problem had arisen. Though puzzled by her behavior, he was relieved by this inexplicable attitude, by her apparent reversal of feelings and intentions. He decided not to risk precipitating another crisis by referring to what had happened on the visit. For several days the household was peaceful and relations between the two seemed at their best. Then one evening he found Eve packing her suitcase as if for a trip. She was calm, matter-of-fact, and smiling. Cautiously he asked why she was making these preparations.

"Why, I'm getting ready to go and visit Flo," she told him, now taken aback herself at the question. She seemed at a loss, wondering why he should ask her this. Before the recent trip that had terminated so strangely, they had often discussed the plan for Eve to spend several days with her cousin Flo who lived about fifty miles away in Columbia. Eve could not understand what she took to be her husband's unfamiliarity with the well-known project. Nor could Ralph convince her that she had already paid the visit. She had not the slightest recollection of this or of the vehement altercation that had made her decide to leave him.

17

In the office she told the therapist that no awareness had come to her of the period Ralph said she had spent with Flo and her husband. This, he decided, was an impressive amnesia. What relation did such a manifestation have to the former blackouts which had been mentioned? Hypnosis was easily induced and in this state Eve found it possible to recall the visit to her cousin in considerable detail.

What she and the congenial cousin had done—shopping expeditions, going to the movies, playing canasta—became quite clear. And recollection of this was retained after she was awakened from hypnosis. About the quarrel with her husband and the causes for it, her remarks were somewhat ambiguous. She said that she remembered about it and made no attempt to deny her responsibility. But to the therapist there seemed something not quite satisfactory and something a little curious about her discussion of the violent scene. At the time he wondered if this feeling was derived from inconsistency between the bitterness and aggressive wrath reported by her husband and the otherwise consistent meekness and propriety of Eve. Flo and her husband, Jack, had witnessed the scene and later confirmed Ralph's account of his wife's participating in the fray with all the fury of a tigress. Though Eve denied nothing of this, something about her reaction suggested that her memory acknowledged the experience as material slightly alien or extraneous, as lacking a little in some dimension of reality, not quite like—but a little like—elements from a weirdly incompatible and disturbing dream. These impressions entered the therapist's thought only vaguely at the moment. They were developed later in relation to subsequent events of deep significance, then unforeseen. Sensing that Eve became more and more tense as the quarrel was discussed, he decided to refrain from pursuing the subject.

Her host and hostess reported later that Eve had been in wonderful spirits during the visit, showing at times an actual gaiety and liveliness they had not seen in her for years. She seemed extremely energetic and had so many plans and engagements that she was seldom at the house, and they had seen relatively little of her during the entire period. She must have been enjoying herself, for she made up her mind to stay longer than she had intended. Evidently she failed to inform her husband of this decision. When she did not return on the date she was expected, he had become alarmed and telephoned.

In curt tones she had flatly told Ralph that she had no intention of coming home at present, that she would come when she was good and ready. Disturbed by such a conversation, he at once got into his automobile and drove the fifty-odd miles to Columbia. On arriving at Flo's house he was received by Eve with haughty antagonism. She refused his request to come home with him, shouting that she was not going back. After a deplorable scene, she told him unequivocally that she was withdrawing from the marriage, that she wanted to see or hear no more of him. It was against the background of this encounter that his astonishment rose when she came back to their house, her sweet, timid self, apparently unaware of the painful events that had occurred.

Later, in the office Eve White expressed alarm about having suffered such a lapse of memory. There was considerable discussion about the relation between spells of amnesia, experiences which are painful to recall, and situations which are difficult to face. She seemed to gain some reassurance in the explanation that unacceptable events are sometimes unconsciously repressed from memory or involuntarily dissociated from awareness. She and her husband left the office in good spirits. Her period of amnesia, as far as could be determined, was now clear. She seemed free now of any intention or impulse to withdraw from her marriage.

A number of days passed. Then came the following letter.

Tues—

Dear Doctor,

Remembering my visit to — brought me a great deal of relief, to begin with.

Just being able to recall the trip seemed enough, but now that I've had time to think about it and all that occurred, it's more painful than I ever thought possible.

How can I be sure that I remember all that happened, even now? How can I know that it won't happen again? I wonder if I'll ever be sure of anything again.

While I was there with you it seemed different. Somehow it didn't matter to[o] much, to have forgotten; but now it does matter. I know it's something that doesn't happen ev—

I can't even recall —'s color schemes and I know that would probably be the first thing I'd notice.

My head hurts right on top. It has ever since the day I was down there to see you. I think it must be my eyes—I see little red and green specks—and I'm covered with some kind of rash.

—baby please be quite dear lord don't let me lose patience with her she's too sweet and innocent and my self-control

What was the meaning of such a letter? Though unsigned, the postmark, the content, and the familiar penmanship in most of the message revealed plainly that this had been written by Eve White. The effect of this letter on the therapist was considerable. It raised questions for which there were no good answers and set in motion thoughts that pursued various and vague directions. Had some child found the uncompleted page, scribbled those additional words and, perhaps as a whim, mailed it in an already addressed envelope? Perhaps. The handwriting of the last paragraph certainly suggested the work of a child. The abrupt change of content surely indicated another's thought. Could Eve White herself, as a puerile prank, have decided to disguise her characteristic handwriting and add this inconsequential note? And if so, why? Eve White had always appeared to be a circumspect, matter-of-fact person, meticulously truthful and consistently sober and serious about her grave troubles. The period of amnesia which she had experienced while visiting her cousin in Columbia suggested, of course, that another somnambulism or brief fugue might have occurred.

Within a week her husband called requesting another appointment for her without delay. He seemed genuinely distraught, saying that serious developments had occurred, that the situation had him at his wit's end. Eve, he said, had gone downtown without consulting him and had bought a great array of expensive clothes. There was a lot about all this that he could not understand. Nothing now seemed to relieve his wife's headaches. Could she come tomorrow?

Sitting in the office again, Eve first discussed the headaches. When questioned about it, she quietly but positively denied having sent the letter. She had, she clearly remembered, begun a letter to the physician, but had not finished it. She could not satisfactorily repeat what she had begun to say and thought she tore up the sheet of paper. For the new clothes which had so disturbed her husband, she had no explanation.

"I never saw them, doctor," she said with simple conviction, her light-blue eyes puzzled and intent. "I never saw them until Ralph took me to the closet and showed them to me."

Their income, though sufficient for ordinary expenses, would not pay for such extravagance. It would take several years of economizing now to get out of debt. Eve's wardrobe was modest, her garments inexpensive. Clever and industrious at needlework, she made most of her own clothing. Only recently had she completed the last dress she allowed herself for the season. When she had looked in the closet and seen half a dozen luxurious evening gowns, several pairs of I. Miller shoes, the new coat, the nylon lingerie with lace, and other items, she stepped back aghast.

"I don't blame him for being outraged," she said. "Those things must have cost hundreds of dollars. I told him I had no idea how they got in the closet, but that I'd surely try to find out where they came from and take them back as fast as I could."

How did those clothes get in her closet? Bewildered and distressed, her imagination searched wildly for an explanation. She thought of the quarrel in Columbia. Ever since then Ralph had seemed to harbor a suspicion that she might be secretly planning to divorce him. If he could show her unfit for the role of mother, he might, if they separated, gain the custody of Bonnie, might take her little girl away from her. Such thoughts, catalyzed by Ralph's anger and his insistence that she was lying, profoundly shook her equanimity.

Telling now of this perplexity, her voice lost its monotonous calm. For the first time her physician saw Eve's eyes grow moist. As if in apology, she mentioned her headache, saying it was now quite severe. Grave and immobile, she stopped speaking. She looked steadily at the man from whom she sought help, as a few tears ran slowly down her cheeks. There was a period of tight silence. She looked as if she wished to speak, as if there were something she *must* say; but strong forces seemed to work against this urgency. The physician, as if to break the impasse, involuntarily took a deeper breath. Without realizing it, he smiled, just discernibly.

"Doctor," the young woman said, "I am not sure I can tell you...." She lowered her head a little as if to avoid something she dare not face directly. Her unfailing composure was at last broken. Her small hands, lying as usual on the arms of her chair, knotted slowly into tight fists. As if summoning all her resolution she looked up, her gentle eyes very wide and steady.

"If you hear voices ... what does it mean ...? Oh, no....
If you really hear it ... with no one there ...?" She sobbed
briefly, very quietly. "I know what it means." Her posture
tightened. "Madness!!" she gasped. "The State Hospital ...
a lunatic forever.... Bonnie...." Her voice was scarcely
audible. Her blue eyes grew warm with memories, then
bleached suddenly with terror. "My little Bonnie girl...."

Auditory hallucinations are indeed serious. Eve White was
not wrong in concluding that they plainly indicate psychosis. After a little while she was able to tell more about the
dreadful experience.

"For several months," she finally admitted, "I've heard it
on rare occasions." During the last few days it had become
frequent; now she could not escape it. It was always a
woman's voice. Though she could not recognize this voice,
at times it seemed somehow familiar. It spoke in a jaunty
tone, often using vulgar phrases.

Though alarmed about this development, the physician
was struck by several points. Psychotic patients who experience auditory hallucinations do not ordinarily find them so
remarkable. Though they are sometimes terrified at what
the voices say, they seldom find the experience of abnormal
perception alarming in itself. Almost uniformly the patients
assume that the voices are real. They insist that the sound
comes to them by radio, by radar, by telephonic projective
radioactivity, by invisible waves playing upon an intrapsy-
chic ectoplasm, et cetra. The psychotic schizophrenic almost never regards the hallucinations as an indication of
mental disorder. No one can convince him that they are
not objectively real.

Eve White's reactions were those of a normal, sane, and
healthy person to what, theoretically, could happen only to
a person with a grave and malignant psychosis.

CHAPTER 3

Having found encouragement in the points just mentioned,
the physician emphasized them to the young woman. He
was able to assure her, despite what she had told him, that
he did not consider her to be psychotic. She spoke of her
incessant dread that she would lose her little girl. Relations
with her husband seemed to be deteriorating dangerously.
No matter what she planned, or intended, or tried to do,

22

events so shaped themselves that intsead of progress only retrogression occurred. The headaches had been more frequent and more severe. There had been more blackouts. She could not tell how long they lasted.

Eve White was clearly frightened and baffled by something she sought to cope with or to escape. Its dreadful threat was palpable to her, and she braced herself as one who awaits what might prove to be an invisible guillotine. But she spoke softly in her characteristic steady voice. The delicate long-fingered hands remained on the arms of her chair as usual. Their immobility conveyed not relaxation but tensions more acute than she had shown on previous visits.

Hoping to avoid a further mobilization of anxiety, the physician endeavored to direct discussion toward the more encouraging features of her situation. She returned, however, to the episode of the clothes. Clerks at the stores where she tried to return them had insisted it *was* she who had bought them. She spoke again of the voice she had heard, apparently wishing to say more and finding herself at a loss for adequate expression. She hesitated. There was perhaps a minute or more of silence.

The brooding look in her eyes became almost a stare. Eve seemed momentarily dazed. Suddenly her posture began to change. Her body slowly stiffened until she sat rigidly erect. An alien, inexplicable expression then came over her face. This was suddenly erased into utter blankness. The lines of her countenance seemed to shift in a barely visible, slow, rippling transformation. For a moment there was the impression of something arcane. Closing her eyes, she winced as she put her hands to her temples, pressed hard, and twisted them as if to combat sudden pain. A slight shudder passed over her entire body.

Then the hands lightly dropped. She relaxed easily into an attitude of comfort the physician had never before seen in this patient. A pair of blue eyes popped open. There was a quick reckless smile. In a bright unfamiliar voice that sparkled, the woman said, "Hi, there, Doc!"

With a soft and surprisingly intimate syllable of laughter, she crossed her legs, carelessly swirling her skirt in the process. She unhurriedly smoothed the hem down over her knees in a manner that was playful and somehow just a little provocative. From a corner of his preoccupied awareness the physician had vaguely noted for the first time how attractive those legs were. She settled a little more deeply into the cushions of the chair. The demure and constrained posture of Eve White had melted into buoyant repose. One little foot crossed over the other began a slow, small, rhythmic, rocking motion that seemed to express alert contentment as pervasively as the gentle wagging of a fox terrier's tail.

Still busy with his own unassimilated surprise, the doctor heard himself say, "How do you feel now?"

"Why just fine—never better! How you doing yourself, Doc?"

Eve looked for a moment straight into his eyes. Her expression was that of one who is just barely able to restrain laughter. Her eyes rolled up and to one side for an instant, then the lids flicked softly before opening wide again. She tossed her head lightly with a little gesture that threw the fine dark hair forward onto her shoulder. A five-year-old might have so reacted to some sudden, unforeseen amusement. In the patient's gesture there was something of pert sauciness, something in which the artless play of a child and a scarcely conscious flirtatiousness mingled. The therapist reacted to the new presence with feelings that momentarily recalled some half-remembered quotation about the devil entering the prompter's box. But the patient remained at ease and, apparently, for some reason of her own, quite amused. The silence went unbroken for a minute or more.

"She's been having a real rough time. There's no doubt about that," the girl said carelessly. "I feel right sorry for her sometimes. She's such a damn dope though.... What she puts up with from the sorry Ralph White—and all her mooning over the little brat...! To hell with it, I say!"

She leaned forward in a little movement that suggested a kitten. With one hand she half-heartedly began to scratch her leg just below the knee. She stretched out the other hand amiably and said, "Would you give me a cigarette, please, Doc?"

He handed her a cigarette, and then lighting it, said, "Who is 'she'?"

"Why, Eve White, of course. Your long-suffering, saintly, little patient."

"But aren't you Eve White?" he asked.

"That's for laughs," she exclaimed, a ripple of mirth in her tone. She tossed her head slightly again. "Why, you ought to know better than that, Doc!" She paused and looked at him intently. Her face was fresh and marvelously free from the habitual signs of care, seriousness, and underlying stress

24

so familiar in the face of the girl who had come into the office. Shifting her position in the chair, she raised her hand and rolled a lock of hair slowly between her fingers. Open-eyed, she looked again directly at him. As an impish smile flickered over her childlike face she said softly:

"I know you *real* well, Doc . . . lots better than she knows you. . . . And I kind of like you. I bet you're a good dancer, too."

After he had disclaimed any special talents for the dance, they exchanged several inconsequential remarks. Then the physician said, "Can you tell me anything more about those dresses that upset your husband so much?"

"I ain't got no husband," she replied promptly and emphatically. "Let's get that straight right now." She grinned broadly.

"Well, who *are* you?" he asked incredulously.

"Why, I'm Eve Black," she said (giving Mrs. White's maiden name). "I'm me and she's herself," the girl added. "I like to live and she don't. . . . Those dresses—well, I can tell you about them. I got out the other day, and I needed some dresses. I like good clothes. So I just went downtown and bought what I wanted. I charged 'em to her husband, too!" She began to laugh softly. "You ought've seen the look on her silly face when he showed her what was in that closet!"

There is little point in attempting to give in detail here the differences between this novel feminine apparition and the vanished Eve White. Instead of the gentleness and restraint of that conventional figure, there sparkled in the newcomer a childishly daredevil air, an erotically mischievous glance, a rippling energy, a greedy appetite for fun. This new and apparently carefree girl spoke casually of Eve White and her problems, always using *she* or *her* in every reference, always respecting the strict bounds of a separate identity.

It was also immediately apparent that this new voice was different, that the basic idiom of her language was plainly not that of Eve White. Eve White regularly gave the impression of a taut fragile slenderness. Perhaps because of the easy laxness of this girl's posture and her more vigorous movements, the lines of her body seemed somehow a little more voluptuously rounded. A thousand minute alterations of manner, gesture, expression, posture, of nuances in reflex or instinctive reaction, of glance, of eyebrow tilting, and eye movements—all argued that this could only be another woman. It is not even possible to say just what all these differences were.

It would not be difficult for a man to distinguish his wife (or perhaps even his secretary) if she were placed among a hundred other women carefully chosen from millions because of their close resemblance to her, and all dressed identically. But would one wager, however articulate he might be, that he could tell a stranger, or even a person very slightly acquainted with her, how to accomplish this task? If the husband should try to tell us how he himself recognizes his wife, he might accurately convey something to us. But when he conveyed, no matter how hard he tried, would be only an inconsequential fragment. It would not be enough to help us when we ourselves set out to find the designated woman. So, too, we are not equal to the task of telling adequately what so profoundly distinguished from Eve White the carefree girl who had taken her place in this vivid mutation.

Talking came easy to Eve Black. She not only answered all questions readily but often digressed or went on to reminisce in exuberant loquacity. This was in sharp contrast with the habits of her predecessor in the chair, who spoke slowly and carefully and sometimes as if her answers cost considerable effort.

The new Eve spoke at length about the expensive clothes which had caused trouble for Mr. and Mrs. White.

"She tried to take 'em all back," she said with relish, "but some of the stores wouldn't do it. Of course, they thought I was her, and they told her she'd bought 'em and she'd have to keep 'em! I'm glad, too. I need something fit to wear when I do get out. She never gets anything but those prim little jobs that make you feel like an old maid Sunday-school teacher or somebody's great-aunt. Just look at this, will you?" she said, with a deprecatory glance down at the neat but inconspicuous skirt she brushed with a lively flourish of her hands.

"What can you tell me about Eve White?" the physician asked.

"Well, I really haven't been paying much attention to her recently," she said, as if ready to dismiss a subject of minor importance. Then her eyes brightened. "But I can tell you plenty, Doc," she added eagerly, with a flash of pride that suggested a child sure she has the answers. "I know just about everything about her—lots and lots of things she don't know herself. For one thing, she's a lot more sick of that husband than she'll admit. She and her fine airs about always having to do the right thing—the *right thing* even if it kills her."

"Is it because of little Bonnie?" he asked.

"Little Bonnie, little Bonnie, little Bonnie! That's all she can think about. Running herself crazy from morning to night with worry about her brat. Oh, the kid's all right—a nice enough kid most of the time. But why the hell should a girl find nothing to do but fret all the time about a four-year-old child?"

"Don't you *love* your daughter?"

"My daughter! I don't *have* no child, Doc. Never will have one either. There's no percentage in it. Not for me. I like to have a good time—like to live. Life don't last forever. Bonnie's *her* child. I got nothing to do with her."

When asked if Eve White's all-absorbing devotion to Bonnie was genuine, she hesitated for a moment. "Yes, Doc, I reckon you'd say that's real.... But it's silly.... To me it just don't make real good sense."

Eve Black did not deny that the body from which she spoke was also the body of Eve White, or that from it had been born not quite four years ago the little girl under discussion. When pressed for explanations about this, she still insisted that she herself was not a mother, that she was not married to Ralph White "or to anybody else either." For many questions she had no satisfactory answers but on these points she was emphatically positive.

"Where were you when the baby was born?" he inquired.

She paused for a moment, flicked the ash off her cigarette. A triumphant flash of mischief lit her face as she replied:

"Now, Doc, that's one for you to answer! There's a lot about it I can't explain," she then admitted, "an awful lot I don't understand. But I do know I'm not her and she's not me. I ain't going to worry myself about it too much, either. I want to have some fun while I can. There's life in me, Doc," she added, with a light little sigh of pleasure. "I've been getting out a lot more recently, too." Her bright eyes snapped with a look of childlike deviltry. "Now, Eve White would worry about all those questions you've been asking, but not me."

"*Does* she worry about them?"

"That's one trouble she's got she don't know nothing about!" replied the young woman in amused tones but with conviction. She went on to say that Eve White was completely unaware of Eve Black's existence.

"She don't know anything about me..." She broke off suddenly and a flash of defiance lit her eyes. "And don't you go and tell her either! When I get out she don't know a thing about it. I go where I please, and do like I please and it's none of her damned business."

She had no explanation to offer for this. She could not tell the doctor where Eve White disappeared to or what happened to her when she herself "got out" and went on her merry way. She was able to maintain awareness, she claimed, of everything, or nearly everything, that the cautious housewife and mother did, and had access most of the time to her thoughts and her memory. She did not, however, always take advantage of this ability. She found Eve White's thoughts and activities so boring that she often withdrew her attention for long periods. On the other hand, Eve White had no contact with Eve Black's consciousness, no suspicion of her existence. Eve Black could not, she admitted, emerge at will to express herself freely in the body of the sober and retiring woman known as Eve White. Until a few months ago it had been only at long intervals that she was able to gain control and then, with one exception, only for brief periods.

The original patient had, during previous interviews, discussed at length a miscarriage which she had suffered about four months earlier. Aside from the physiologic stress of this event, there had been other and more serious complications. Sensing some disturbance, full of an apprehension she could not explain adequately, Eve White had requested her husband not to leave the house but to stay with her. It had seemed to her that he made light of her uneasiness. Trying to reassure her, he had repeatedly told her that she would be all right. Naturally he could not foresee what would occur. There was no way she could explain how she felt and she could give no concrete reasons for insisting that he stay. He had been forced to lose time from work and to change his plans repeatedly since his wife had become so uneasy. Some of his friends seemed to regard him as henpecked. After all, he could not be completely governed by every whim of a pregnant wife. The doctor had assured him nothing serious was wrong with her. But the usually docile Eve had persistently urged Ralph to humor her.

He had planned for weeks to attend a certain barbecue. To

him his wife's insistence seemed like unreasonable nagging. Though ordinarily a kind and agreeable man, he eventually became impatient and at last angry with her. An unpleasant quarrel developed. As Ralph remembered the scene, Eve had seized him by the arm in an effort to make him stay home with her. In freeing himself, he had inadvertently pushed her in such a way that she interpreted his action as a slap or a blow. He did not realize this at the time. It is difficult to reconstruct the incident in detail through two differing accounts, each given by a person who was in a state of considerable emotional distress. Eve felt that her husband had struck her across the face with the back of his hand and had callously turned his back on her and walked out of the house.

This was the night her miscarriage occurred. With no one but little Bonnie to help her, she was unable to obtain medical attention until hours of pain and alarming hemorrhage had gone by. She lay in the bed struggling to stifle her groans with little Bonnie in tears trying to comfort her.

"Why, Mommy...oh, why do you and Daddy fuss like that?" the child asked plaintively. Later when the bed sheets were red with blood, she whispered in terror, "Mommy, you're not going to die are you? Don't, don't die. . . . Please Mommy, don't die now!"

The marital relations, which had been difficult for a long while, after the miscarriage grew rapidly worse. In Eve there was now a coldness toward Ralph and a hurt she could not express. Without any reconciliation having occurred between them, some days after the miscarriage she took Bonnie and went to stay for a while with her parents. Though in time she returned at his urging and superficially resumed her former attitude toward him, a deep alteration of her feelings, which she could not influence, persisted and progressed.

Shortly after this experience Eve White's headaches and blackouts began, and Eve Black found herself able to emerge more frequently and to stay out for longer periods.

"What gave her those headaches," the new Eve said, "was trying to keep me from getting out. She didn't know what was going on but when she tried to stop me and had trouble doing it, her head would give her hell."

Sometimes, but not always, after Eve Black had been out Eve White was left with the memory of a blackout. There were occasions too when the innocent housewife had been left with other consequences of her unrecognized twin's activities. Eve White neither smoked nor drank and kept judicious hours. When Eve Black emerged, if the occasion permitted, she often made herself attractive to various adventurous men she encountered, men not acquainted with Mrs. White. She was always ready for a party and liked nothing better than to dance until the small hours of the morning.

"What does Ralph make of you?" the physician now inquired.

"Why, he don't know anything about me," she promptly replied. "Naturally I wouldn't try to come out if he's going to be around. If I ever happen to run into him I take on airs and try to act just like his wife until I can get out of his sight."

Softly humming the tune of a favorite rumba and moving her smooth shoulders just a little in beat with the rhythm, this bold figure of a girl began to laugh. With a flashing roll of her eyes she averred jubilantly, "About a week ago I was out nearly all night and got right well polluted with gin. You ought've seen her thoughts when she woke up the next morning and found herself with the hang-over! It was a dilly of a hang-over. She didn't know what the hell it was, or what to make of it. She didn't like it a bit and was scared half to death."

"But didn't you feel the hang-over yourself?" the physician asked. "Me? Naw. *Of course* I didn't feel it! I wasn't out then. And anyway, it was a time I wouldn't have cared to be out. She was out and she's the one that felt it, but I could tell every damn thing she thought about it."

This lively Eve told of several other occasions when, being out, she had pursued mischievous or injudicious ways and then, as trouble loomed ahead, had slipped back into retirement, leaving the other conscientious and innocent Eve to face various puzzling and unpleasant consequences. According to her she could sometimes, but not regularly, do this of her own volition. Thus she explained the visit to Eve White's cousin Flo in Columbia. She had, she said, succeeded in emerging and had stayed out most of the time. But when Ralph White called up and told her to come home, the capricious Eve, owning no obligation or attachment to this man whom she disliked, not only refused, but tore into him with scurrilous abuse and gave him a piece of her mind, a mind that had nothing in common with that of his self-effacing wife.

Little wonder then, the physician now told himself, that Ralph White sometimes lost his temper or that he had sometimes behaved toward his wife in ways she could not understand. According to the new Eve, she herself had had a wonderful time in Columbia. In the city where she was a stranger, and often away from Flo and on her own, she was able to do nearly anything she chose without risk of being mistaken for Mrs. White. During this period she had entertained hope that she might "stay out" indefinitely and continue her life as Eve Black without interruption. Typically she had ignored all the difficulties that would arise. But despite all her efforts to maintain control, the other Eve had reappeared and returned to Ralph.

The physician now brought up this point: suppose Eve White were to become aware of Eve Black's presence. She would surely do everything in her power to keep such a force and such inclinations in abeyance. What then would Eve Black do?

"I'll fight," she said with vehemence.

"How?"

"I don't know, but I'll sure fight her." After a moment's pause, she added, "I'm getting stronger than she is. Each time I come out she gets weaker."

The physician asked what would happen if this continued.

"Then the body will be mine," she replied with assurance.

She talked freely, often expressing disdain for Mrs. White and for Ralph. Speaking of those two she said that she could have no respect for the wife because of "the way she lets him push her around." In reference to their sexual relations she commented sharply, "He doesn't care how it is to her—just for his own pleasure."

When asked if she herself had ever had intercourse with Ralph, her eyes flared with indignation. The quick reply snapped out, "Definitely not!"

Though indubitably of the same flesh, this vibrant devil-may-care yet somehow childlike creature bore so little resemblance to Eve White as he had known her that the physician found himself asking a question that later he recalled with astonishment:

"If it was you in Columbia with Flo and Jack, why didn't they recognize you? How did they go on believing it was Eve White?"

"Well, for one thing, they don't know me, you see. And I've been around Eve White long enough to know exactly

31

how she talks and how she does. When I have to, I can put on a pretty damn good job of acting like her— even to saying dopey things, being real mousey, and mimicking all her proper little ways. It's a real strain, I tell you, but I couldn't very well act like my own self around her family, could I? Or around anybody who knows her real well? Then it'd really be hell to pay." She chuckled to herself. "Flo and Jack did seem to feel she was mighty lively and happy, at that. They talked about it several times and seemed tickled to death. Once or twice I almost busted out laughing at them."

Eve Black said she could explain the voice that the other Eve had heard with such alarm and such distress.

"It was just me," she said. "I've never been able to influence her thoughts or make her do a thing I wanted her to, and not till the last week or so was I ever able to make her hear me like that. Once I found out I could sometimes do it, I kept on trying. It seemed to help me when I wanted to get out. She'd get so upset about hearing such a thing, she couldn't do much to stop me. You really ought've seen her the other day. Ralph was giving her hell and I got kind of sick of it. Before I knew it I shouted to her, 'Knock the damn old creep's block off!'"

"Did Ralph hear you?" the physician inquired attentively.

"Naw, *of course* not, Doc! But *she* did. *She* heard me all right and it scared her so she almost wet her sweet, prissy little panties."

CHAPTER 4

During this first hour's interview with the energetic and capricious woman who called herself Eve Black, the physician had often reminded himself that Ralph White was outside in the waiting room. Trying to put himself in this husband's place, he found it difficult to say what his own reactions to such a situation would be. Eve White's auditory hallucinations established beyond a doubt the deep gravity of her psychiatric illness, and he deemed it advisable that she enter the hospital. Would the husband believe such a report as the physician must give him? Suppose Eve Black denied him permission to inform Ralph of her existence? She had schemed and worked carefully and long to prevent this man from discovering her. What would Eve White's parents say to such a story? This Eve before him had emerged spontaneously. How was he to dismiss her? How recall the other?

Fearing that Ralph White would not otherwise believe what he had observed, the physician decided that the husband must meet Eve Black in person, must see her himself, and speak with her directly. Otherwise he would probably lose confidence in the physician and, perhaps, refuse to let his wife be admitted to the hospital.

With such thoughts in mind he asked the patient, "What do you think we ought to do now?"

"Lord Doc," she said smiling amiably as she rocked the crossed leg gently over the other smooth knee, "how in hell would I know? Watching you work with her so long I've got to kind of like you. I'm willing to try most anything you say."

He asked her if she would be willing to talk with Ralph White.

"Why should *I* talk with him, Doc?" she answered, a little startled. "I don't like the man and I don't want to have nothing to do with him, either."

She said finally that she would be willing to do what she could to make things better for Eve White, but her statement did not carry great conviction. It seemed likely that she bore her alternate no active animosity, but it was hardly possible that she could be counted upon to put herself to any pains to cooperate in medical efforts to help. The physician explained that he felt it necessary for Eve White to come into the hospital, a general hospital connected with the University Medical School, and to stay for a while in the psychiatric section. Eve Black admitted that it was none of her business what the other Eve might decide to do, but made it plain that she herself did not relish the idea of finding herself on a "bughouse ward." She did not want to be limited by its restrictions if she succeeded in getting out during the period of Eve White's hospitalization.

"I've already got a date for the dance out at Ten Mile Tavern next Friday night," she said. "Her husband's planning to be away for the night on business and she'd made plans to take Bonnie and spend the night at a girl friend's house. There's a good chance I might get out that night."

The seriousness of Eve White's disorder was then carefully explained. The girl listened politely but showed little serious

33

concern about the prognosis of her associate. Occasionally her glance wandered about the office inattentively.

The physician decided it was necessary to be more frank, to emphasize some points he had hoped might be left unspoken. He told this girl that he did not know what course Eve White's illness might take. The auditory hallucinations, no matter how one might account for them, suggested that she might become much worse. If she became profoundly irrational, perhaps dangerous to herself and others, she might have to remain confined in a institution for many months, perhaps for years. Because of her husband's limited financial resources, commitment to the State Hospital would be her only choice. With Eve White confined thus, there would be no place to go, nothing very interesting to do when Eve Black emerged for her "times out."

Eve Black had already expressed a blithe and sanguine confidence that, no matter how psychotic the other might become, her own mind, since it was a thing apart, would suffer no ill effects, no change.

"However looney she may get," she insisted, referring to this point, "it won't have nothing to do with me. Let her rave if she wants to, it'll be no skin off my nose."

Now as the point about confinement sank slowly into the debonair girl's awareness, she momentarily took on a more serious air. She was forced to agree that her own future would be jeopardized if Eve White grew worse; prolonged confinement of the other would mean confinement also for her. None of the activities in which she took such childish delight would be possible for her.

"I think you got something there, Doc," she said reluctantly.

She agreed then for the cotenant of her body to go into the hospital, and promised not to exert any force or influence available to her to prevent this step or to impede or disrupt treatment. She also agreed to refrain from whatever she did that (according to her) resulted in Eve White's hearing voices. But she would not promise to do all she could to relieve the other's headaches.

"Why, if I did that, Doc, I might not ever be able to get out again."

The physician then emphasized the precariousness of Eve White's condition; if she developed a psychosis that held the threat of confinement, then Eve Black was threatened also. He urged the attractive girl who smiled at him from the opposite chair *not* to increase the vigor or aggression of her contest for predominance with the now absent opponent. She was warned that attempts to "come out" more often, or to stay out longer, would be likely to jeopardize her own freedom no less than the other's. He also pointed out that for the same reason she must refrain from any sort of behavior that might cause more trouble between Eve White and her husband; she must resist impish pranks that would bewilder the other woman and shake her already crumbling confidence.

Eve Black made inquiry about the psychiatric section of the hospital and about what sort of treatment might be necessary for Eve White. With the excited curiosity of a child who hears that a playmate is going to have some teeth filled, she asked, "Do you think you'll have to give her electric shock?"

That could not yet be decided, the physician said, but there was a possibility this measure might promise benefit.

"If you do it, Doc," she said eagerly, "please be damned sure nobody gets the bright idea to start it if I happen to be out. I sure don't want anybody poppin' that juice to me. No sir! If she needs it, that's O.K. by me. But I'm all right, myself, and I sure wouldn't like to catch no jolt like that."

Eve Black had agreed to reveal her identity to Ralph White and to discuss the situation with him. Sitting with him in another office the physician wondered how the exasperated, deeply worried, and already bewildered husband should be prepared for what he was to encounter. It was deemed inadvisable to offer him at this point any theoretical explanations of dual personality or to emphasize the fact that a few similar manifestations had been extensively described in the medical and psychologic literature. Ralph White was, understandably, worn out with what he had been going through for months. Any effort on the part of the physician to account for his wife's puzzling behavior through the assumption of "another personality in her body" might well impress him as some glib and far-fetched psychiatric sophistry. It seemed wise, also, to avoid any preliminary discussion that might compromise this husband's status as an unbiased observer, as one free of second-hand explanatory concepts that could be projected prejudicially into his reactions and appraisals.

So it was decided to let Ralph first *see* this woman who called herself Eve Black. He had lived with his wife for almost seven years. Certainly he should be able to recognize her through any disguise, be it of play-acting, hysteria, or of psychosis. No matter what changes might have occurred in this woman, he should be able to discern features inaccessible to another that would establish for him her inimitable identity as Eve White.

When brought into the presence of Eve Black by the physician, this husband was, of course, immediately confronted by an infinity of detail to him long and profoundly familiar. The hair on the woman's head, every strand of it, was his wife's hair. The nose, ears, eyebrows, all the lines and contours of the face were intimately known by him as her very own. Though it may not be possible for strangers to tell one identical twin from the other, either's husband or a parent seldom has difficulty. The recognition is probably achieved through thousands, perhaps millions, of small items of preception, data from the dim periphery of awareness, through subliminal minute elements never consciously recognized or clearly labeled, by indescribable distinctions vaguely sensed in nonlogical reactions, by some loosely called *intuitive*.

Contradicting all this came the brash, unfamiliar voice in which Eve Black said that she had never married him, that she was no wife of his. Anatomically this face was the face he knew, but all that it expressed was alien. The physiologic functions, the small involuntary movements through which a countenance reflects feeling were not those he had ever seen in the face of his wife. Her denial of their relationship, her amazing insistence that she was not Bonnie's mother might, he realized, be the result of mental confusion, the irrational product of ordinary psychiatric illness. So, too, the profound alteration in her attitude toward him might be explained, and the general transformation of her emotional status. He told himself repeatedly that serious personality disorder may bring about drastic changes in any patient, erasing habitual reactions, characteristic qualities and attitudes, that it often brings out or introduces moods, viewpoints, and behavior unimaginable in that individual while sane.

At the beginning of the interview, it seemed to the physician that Ralph White, though amazed and genuinely distressed, clung to the idea that hurt, nervous instability and emotional stress had led his wife, through some fantastic caprice, to adopt voluntarily this unheard-of attitude. Patiently he tried to reason with her as one might with a child who, in speech and behavior, is carrying out the absurdities of a weirdly atypical tantrum.

In the discussion with Ralph, Eve Black repeated most of what she had already told the physician. And as Ralph, for whom she acknowledged only an impersonal acquaintance, found himself unable to break down any pretenses or make her admit the folly of her statements, as he persistently struggled against the invulnerable consistency she maintained, despair and, finally, something akin to awe seemed to possess him.

These rounded cheeks seemed to flush with a healthy pink not to be seen in the pinched features of his wife's quiet tense little face. The language this woman used, not in deliberate or studied speech, but in quick, spontaneous, volatile reactions unknown to Eve White, he had never heard from her in his home. The bold eyes that from time to time surveyed him, now in scorn, now with unapproachable indifference, contained no hint of a secret recognition. Open, unveiled by anger, hurt, or discernible affectation, they were to him simply the eyes of a stranger.

The obvious energy, the naive equanimity of the carefree figure that confronted him, gradually infiltrated through the barriers of incredulity demanded by common sense. He could imagine his wife in moods unfamiliar to him and conceive of improbable and even drastic changes occurring in her outlook and her convictions, but in this coarsely buoyant, unfamiliarly provocative girl who sat before him in the very clothes he had seen his wife put on that morning, there was nothing he could recognize of the human being with whom he had shared bed and board for all these years. Had the color of her hair and eyes changed suddenly as he watched and the features of her face and body miraculously taken on gross and unrecognizable deformity, his amazement would have been more swift, but no more convincing and disconcerting than the slow but pervasive realization that now struggled with his reason.

Grasping for what he knew to be his wife's deepest feelings, for what he had long sensed as the changeless core of her being, Ralph White, after a moment of perplexed and tense silence, slowly said, "Bonnie ... our little girl ... what about Bonnie ...? what shall we ... what can I ...?"

"Why ask me?" she interrupted him carelessly, speaking with ease and assurance. "Do what you like about the kid.

How many times am I goin' to have to tell you I got nothing to do with your child—or with you either." Her eyes drifted from him, as if her attention had turned to other matters. She leaned forward a little and absent-mindedly began to scratch a knee.

"These damn nylon stockings she puts on! They always make me itch!" Having apparently relieved herself of the petty annoyance, she turned to the physician, smiling agreeably. With a barely discernible inclination of her head toward Ralph White, a naively pert arching of the dark brows, she now asked, "How long, Doc, does all this have to go on?"

After leaving the room Ralph and the physician talked at length. Permission was freely granted for the patient to enter the hospital and receive treatment.

"The longer I looked at her," said Mr. White, "the less I could make of it...the stranger she seemed to me. I got to feeling after a while that I didn't know her at all. It's no different from the way it would be if I'd never seen her before in my whole life."

Returning to the office where Eve Black, sitting relaxed and apparently unperturbed, awaited him, the physician was faced with another problem. This personality, or manifestation, with whom he now dealt had emerged spontaneously. Would she be willing to withdraw and thus allow his original patient to return so that he could discuss treatment with her? If the present Eve Black were indeed another personality, at least in some degree, or in some aspects of such a term, where then was the one who had been replaced, the other functional manifestation known to herself and to others as Eve White? Was it misleading to speak and to think of them as *separate personalities?* Would it be more accurate to regard them as two aspects, or two parts, of a single human entity that had somehow undergone functional separation? When asleep anyone may, in the thought and feeling of dreams, pursue aims inconsistent with what appear to be the physiologic purposes of repose. People sometimes walk open-eyed in sleep, answering questions and perhaps carrying out complicated acts. They appear not to be fully themselves at such times, as if only a small part of their full capabilities were available. If we regard the two Eves as merely two differing and dissociated aspects or sides of a single mind, character, or personality, how shall we account for the present inactivity and inaccessibility, the

38

apparent absence, of the other Eve? Is she (or it) to be regarded as literally unconscious? Can we say that, veiled behind the sparkling alertness of Eve Black, the other merely sleeps? If so, how can she be awakened or called forth from her invisible quiescence?

Plans for hospitalization having been completed, it then became appropriate, one might say, to locate the patient who was to receive treatment. Eve White on a previous occasion had gone into hypnosis without difficulty. Perhaps if the present Eve could be hypnotized the other personality might emerge or somehow be brought out. This girl said she had no objections to the procedure. Though she seemed cooperative, several attempts were unsuccessful. It may be noted here that, though Eve White was subsequently put under hypnosis on many occasions, Eve Black remained refractory though numerous other attempts were made.

After some discussion the girl suggested that the physician call Eve White by name. As he paused to seek emphasis or persuasion that might be appropriate in bidding the absent one to emerge, his companion fell silent. Quite immobile, she appeared to concentrate or in some way to make herself receptive or cooperative in the attempt. Her eyes closed as the name "Eve White" was called.

A moment later they slowly opened, now quiet, cautious, looking to the physician more pale, as if they had actually been drained of color. This face wore the habitual expression of Eve White. Instead of the animation and vitality it had reflected only a few minutes ago, there was now an inconspicuous sweetness, a delicate poise almost masking the faint lines of tension. Automatically she moved a little in the chair, apparently finding the easy posture that had been adopted by her alternate unfamiliar or a little incongruous. Her legs, as if without volitional prompting, assumed a more sedate position, with knees and feet together.

Her composed features gave the impression of one who feels a little surprised but no great amazement. So might a person look whose attention has been momentarily distracted, who suspects she may have missed a few words of the conversation but is not sure of this.

"What happened?" asked the physician.

She paused as if to think back, her soft eyes still and serious. "I don't know," she said in her slow, precise voice. "Was it anything very much . . . ? I might have had a blackout . . . but I'm not sure." She smiled as if just becoming

39

aware of something pleasant. "My head, Doctor, the pain has all gone."

He now recalled that Eve White, shortly before she vanished, or was replaced, had told him the headache was then troubling her. The physician now talked with Eve White at some length, reviewing particularly all items that it seemed logical to think might stir some latent awareness or still unrealized capacity for recollection that might serve as a link between the two manifestations. After a number of similar but less direct inquiries, he finally asked:

"Do you ever have the feeling, perhaps for a moment, that deep down in you there's still somebody that you used to be, somebody you can't quite reach?"

She looked up at him with puzzled eyes. After pondering a few moments, she said, "I...I don't know what you mean."

He suggested then that she enter the hospital and, discussing plans for this with her, he noted that her reactions were those of one who had heard nothing of what he had said on this subject a little earlier to Eve Black.

CHAPTER 5

During many years of clinical experience in psychiatry we had both often encountered the inexplicable, had grown accustomed, one might say, to various manifestations that the layman would find strange or even weirdly astonishing. Why, then, did we find ourselves regarding this patient (or should one say these patients) with such uncommon interest? Was there in the problem we confronted something seriously enigmatic, some element of marvel?

The psychiatric manifestation called *dual personality* has been extensively discussed over several decades. So too have the unicorn and the centaur remained figures familiar, in a sense, over thousands of years. Can one doubt that during medieval times twilight encounters with the unicorn were accepted as commonplace events? Surely in the days of Homer there were men of Thessaly or Boeotia who convincingly spoke of having seen centaurs almost as wise as Chiron. But who today, confronting a centaur in the flesh, could summon the sophistication to contain his astonishment?

A few examples of dual or multiple personality were reported in medical literature during the first half of the nineteenth century, one or two in its very early decades. The concept was not entirely novel when Robert Louis Stevenson in 1886 published his story of Dr. Jekyll and Mr. Hyde. In these gifted hands the subject took on sinister and eerie overtones. Gross and impossible bodily alterations were described as accompanying the sudden changes of personality. But running through this vivid and poetic extravagance we find a texture of plausibility, a thread of reality that cannot be dismissed forthwith as mere supernatural moonshine. This, perhaps, contributed to the effect of the appalling story, weaving into it just enough fact scarcely less strange—to multiply its force, and solidify its impact.

One totally without belief in ghosts or human vampires may experience thrills of horror in reading such novels as Bram Stocker's *Dracula* or Bulwer-Lytton's short story, *The Haunted and the Haunters*. Such reactions would be more profound if the uncanny and gruesome events described were not dismissed as pure fantasy but accepted as distorted and sensationally applied versions of a still scarcely comprehensive reality.

Several generations have read with fascination *The Strange Case of Dr. Jekyll and Mr. Hyde*. The motion pictures have repeatedly presented these two personalities (souls, or beings) who alternate in and finally struggle for the privilege of inhabiting or controlling a single human body. Old and terrible superstitions, some of the most weird and savage beliefs that ever afflicted mankind, are reflected or shadowed in this theme. The concept of an evil and criminal presence or spirit gaining ascendancy in a hitherto benevolent and honorable person can scarcely be presented without arousing in the human heart some echoes or stealthy overtones of witchcraft and demonology.

Instead of a theological devil or some lesser vile and supernatural spirit entering and possessing the body, we find in Mr. Hyde its seizure and operation by forces of human evil. Though a drug is described as producing or facilitating the transition, no satisfactory explanation of how this comes about is offered by Stevenson. Most readers are probably left with an impression that the motivations and character of the hideous Mr. Hyde have germinated in and developed from latent potentialities for depravity formerly subjugated, chiefly unconscious, in the splendid Dr. Jekyll. The implication is definite that in each of us similarly malign forces perhaps lie dormant.

Though Stevenson's remarkable story, like the story of Faust, carries faint reverberations of the witches' Sabbath, some indirect evocations of the warlock, the sorcerer, and the familiar spirit, the words *Dr. Jekyll and Mr. Hyde* are probably used by most people today to express what they consider a commonplace matter. The two famous names in conjunction serve as a rough equivalent for such popular expressions as "she's a street angel but a home devil." If we hear that someone is "a wolf in sheep's clothing," we feel he is being accused of deliberate hypocrisy. With *Dr. Jekyll and Mr. Hyde*, in casual use, the imputation of hypocrisy is sometimes definite; but more fundamental implications are that someone has two sides to his nature, that his behavior under certain circumstances will be incompatible with what one would expect of him.

Serious medical reports, scarcely less than Stevenson's memorable story, seem to arouse in the lay public, and also among scientific groups, complex and widely diversified reactions; they provoke contrasting mixtures of feeling that it has become popular to call *ambivalent*. The layman who years ago took a course in psychology at college may feel that for him *dual personality*, or *multiple personality* is a familiar subject. Some psychiatrists tend to dismiss the subject more or less as if it were old hat, something long ago discovered, already sufficiently discussed and satisfactorily explained. Others, though interested theoretically in these spectacular dissociations of psychic function described in detail by observers long ago, seem to feel that enthusiasm must have exaggerated and distorted these pictures into something not to be met in actual experience. A sense of something too marvelous *not* to be misleading is likely to follow the initial excitement this subject usually evokes in the classroom.

The persistence of a peculiar curiosity and concern aroused by this subject is reflected in an article, "The Strange Case of Miss Beauchamp," by Kenneth Walker published in the *London Courier*,[1] May, 1955. This interesting discussion deals briefly with the origins of *Dr. Jekyll and Mr. Hyde* and at some length with the remarkable case studied in the closing years of the last century by Morton Prince. More will be said about Miss Beauchamp and the alternate Sally who contended with her for the possession of consciousness, when we have proceeded further with the report of our own patient. It is enough to note here that the concealed manifestations of personality in Miss Beauchamp were first brought out through hypnosis; whereas our Eve Black emerged spontaneously, with no prompting, at a time when Eve White was in her ordinary state of consciousness and entirely free from hypnotic influence.

In some respects dual personality, despite vivid descriptions in popularized books on psychology, is not commonly encountered in the full reality of life. In 1944 a careful survey of the literature by Taylor and Martin listed approximately 76 cases that displayed fully and impressively this disorder.[2] One should not forget that many reports describe only minor or incomplete manifestations, often not particularly remarkable reactions, that give little idea of the rarely seen disorder in its full spectacular scope. Nearly all those stimulating and perplexing medical accounts of two or more people in one body, so to speak, that arouse a unique interest in the classroom are reports of observations made in a relatively distant past. The most significant manifestations of this sort, those that still furnish the chief material for discussion in current literature, occurred and were directly studied half a century or more ago. Never in long years of practice having observed anything remotely approaching the fascinating and almost incredible transformations Morton Prince described in Miss Beauchamp, it is scarcely surprising that practical psychiatrists today might hold a tacitly skeptical attitude toward such archaic marvels and miracles.[3]

In chemistry or internal medicine the last, or even the middle, decades of the nineteenth century appear relatively close to us. There, as compared with the still inexact and primitive field of psychopathology, one feels he can see more clearly or follow a more reliable continuity into the past. In psychiatry, a relatively new and unexplored area of medicine, those decades seem to many almost primeval, a dim dawn era in which we find it easy to believe that a glimpse of a rhinoceros might have led to quite honest descriptions of the unicorn, or the sound of thunder could have been literally interpreted as a god's voice.

Dual personality is a term which usage has endowed with considerable elasticity. To some it may convey concepts of what is mystic, supernatural, or plainly impossible. Others may think of it as indicating little more than an exaggeration of the changes in outlook and behavior that accompany sharply varying moods. Those who have for the first time been freshly impressed by the old reports sensationally describing patients observed long ago often develop a striking enthusiasm for the subject. The receptive senior medical student, or new resident, has been known to discover in the typical products of hypnosis, in the simplest conflicting impulses, even in the most ordinary disturbance of awareness or volition, clues to additional personalities which he thereupon begins to imagine as lurking submerged and invisible in fastnesses of the unconscious. We have known young physicians who became confident that they were discovering several hidden personalities in each new patient. Since our report of this case, some of these zealous explorers of the unconscious have solemnly told us that they have devised complicated digital signals and other shorthand methods to establish contact promptly with various disparate intelligences which they felt sure were thus rendered accessible and articulate.

If investigators can become sufficiently stimulated to feel they can discover so much about additional personalities that never emerge or reveal themselves directly, it is little wonder that those who have worked with overt, rare, and spectacular manifestations have been suspected of overcoloring their reports.

Multiple personality is often classified as a form of hysteria. Some of the cases reported have shown, aside from a dichotomy of consciousness, many classic and unmistakable signs of conversion disorder. Every physician knows that many hysterical patients are notoriously suggestible and dramatic. It is not difficult to believe that such a patient, in response to the enthusiasm of a therapist who sincerely feels he is discovering evidence of something remarkable, might be stimulated to produce elaborate and almost incredible manifestations to conform with or even surpass the observer's expectation or his wildest surmise. Some of the most bizarre performances attributed at first to poltergeists —astonishing and apparently supernatural feats of levitation, teleportation, and necromancy, that in our times have convinced learned men they were dealing with ectoplasmic spirits of the dead—have been produced by naive girls with hysteria responding cooperatively, and perhaps unconsciously, in situations that grew progressively more histrionic and unbelievable.[4,5]

Despite Morton Prince's exquisitely thorough study of the celebrated Miss Beauchamp, it is not surprising that decades later McDougall should have warned us:

It has been suggested by many critics that, in the course of Prince's long and intimate dealings with the case, involving as it did the frequent use of hypnosis both for exploratory and therapeutic purposes, he may have moulded the course of its development to a degree that cannot be determined. This possibility cannot be denied.[6]

It is perhaps significant that, despite the light (or at least the half-light) they seem to throw on many of the puzzling manifestations of psychiatric disorder, the studies of Prince and others on multiple personality are not even mentioned in some of the best and most popular textbooks of psychiatry used in our medical schools today.[7, 8] When mentioned at all in such works, the subject is usually dismissed with a few words.[9, 10] And Freud, during all his years of assiduous investigation apparently displayed no appreciable interest in the nature of such disorder. Erickson and Kubie cite one brief allusion which they term "his only reference to the problem."[11]

In his recent text, *The Practice of Dynamic Psychiatry*, Masserman in a footnote refers to "the concept of 'dissociation' . . . developed in this country by Morton Prince into an elaborate theory of 'multiple personalities' according to which one person not only could be both a Dr. Jekyll and Mr. Hyde but could also rotate among a number of different personalities which had only a tangential knowledge of each other." Masserman, though expressing respect for Prince's work, finds in it "uncritical receptivity in accepting his patient's reports," and concludes, "This type of formulation though popular in psychiatry and literature fifty years ago is now considered questionable."[12] In another footnote referring to patients who are regarded as shifting from one personality to another, Masserman adds,

"This . . . is still avidly acceptable in Hollywood and in radio serials, but in a literal sense progressively less so everywhere else."[13]

Psychiatrists who would not deny outright the truly remarkable things reported long ago about multiple personality, even when accepting them passively in good faith, seem often to do so perfunctorily. In the midst of clinical work with its interesting immediate experience and pressing demands, few are likely to focus a major interest on what is accessible to them only through dust-covered records of what they have never encountered and do not expect to deal with during their lives. During the complications and excitements of a stormy sea voyage, even the most sincere believer in the miracle of Jonah will probably not look to whales for his chief solution to any problems that might arise from shipwreck.

Neither of us, at the time our quiet little patient Eve White changed so spectacularly in the office, had ever seen anything that even remotely resembled a dual personality as described in the old reports. Nor had we ever met another psychiatrist who had seen such a patient. We had grown progressively more skeptical about the subject. The impression given by this young woman when she considered herself Eve Black was such, however, as to arouse our immediate and profound interest. Whatsoever one might choose to call what we witnessed—hysterical dissociation, dual personality, return of the repressed, somnambulism, role-taking, legerdemain, play-acting, or deliberate pretense—it was a performance or manifestation that plainly demanded attention and study.

CHAPTER 6

What, we both wondered, would evolve during the period of hospitalization that had been arranged for Eve White? During her occasional office visits in the past she had seemed not only tense but frightened. Invariably reserved, she was never sufficiently articulate or explicit for one to divine much about the form or essence of this feeling as she experienced it within. Her unhappy and deteriorating marriage and the dangerous uncertainties of her child's future were natural and obvious sources of anxiety. These matters she spoke of, reticently but apparently without evasion. For several months, however, there had seemed to be other components in her fear, threats more internal and unspecific that she found no way of discussing adequately or even of clearly naming. Though it was often an exacerbation of the headache that she or her husband mentioned in requesting another appointment, there were probably more complex and urgent distresses that prompted her to return. There is little difficulty in explaining that one has a headache; but for some of the emotional experiences we suffer there are, perhaps, no corresponding words. This is not to say that Eve White's headaches were not real and sometimes severe.

After she had spoken of hearing imaginary voices, it became less difficult for the physician to grasp that some of the unnamed threats and stresses she felt from within might well be extremely disturbing. These, she was eventually able to make clear, had begun many months before she heard the voice. She seemed .deeply relieved at the prospect of staying in the hospital, as if she hoped it might afford, temporarily at least, a shelter from she knew not what.

"I don't believe I could do otherwise, Doctor," she said with well-controlled but impressive apprehension. "I don't see how I could go back home at present.... Somehow, I dread the thought of being alone."

No alteration in Eve White's characteristic appearance was discernible. Nothing suggested that she had undergone a disturbance or change since she sat down for the interview. She seemed altogether unaware of the role that had been enacted by Eve Black, or even that such a manifestation had come to pass. No trace or hint of that brash vitality could be detected in this slender body as it finally rose from the chair to stand for a moment in the familiar sedate posture before leaving for the Hospital Admitting Office. The shoulders drooped just a little, as they had when she entered the office that morning. An unobtrusive but unmistakable circumspection seemed implicit in every small movement of her body, every line of her face. In these steady timid eyes lurked no glimmer of that blazing light that seemed to flash when the other Eve, such a short time before, had carelessly tossed them about in bold provocative glances. No matter how searchingly the physician looked, he could discern no faint submerged spark, no echo of the bravado or teasing mirth of the subliminal Eve Black.

It was difficult for him to believe that these gentle eyes were composed of the same irises, the same conjunctivae, lenses, retinas, the same humors (aqueous and vitreous) as those which had looked at him scarcely twenty minutes earlier. It was more difficult still to realize that the extraocular muscles of the serious eyes now before him had made dance in such quick spontaneous animation. Where now were the synaptic neural patterns that had so differently activated the play of those eyes such a short time ago? Where were the light and lively emotions they had so sparklingly reflected?

Perhaps it is less than remarkable, the physician told himself, if during medieval times superstitious observers convinced themselves that sudden, gross alterations occurred when the Prince of Darkness entered and possessed a human body. One not knowing this to be impossible might indeed be persuaded to believe that the tired, delicate little figure before him was several pounds less in flesh than the boisterous girl who called herself Eve Black.

The illusion, though impressive, was, to be sure, *illusion*. The slightly pinched cheeks of this tense face did not look as if they were of identical substance with the cheeks to which full relaxation had given a different contour and to which easy gusts of merriment had brought a distinctive flush. Tight-lipped, a little drawn by the specific and involuntary tonic patterns of unremitting care, Eve White's face appeared thinner than when it was expansively activated by the other Eve's vigor.

No structural or true anatomic change need be supposed if we say that this contrast between the two Eves may rest on something more substantial than mere illusion. Real physiologic processes, many of which are not subject to volition, contribute to the distinguishing features of a countenance, to its lines, its color, and to the complex patterns of minute muscular activity that we call *expression*. Few physicians have difficulty remembering faces impressively transformed by an hour or more of severe and unrelieved physical pain. Perhaps alterations of autonomic neural balance contribute an element of true enophthalmos to the haggard look of such a sufferer. The patterns of muscular tonus that underlie posture and carriage are seldom consciously regulated. A subjective sense of energy and well-being, or its opposite, is, however, likely to influence these patterns profoundly, as well as the countless small movements of hand, head, eye, lips, and scalp that enter unnoticed into the complex idiom of recognizable identity. If we are requested to smile we can oblige with a facial movement. But even the obtuse observer can see that this is not really a smile. Talented and well-trained actresses are reported to be able to summon tears at will when their parts require that they weep. It is doubtful if ordinary volition unaided can bring such tears. Is it not more reasonable to believe that the process is indirect, that such an actress has the means to summon into her awareness some emotional component or shallower representation of the real feelings that might cause one to weep?

While discussing plans for Eve White to enter the hospital, Eve Black had made it plain that she considered herself in excellent health and spirits, that she neither wanted nor needed treatment. Her robust appearance in every way supported this claim. But the unassertive little figure of Eve White now leaving with cautious step seemed almost spent, virtually defenseless. There was more about her than the physician could readily describe that promoted fear that her illness might become critical.

How should treatment be planned for this patient? Whether one thinks of Eve Black as another personality or as a congregation of tendencies long denied expression which have surreptitiously organized into a functional unit, it seemed plain that Eve Black's activity played a major part in our patient's illness. Whoever, or whatever, might be regarded as morally or legally responsible for running up the disastrous debt for clothes, the continuation of such occurences would be likely to destroy the Whites' marriage. The imaginary voice which had so seriously and justifiably alarmed the unhappy wife was claimed by Eve Black as her own. The headaches and the far more serious attacks of almost unbearable anxiety, and the feeling of impending disintegration seemed to spring from Eve Black's efforts to gain control and to supplant her rival and emerge. In this contest the disruptive forces seemed to be growing stronger. If Eve Black found it possible to get out again in the physician's presence, would she choose to do so? Or would she, instead, deliberately evade him in order to utilize her time out for her own purposes? If she could be interviewed again would it be possible to influence her favorably, to persuade her to cease, or at least to limit her adverse activity, and, perhaps, even to cooperate in the efforts to help her alternate?

Both of us felt confident that Eve White should know more of what was going on. Was she, as the other Eve claimed, entirely unaware of this lively and irresponsible manifestation's existence? So, indeed, she appeared. Would such knowledge add to the burdens she already found overwhelming? Would it, perhaps, dissolve her remaining powers of integration and precipitate a schizophrenic psychosis? We had no reliable answer to any of these questions. It seemed a situation in which we must proceed cautiously.

After some deliberation we decided against using electric shock or insulin coma treatment. In depressive illness electric treatment, we believed, would almost surely give satisfactory relief. Both these measures had for years proved helpful in dealing with psychotic manifestations of many types, and sometimes with severe disorders generally regarded as neurotic. In our experience with thousands of patients, we had not observed adverse effects on a psychiatric disorder from either of these methods. The risk to life in such a patient as Eve White from the administration of electric treatment would, we estimated, be far less than the risks of tonsillectomy. The chance of fatal complication from insulin coma, though appreciably greater than from electric treatment, would not be imposing—perhaps about equal to that involved in tonsillectomy. In other cases where it seemed that these treatments could offer a reasonable chance for relief in serious trouble, we had never hesitated to advise them and to administer them.

But now we found ourselves confronted with a manifestation of life unique in our experience, with a disorder that seemed to pose problems and bear potentialities never encountered before in the approximately twenty-five years of our collective practice in psychiatry. In textbooks dual personality is often classed with other dissociations of consciousness under the familiar term *hysteria*. Neither of us felt justified, however, in assuming that this patient should be so labeled, or that she would be likely to react in the ordinary patterns of that common disorder. There was about this woman something that made us distinctly aware of the limitations of our knowledge, of the immense mysteries of human entity and of life surrounding the small core of fact and the elaborate and dubious theories of psychopathology.

We decided to approach this problem modestly, to feel our way as best we could, there being no distinct or reliable path that we could see to follow. Psychotherapy is often spoken of as if it were a well-charted procedure based on scientifically established facts about a thoroughly explored unconscious. Our experience had led us to be more skeptical than we once were about some of the psychodynamic processes that are popularly believed to operate in therapy. But we remained deeply impressed with the value of communication between patient and physician, with the many and sometimes powerful emotional forces that develop in such a relationship and that seem occasionally to solve problems too profound for explicit verbal exposition. When we had seen ordinary patients obtain relief from psychotherapy, we often realized that what we understood of the process was at best incomplete. Often what seemed to happen had little or no relation to the more ambitious and elaborate formulations of popular dynamic theory.

With Eve White in the hospital, we planned to encourage her to talk in order to learn as much as we could about her life and feelings. Should Eve Black reappear, we hoped to evoke communication from her also. The immediate and perhaps the chief purpose of hospitalization was to give Eve White relief from a situation that had become acute, that she found inwardly threatening. We hoped to establish through daily interviews while she was there, a helpful relation that would encourage her to return for the many subsequent interviews it seemed likely she would need.

It was the tense, serious little wife and mother, and she only, whom we saw and talked with during the first few days that followed her admission to the hospital. Eve Black did not appear. Nor did any faint suggestion of her manner, of her attitudes, or of her voice slip out during this period when her alternate was under constant and carefully planned surveillance. As might be expected, she was a docile, cooperative, and uncomplaining patient. We considered it important to learn what she might do when alone and, so far as she could know, entirely free from scrutiny by eye or ear. Nurses, interns, attendants, and other patients reported no change in her demeanor, or rift in the orderly routine of her days on the ward. Even in the privacy of her room, it was several times noted, she carefully arranged the dressing gown in which she then walked with discreet gait to the bathroom down the empty corridors after bedtime. Though always quietly courteous, she seemed inhibited in establishing easy, casual contact with others.

Often she sat alone in her room reading a copy of *Palgrave's Golden Treasury* which she had kept from high school days, or verses clipped from newspapers and magazines which she had over the years pasted into a scrapbook.

The poems she liked best were those dealing with age-old orthodox values and the basic virtues often regarded by the sophisticated as simple, or even as banal. She had committed to memory a considerable number of short verses and fragments. She particularly liked these lines:

Love took up the glass of Time, and turned it in his glowing hands;
Every moment, lightly shaken, ran itself in golden sands.
Love took up the harp of Life, and smote on all the
chords with might,
Smote the chord of Self, that, trembling, passed in music
out of sight.

This pleasure in verse was not freely exhibited by Mrs.
White. Like most of her personal interests it had remained
a solitary preoccupation. She had been too reserved to risk
the misunderstanding one often finds in the effort to share
one's own little emotional discoveries. Though many of the
poems and rhymes she valued are generally regarded as
sentimental or trite, her reaction to these, as well as to
more serious material, was never effusive or pretentious.
In her shy, uncommunicative fashion she had, apparently,
found solace in things that ranged from Shakespearean lines
too well-known to retain interest for the learned to Edgar A.
Guest's jingling stanzas in praise of household virtues and
hard work. This interest of Eve White's was not discovered
by us until she was in the hospital where it could be observed that she turned to her large scrapbook and to *Palgrave* as if to a familiar refuge.

In discussion it was difficult to elicit from her much indication of what emotional response she obtained from the
lines she liked. Formally and quietly she discussed her pref-
erences, her voice never quickening with enthusiasm. Her
reserve never suggested affectation, unfriendliness, or emotional paucity. She was anything but indifferent but she lacked
the impulsiveness to communicate affect freely. It seemed
plain that she would share her personal feelings if she had
the means to do so. Not in the tranquillity that her controlled appearance often suggested, but in forlorn need of
unattained communion, she seemed to continue purblind
the unformulated quest of some substitute for being adequately understood by another. She could talk without difficulty about intimate matters, but she was too timid to allow
her own specific feelings about them to emerge from within,
except in diluted tinctures of generalization. She said that
she was able to find some measure of relief from worry in
reading. Among the favorite lines committed to memory
that she often dwelt on silently, she mentioned this stanza
from Tennyson's *In Memoriam*:

I held it truth, with him who sings
To one clear harp of divers tones,
That men may rise on stepping-stones
Of their dead selves to higher things.

In the hospital environment Eve White seemed to feel some degree of security or protection. She impressed all observers as a woman of even disposition, showing no unwarranted shifts of mood or flashes of temperament. She freely discussed the early years of her life. Her father, a farmer and country storekeeper, had been able to provide a comfortable living for the family but very few luxuries. So far as she recalled, she had felt wanted and loved. There had been special occasions of pleasure and also ordinary little disappointments that at the time had seemed rather serious, but only for the moment. Yes, she supposed she could say that both her mother and her father seemed warm and understanding. They were not arbitrary or severe about discipline; nor did she remember them as pampering or spoiling any of their children. Most of the scoldings and punishments she received had been given by her mother. The father was away at work nearly all day. She believed that her mother had been fair and not unduly strict.

Important in her memory of early childhood was the birth of twin sisters when she was about five years old. She recalled this event as chiefly exciting. The sudden appearance of two new babies had seemed to the little girl something pleasant, an exciting sort of prodigy in which she too, she vaguely felt, since they were her sisters, played an important part. She must have felt jealous of the twins sometimes she supposed, or resented the attention they demanded of her parents, but she could recall no bitter or enduring sense of rivalry, no tragic sense of displacement and rejection. Though she was an only child until the twins were born, she had always enjoyed the close companionship of Flo, her cousin who lived nearby.

As she talked with us at great length during the first days of hospitalization, the story of her early life seemed more ordinary than remarkable. She brought out nothing to indicate malign or distorting influences, unusual emotional conflicts or deprivations. She could recall no unusual erotic preoccupations or experiences, no precocious striving, and no adventures that might have confused her aims or disturbed her normal development.

53

A long time before the twins had been born, she had experienced a good deal of apprehension about an incident she still remembered vividly. There was a large ditch of stagnant, slimy water under a bridge in the woods nearby. This spot had seemed a long way from home; the woods, particularly in twilight, seemed mysterious and beautiful but haunted with danger. A man, perhaps a drunken tramp, had fallen into this ditch one night and drowned. His body was dragged next day from the murky depths. Eve White believed she had been present when this occurred, for she recalled her specific horror and fear at the sight of the body, and her vague but powerful new realizations and surmises about death.

Such an event naturally caused much talk in the little community among both adults and children. What she actually saw as a small child soon became entangled with overheard snatches of grown people's conversation, with elaborate fantasies spun by older boys and girls to dazzle and shock the hearer. Various products of her own imagination, along with incomplete bits of rustic superstition about ghosts that walked in graveyards during the new moon and witches that "rid you till they's tuk all yer breath," which field hands sometimes mentioned, accrued to the actual happening, eventually cloaking it with enchantment and terror.

By one way or another she had come to believe for a while that a malign and dangerous monster dwelt in the stagnant waters of the ditch. Perhaps she had never been fully convinced that this creature was real, but she had thoughts about it and uncertainties accompanied by lively apprehension. She recalled dreams in which the monster of the ditch threatened and pursued her in vague and various forms. The deadly thing was pictured as predominantly reptilian, as a great scaly form larger than a grown man. There were features of the image that suggested an alligator, but it had also some attributes of the sea serpent and the dragon. The eyes were baleful and merciless. Imagery from the dreams afforded additional features with which she endowed her creation in daylight fantasies. But on the whole Eve White felt that her childhood had been happy; even those ideas about the dangerous inhabitant of the ditch, she now felt, probably had afforded more interest and excitement than distress.

Some narrators through their own exuberance, their freely displayed personal reaction to details of experience, make intrinsically ordinary events take on a special quality and even become remarkable. The simplest and most familiar matters may evoke subjective responses that are fresh and notable. In contrast, Eve White was never quite able to free herself from an element of formality that seemed to keep the facts she imparted, however intimate these might be, at some distance from the individual and unique feelings with which she must have met them. By a small unobtrusive step of circumspection, she stood apart from what she related just enough to blur its emotional specificity, just enough to make what might have been subjectively a rather sensational experience take on, in the process of its expression, a generic quality.

"As a child," she said, "I must have been very sensitive to criticism and to punishment." She felt quite sure that her parents had not punished her too frequently or severely. "Perhaps it was because they did it so seldom," she suggested, "that it sometimes hurt my feelings and I couldn't understand."

During the period of observation nothing was observed in Eve White that suggested a masked or incipient schizophrenic disorder or even schizoid traits. Her gestures and posture revealed no hint of the odd or bizarre little manifestations that so often reflect evanescently subtle schizoid changes deeply concealed behind flawless rationality. There was in her restraint and propriety only the flavor of normal timidity, nothing of the chill and glassy aloofness, the inexplicable withdrawal from life and its basic warmth that form the untranslatable idiom of schizoid feeling. Where she differed from the average or the typical, it seemed not in the direction of queerness but of conventionality.

After much consideration, we decided to seek another audience with Eve Black. Both of us felt some reluctance about simply confronting our cooperative and insecure little patient with a forthright account of what we had learned about her alternate. If Eve White's apparent unawareness of the other modality of behavior was indeed genuine, would this not be a dangerously shocking revelation? If one assumed the entire business to be only an elaborate pretense, consciously, or less than consciously, enacted, it must have some purpose. Perhaps it might play an important part in this woman's inward efforts to survive. Whatever one might conclude about the degree of real disparity between these alternating manifestations, he who had dealt with them directly would not be likely to believe that they represented the sort of ordinary chicanery that could be dispelled by a frank accusation of deceit.

On the two occasions that Eve White had been hypnotized, amnesia for the period of "sleep" or "trance" had been obtained. Hypnosis was therefore induced again. While the demure little patient sat with eyes closed in this (still little-understood) state of altered or incomplete consciousness, Eve Black was called by name and requested in tones of confidence to speak.

The eyes opened promptly. Even before they moved, or so it seemed to us, there could be no doubt about whom we dealt with. Like one awakened who has been sleeping in a cramped uncomfortable position, her body shifted slightly its center of gravity, carrying out by reflex, it seemed, numerous but scarcely discernible little readjustments. Almost instantaneously the figure had relaxed into the buoyant ease of Eve Black.

"Well, Doc," she said in the husky, brisk voice so unlike that of the other, "what you did just now sure made it easier for me to get out."

Her bright eyes roved briefly about the hospital room as if in amused curosity. "I know pretty well what this place looks like all right," she explained, "but I just thought I'd like to see for myself." She smiled, her affable face at ease, and then said casually, as if referring to a matter that did not particularly concern her, "She's really feeling a lot better. Of course, there ain't anything could bring her to her senses. But, Doc, I do think you somehow done her some good. She's still scared, all right. I can tell that. But nothing like what she was a week ago."

After considerable discussion, this Eve granted permission for the other to be informed of her existence. She was at first skeptical and a little negative to the suggestion. She questioned the influence this might have on her own ability to come out and be herself. The physician suggested that compromises might be worked out, that, with Eve White cognizant of her, there might be some lessening of the peculiar conflict. In some respects she seemed like a child bargaining for a toy, naively flourishing the cards she knew she held and at the same time lured by what might be offered. There was a way, she admitted, in which her alternate could oppose her and often, though not always, actively prevent her from getting out. This power, according to

56

Eve Black, varied with the other's state of health, strength, and security. Just what the other did in her efforts to suppress her she could not explain. "She don't really know what she's about, either, but just struggles hard to keep herself from what she thinks of as going to pieces." In the improvement that had occurred since Eve White came into the hospital, this Eve found added difficulties. She had, she admitted, tried unsuccessfully to come out "a couple of times for just a little while" and investigate the psychiatric ward.

She was apparently impressed with the effects of hypnosis on the other Eve and its influence in facilitating her emergence. "I think it made it easier on her, too," she said, with a bright canny glance at the physician. She was again requested to avoid conduct during her periods of ascendancy that would damage the other. She was also told that it might be dangerous for her, while submerged, to increase the pressures she exerted on the other or to seek new ways to harass and exhaust her in anticipation of a full-scale attempt to break out. It was again emphasized that if Eve White lost ground and finally became psychotic, there would be poor opportunities in the state hospital for a girl who enjoyed highballs, new acquaintances, and late hours in night clubs.

The confident girl before us was not immediately compliant to all these sugestions. Nothing could bring her to admit responsibility or a personal concern for Eve White, Ralph White, of their daughter. She did not seem in the least cruel or vengeful, but rather stood in the role of a disinterested observer who was sure of her ground and determined not to be saddled with problems not of her own making.

"I got nothing against her," she said, speaking of Eve White. "I don't wish her any bad luck. But I got myself to think about, too; I can't keep my mind on her and her doings and her worryings all the time."

When Eve Black did agree to behave with reasonable discretion, her final words of compliance seemed too easy and sweeping, a little too glib to rely on. But she finally gave wholehearted consent for the physician to explain about her to Eve White. Mentioning several minor adventures she had enjoyed in the past few months, she began to laugh softly but with warm amusement. She told about several flirtations she had begun, and lively and extremely contagious little gusts of mirth interrupted her as she explained how she had successfully evaded the consequences of each adventure. Leaning over, she rested an elbow on each knee and put her forehead in her hands. The knees, as she struggled to control her laughter, sprawled a little apart. In this there seemed only a little that was erotically provocative. It was chiefly the carelessness of a pubertal girl forgetting for the moment that she is no longer a child.

"Her face will be a sight to see if you tell her about the time I was out at the Lido Club. Had some champagne cocktails with a fellow there. I like to sing, you see. Well, about two o'clock I couldn't stand it any longer. I got out in the middle of the floor and really let 'em have it. They liked it, too. Everybody stopped dancing. The orchestra quit. I got better and better. The pianist started up again to accompany me. They kept on clapping and stomping and cheering. I put some charge in it when I got to 'Rockin' and Rollin' '—*Rockin' and rollin' All night long....*"

With a little toss of her head she carried a snatch of the tune for a moment. "But what really sent 'em," she said, "was when I stood there in the middle of that dance floor with the spotlight on me and let 'em have 'Sixty Minute Man.'"

CHAPTER 7

In our attempt to tell Eve White about the other personality we proceeded circumspectly. From the subject of her black-outs, discussion led from such commonplace matters as sleep-walking toward more complicated automatisms and fugues. She was confident that during the occasional periods of unconsciousness of which she had complained, nothing more than a passive state of sleep prevailed. Her attitude indicated the assumption that these had been of brief duration, probably nothing more remarkable than transient faint-ing spells caused by the severe headaches which preceded them. Sometimes when she came for an office appointment, however, on occasions shortly after suffering from a black-out, she had sometimes seemed more uneasy about them, less assured that they had lasted only a few minutes. As time elapsed and the experiences became a little more re-mote, she was apparently better able to accept them as minor episodes. Her curiosity about them seemed to de-cline. Members of the family had not recently observed Eve White to faint. She had not checked with watch or clock to obtain evidence of their duration. From her parents we learned later that many years ago she had suffered from periods of stupor or delirium that varied in length from a few minutes to an hour or more. Her husband told us that several months ago, after a quarrel with him, she had impetuously rushed out of the house at night in a hard rain, and he had found her an hour later, unconscious at the foot of a pine tree with which she had apparently collided. Later she was unable to recall the quarrel or that she had left the house.

Had Eve White shrunk from investigating these occurences?

Had there been some inner feeling, perhaps only vaguely realized, warning her that investigation might lead to further trouble, might raise questions that would add to her stress and bewilderment? She denied awareness of any such motivation. Even in much less unusual situations we often involuntarily turn from matters that might prove to be unpleasant, and often without realizing our own evasion. Has not every thoughtful person, occasionally, on being plainly confronted with some distressing situation, realized for the first time that latent awareness or at least grounds for suspicion of the danger had lain within him for many months, somehow disregarded or unrecognized?

The patient remembered that during early childhood she was told that she often walked in her sleep. Her parents had spoken of this many times. What she recalled chiefly were references to the habit after it had ceased, or almost ceased, stories that her mother or father told humorously as if it were some minor but amusing idiosyncrasy in a distant past. She had, she felt sure, never waked up while out of bed during the night. She never had any recollection next day that she had gotten up and gone about the house. She could remember that when she was very small her parents had discussed means of preventing her from walking in her sleep. Yes, they had for a few nights put a tub of water at the side of the bed. They had been told that if one arises while still asleep and puts his foot in cold water, he will be likely to wake.

She recalled no particular uneasiness about this on the part of her parents. Never having waked up in a strange place, there was nothing about the matter that alarmed her. So far as she knew, she had done nothing unusual or dangerous while carrying out simple activities in her sleep. It must have begun very early, perhaps a few months after the twin sisters were born. After a year or two it became progressively less frequent and disappeared. It did, however, recur once or twice in her early teens, but never again, as far as she knew, after that.

Though she looked back on the sleepwalking in early childhood as a relatively ordinary matter, she recalled having some curiosity about it when it returned briefly during adolescence. Once then she had walked out into the living room where the light was on and her parents, who had not yet gone to bed, were sitting. Next day she asked them to tell her exactly what she did and how she seemed.

Her eyes had been open, they said, and apparently she could see what she was doing, for she avoided furniture and other objects that lay in her way. She had stopped and turned toward them when they addressed her and, indeed, had spoken in reply. Her eyes, they told her, had a vacant look, her gaze seemed abstract and inattentive to the immediate surroundings, but not troubled or unnatural. Though her appearance must have differed immensely from that of a person asleep, she was also noticeably unlike herself during ordinary wakefulness. She seemed not so much sleeping as dazed. Her reactions indicated consciousness and purpose; but she seemed incompletely or differently conscious, reacting with less than her full, ordinary motivations. They had told her she was responsive to persuasion. After being led back to bed she had slept on through the night. Next morning she was unable to remember getting out of bed in the night, or anything at all about what she had said and done.

She had never thought of these episodes as bizarre or dangerous. Would she be upset if such a manifestation should occur during one of her blackouts? Eve seemed to have given this possibility little thought, but said she found nothing particularly alarming in what she remembered being told about her sleepwalking long ago. No attempt was made at this point to hurry the patient toward any concept of serious personality dissociation. What she remembered of her somnambulism was utilized in discussions that dwelt on varying degrees of consciousness in commonplace situations.

Quarterbacks have played brilliantly after a blow on the head, displaying not only physical coordination but also planning and executing an effective strategy of offense. Sometimes such a quarterback retains no memory of what he thought and what he did during such a period. So far as he himself will ever know, he was unconscious. His performance, nevertheless, was versatile and impeccable. He gave no indication of being dazed. Anything of function, would, one might think, have become evident during the considerable period of amnesia when he was directing the team successfully in its complicated and varied maneuvers. Physicians, aroused by the persistent ringing of a telephone from the depths of sleep, have been known to discuss at length some urgent medical problem with an intern without being able next day to realize their night's rest had been interrupted. If the caller brings up again the details of such a conversation during the physician's rounds at the hospital, he may then obtain memories of the incident. Occasionally the physician may display his best knowledge and judgment in what he says over the telephone and yet find it impossible ever to recall that he had been aroused.

It seems reasonable to think that almost any person might experience alarm and bewilderment on being told for the first time that he had frequently walked around town during periods of amnesia. Will he not wonder what he may have said and done? Was he strange in his appearance and manner or conspicuous in public? What impulses and intentions determined the activities that were carried on without his present knowledge? In the absence of whatever he regards as *himself*, what other reasoning or judgment controlled and directed his behavior? Patients with narcolepsy and psychomotor epilepsy, who frequently have periodic lapses of consciousness, show great concern about these points.

In any serious consideration of losing the customary control of oneself, many people find a specific dread. Not to be quite oneself because of drunkenness would loom as a disturbing proposition to many responsible men who nevertheless enjoy drinking in moderation. An extreme example of the alterations occasionally brought about by alcohol is afforded by an isolated incident in the life of a circumspect young schoolteacher. Unaccustomed to whisky, she decided at a large dance to take a few highballs, more or less as an experiment. Next morning she woke up, as she shamefacedly expressed it, "with company in bed." She had not intended to drink much. She never recalled any of the events that led to the man, whom she had regarded only as a pleasant, casual acquaintance, escorting her home and spending the night with her. One who has ever lost his temper to the point where he is plunged into alien behavior is likely to be uncomfortable at the thought that this may recur. Those who suffer from phobias that center about the idea of becoming psychotic, of suddenly losing rational command of volitional activity and of sane demeanor, sometimes experience terror not altogether expressible.

How would the conventional mind of Eve White react to information that at times she so far forgot herself as to dance and drink with strangers in a night club? Would she be less incredulous or less confused, if told that, without her knowledge, a constellation of tendencies and aims foreign to her own awareness emerged and directed her own physical self in activities she regarded as distasteful and strictly impermissible? What sort of anxious insecurity might a deeply conscientious and cautious person feel who never knows when such an episode might occur?

If this patient was completely noncognizant of Eve Black, truly unaware of what the other manifestation did and thought and felt, would she not reject as fantastically impossible any explanation of this sort that we might offer? Surely even the most credulous of people would hesitate to accept anyone's word for such a story. Would this staid and retiring little person ever be able to formulate in her imagination a convincing image of that other vital and reckless figure? True imperturbability would be necessary to accept anything so alien as an unknown part of oneself. Even more of this quality would be needed to face the concept of a being or personality so uncongenial and incompatible as, somehow and incomprehensibly, a coinhabitant of one's own flesh and blood.

After a week in the hospital Eve White, now considerably encouraged and improved, accepted without undue apparent apprehension our statement that during her blackout in the office more than an hour had elapsed before she again seemed aware of her surroundings. She did not, we assured her, show any signs of physical shock, nothing to suggest that her life might be in danger. With what seemed to be well-controlled surprise she listened as we told her she had spoken and had opened her eyes soon after losing consciousness. She knew from previous discussions that while hypnotized she had carried out these and other acts without retaining memory of them on awakening. Was her state during the blackout similar to hypnosis, she inquired? We told her it was, as far as we knew, in *some* respects similar but not in all.

We explained that her manner and voice had changed considerably and that she had seemed remarkably free from worry about her problems. She was encouraged to think of the lapse as having some points of resemblance to the sleepwalking of her childhood. Our experience with several patients who had suffered brief and relatively unspectacular fugues was discussed. One of these had persistant amnesia for a period of almost one week during which he had traveled to another state. His behavior there had been socially acceptable and rather ordinary. Though apparently purposive and well-executed, his activities had no relation to his recognized inclinations or habitual aims. Awakening from, or passing through, the period of alteration, he had found himself in a strange town without knowledge of how, or when, or why, he got there. Unlike Eve White, he had immediate and vivid awareness that an unusual and major lapse of consciousness lay behind him and that something astonishing had occurred.

Characteristically laconic, never idly talkative, Eve White seemed to react with mixed feelings. To be faced with evidence that she had, without realizing it, passed through periods of unconsciousness during which she carried out activities unknown to herself was inevitably disquieting. A new sense of vulnerability could not be avoided. On the other hand there was an advantage in the patient's having now some explanation for the disturbing events which heretofore had confronted her only in the form of a weirdly impossible paradox. Ralph White, after his first meeting with Eve Black in the office, though his thoughts still seemed to stagger from the unanticipated revelation, had said:

"Well, Doctor, this throws some light on a lot of things that have happened. I never heard of any such thing as what we just saw. I don't understand it at all. But it does bring some kind of sense to a lot that's gone on, a lot that just didn't fit together anyway you tried to look at it."

So, too, Eve White might now account to herself for the quarrel while she was visiting Flo in Columbia. If at times during that period she was not, in the ordinary sense, conscious, if she was dazed or confused and not herself, she might have been unreasonable and even disagreeable in speaking with Ralph. Theoretically at least, this seemed to afford some interpretation for what had heretofore been un-

63

approachably inexplicable. In a twilight state, acting as people sometimes act in delirium or nightmare, one might, indeed, do unusual things. Could she actually have gone downtown to the stores and heedlessly bought all those lavish clothes while in such a state? As if with one hand she seemed to grasp for relief in such an explanation, with the other she held it off, and appeared, indeed, as if trying to push it away as implausibly fantastic, and in some new way bizarrely terrifying. Her face looked pale and pinched and her thin fingers clenched the arms of her chair as she sat for perhaps a minute in silent contemplation. Her pupils had dilated, giving her intent eyes a darker hue. The consequential details of the situation, all that must follow if one accepted such an assumption, seemed to sink slowly into the grave young woman's realization.

But was it not true, she finally asked, that anyone in such a trance would be detected? If any person were in a state that would allow her to carry out a deed so purposeless and inappropriate, so downright foolish, surely the confusion would be obvious. Would any clerk show such poor judgment as to transact serious business with a dazed and incoherent customer? Can't most people tell that someone walking in his sleep is not really awake? Why, of all things, would she, even in some clouded or semiconscious state, choose, or be led into, a performance so contrary to her desires and so self-damaging? Such a debt would be no less painful to her than to her husband. Even if she could easily afford them, she would never want such conspicuous hats and gloves, such lingerie and perfume, such vivid and daring gowns.

"Really, Doctor" she said in a low, serious tone, "there wasn't one of those dresses in which I could have felt ... well ..., in which I could have felt quite like a decent woman."

As something remote or generalized, the concept of people during periods of amnesia occasionally carrying out complicated activity had seemed more credible, less strange and alarming than the prospect of accepting such a supposition about herself. She was not urged to do so. During the following days amnesia and automatism were discussed from many approaches. Encouraging examples were cited of people who, after serious and elaborate episodes of fugue, had recovered and led normal lives. Gradually emphasis was shifted to descriptions of "how a person might seem" during an extended fugue, and eventually some of the striking differences in manner, appearance, and behavior of those manifestations, often referred to as *alternating consciousness* or *dual personality*, were discussed.

Any suggestion of the Dr. Jekyll-Mr. Hyde concept of a malevolent subterranean force or an organized entity of evil was carefully avoided. So, too, were all terms that might stimulate the imagination toward overcolored or mystically tinted notions and fears. We did not, at this point, speak of dual personality or multiple personality, feeling that these expressions might carry implications more likely to cloud, distort, or artificially influence her ideas than to clarify or help. If the pathologic situation we confronted was indeed the result of functional dissociation, then it seemed logical to believe that amelioration might lie in the direction of *rapprochment* between the disparate elements.

Eve Black admitted no point of identity with the other Eve; she consistently drew a sharp line of demarcation between everything ascribed to "her" or recognized as "me." She boasted that she was now able to force her way into control more and more frequently. If real progress was to be made, might it not be necessary for Eve White eventually to regard whatever occurred during periods of amnesia as of her own doing, however impaired her judgment might be, whether or not she might, in the ordinary sense, be held responsible? We did not therefore promote or encourage in the patient tendencies to sequester herself from any act that might have been carried out during amnesia and thus contrive, one might say, a synthetic scapegoat to bear whatever blame might be incurred.

Though Mrs. White came to accept the fact that behavior alien and incomprehensible to her had taken place during periods of amnesia, and that this might recur, she seemed instinctively or automatically to strive against or to evade some aspects of realization. If adequate progress was to be made, must she not clearly recognize and better understand the seceded and rebellious tendencies integrate but invisible within herself? Must she not more realistically appraise this curious adversary?

During this period we also had a number of interviews with Eve Black, hypnotizing Eve White to obtain the other's presence. Without reluctance this debonair girl granted permission for her alternate to be informed of anything she confided concerning her own thought or conduct that we deemed it advisable for Eve White to know. She seemed to feel that this would enable her to gain ascendancy more often, to obtain more freedom at the other's expense. She agreed also to help more directly in the attempt to acquaint the other with herself.

"Eve White's not like me," she said with a kind of easy pride. "She don't know a thing about what I think, but I know her thoughts like she does herself. I don't think 'em, of course, but I can nearly always tell whatever's in her mind."

She had, as we have said, on those few occasions in the past (or so she claimed) been responsible for the objectively unreal voice that Eve White in profound fear had reported as an auditory hallucination. There was, apparently, no means by which Eve White could behold the figure now so pleasantly relaxed in the chair before us, or see for herself this volatile face, those careless sparkling eyes. But perhaps, through the hallucinatory or quasihallucinatory modality of communication, this Eve might manifest herself to the other directly and convincingly. She agreed to try, though her attitude appeared to be that of one who good-naturedly consents about some trivial point in a matter of no great concern. After Eve White had been summoned in the usual way and had for some time been discussing her problems with the therapist, Eve Black was addressed by the name she used and requested to speak directly to her apparently unsuspecting alternate.

The response was immediate and impressive. Eve White's familiar face was suddenly blank almost beyond recognition. The deeply ingrained control that had kept it so consistently molded in lines of timid reserve shattered like an eggshell. The habitually guarded eyes shone luminous. The momentary absence of all expression was followed by naked astonishment. In silence her features regained a good measure of their customary composure. Catching her breath with a scarcely audible sigh she slowly whispered, "It just can't be."

The patient was profoundly shaken and disturbed. Her physician deemed it necessary to remain with her the rest of the afternoon, doing what he could to reassure her and help her adjust her feelings to a realization that she found weirdly terrifying.

66

CHAPTER 8

Eve White remained in the hospital for approximately two weeks. She received no specific treatment other than psychotherapy. She seemed to gain steadily in strength and confidence and to make general improvement. How to proceed in our efforts to help her was not always easy to determine. Precisely what aims to set, what steps to attempt next were not always clear. In this patient processes were at work which we did not have any means of controlling directly. Our position was one of expectancy. At times it seemed that we could do little more than stand in readiness, hoping for new features to emerge that would offer a better grasp on the problem and by which we might exert some more specifically helpful influence.

After a brief period of consternation on hearing the alternate announce herself, Eve White seemed to benefit from the experience. She now had an explanation, however strange, for the voice which she had heard previously and found in it relief from the fear that psychosis was impending. She never again heard Eve Black's voice or in any other way came in contact with her directly. Only by what she was told and by inference from situations into which she suddenly awoke, could she gain any knowledge of the alternate's nature, or of her habits, tastes, and caprices. Some of the predicaments in which she found herself, usually without the sense of a preceding lapse of consciousness, were novel and disturbing.

During long interviews each day we were gathering a good deal of detail about Eve White's career. She discussed her childhood recollections at length and was able to give a substantial picture of her development through the teens. Though not a spontaneously talkative person, she never seemed evasive, and as time passed she became increasingly articulate. There were, apparently, no events she was too reluctant to reveal, and it seemed helpful to her to express herself. Despite this, one felt that she was in some important respects a person for whom real intimacy was peculiarly difficult. She seldom hesitated to speak of her personal feelings but, though her words referring to such matters were quite clear, the affect itself seemed guarded, reserved, not an active or palpable ingredient of the communication.

She did not impress one as voluntarily attempting to hide or to suppress her emotion, but rather as lacking in some subtle way the facility through which simple personal reactions color and warm and identify the content of ordinary speech. Under hypnosis no essential change was ever noted in her personality. Some degree of relaxation often occured and she could react with less reserve to the feelings she discussed; but she never showed under hypnosis any characteristic or suggestion of Eve Black, or of anyone but her distinct self. Though hypnosis was used several times while Eve White was in the hospital and occasionally afterwards in the office, it never led to the recovery of specific memories withheld or repressed during ordinary wakefulness. Nor could we ever succeed in bringing about a regression to earlier stages of her life and have her relive incidents that occurred in childhood. Under hypnosis she could occasionally shed tears in our presence and otherwise reveal her feelings more fully, but none of her basic attitudes showed real alteration. Hypnosis repeatedly failed to bring her into any personal awareness of Eve Black, or into any direct contact with the impulses or thoughts that animated this other figure. Over the years hypnosis seemed to play no important part in the relations between therapist and patient or in the developments that are to be recounted.

Prior to the period of hospitalization Eve White had had no means whatever of accounting for the strange and apparently impossible situations which occasionally confronted her. From this time on, however, she concluded that on such occasions Eve Black must have been out. How long had she been out? This could be estimated only by checking with a watch or calendar.

Where had she been? And what had she done? Sometimes the rank scent of cheap, unfamiliar perfume might offer a clue. Or perhaps the telephone would ring and some strange, self-assured male voice would ask for Eve Black. Occasionally when she awoke in the morning, a taste like dry ashes in her mouth aroused suspicion that the adventurous stranger with whom she lived on such peculiar terms had celebrated excessively with drink and cigarettes. During the months that followed her period of hospitalization, Eve White gradually learned a good deal about her invisible associate's habits, predilections, and escapades. Every detail of the concept furnished by inference of the other's motivation and viewpoint—of self or being—remained unapproachably alien to the

68

decorous and unassertive housewive. Despite the long association in a relation uniquely intimate, Eve White remained invincibly isolated from that other life. No intimation of its feeling, thought, or desire ever touched her awareness directly.

Before our patient left the hospital Eve Black emerged spontaneously on several occasions. A young man, admitted about a week previously to recuperate from a relatively mild alcoholic episode, had, during his first hours of discomfort and remorse, found in Eve White a patient confidante, a soothing, uncritical, and maternal figure to whom he turned for support and encouragement. Recovered from his malaise and dejection, one day this man sat alone with an open book in a small recreation room, his attention wandering, off and on, back to thoughts of the modest, almost nunlike little companion whose consideration he had found so helpful.

Glancing up with eyes still meditative, he saw what at first he took to be a familiar figure. Eve Black had playfully tiptoed into the room, and now stood poised in anticipation of the surprise in his glance. Like a child who has succeeded in slipping up on an adult to startle him by saying "boo," she broke into soft warm laughter. He was aware of a teasing merriment in her eyes flagrantly incompatible with the woman he thought he saw before him. Pouting her lips at his intent face, this Eve took a few buoyant steps forward and casually sat on the arm of his chair. For a moment she softly hummed a light tune, rocking one small foot in time with the beat. Silent again, she suddenly nudged his shoulder with her hand.

"How you doing, boy?" she asked.

Like an energetic kitten that has lots to do, she was up and, an instant later, had swung with a strong supple step to the phonograph across the room and was putting on a record. Turning toward her companion as the lively tune sounded, she stood for a few seconds, her shoulders and hips responding just perceptibly and perfectly to the rhythm. In contrast with the frail, retiring Eve White, in whose dress she stood, this lush apparition pulsated with energy. Catching and holding his glance with bold bright eyes, her whole face lit with a fresh inviting smile.

"Come on, boy ... dance with me," she urged softly.

A minute or two later the floor nurse came in. Having known only Eve White, she was astonished and delighted to find this quiet and troubled patient throwing herself with such spirit into the dance. After a brief observation of the pair she decided, however, that it was time for Mrs. White to return to her room. Reminding her that the nightly vitamin pill awaited and that it was the hour for temperatures to be taken, the nurse accompanied her there.

Nothing unseemly had occured, the nurse reminded herself. Perhaps her sense of uneasiness came from the incredible change in Mrs. White. The stimulus or influence that could make a woman as staid and retiring as this patient flash suddenly with such fire might lead the next moment into almost anything. Mr. Smathers, the male patient, had also seemed excited and a little confused. There was nothing grossly improper in the way they had been dancing. But Mrs. White—*Mrs. White* of all people!—had in some inexpressible way seemed stimulating and provocative. As she left she had said nothing out of the way to Mr. Smathers. But even the husky tone in which she had murmured good night, with a sudden flash of the eyes and a deliberate lowering of the lids, made you stop and wonder. The man's face had looked a little flushed as if he were unduly exhilarated or somehow shaken in his equanimity.

Later, Mr. Smathers talked at some length with the intern about his personal reactions. Nothing extraordinary that you could quite put your finger on had really happened, he said, and kept, in various forms, repeating. Looking back, he didn't know how to describe the peculiar feeling he'd had. It seemed for a moment he was about to lose his grip on himself. Well as he knew Mrs. White, he found himself thinking someone else must be impersonating her. The sensation he had was stranger than that. He didn't know how to put it. Instead of an impersonation this just wasn't like her at all! In the confusion that arose he began to doubt his own general orientation. Though he was not exactly dizzy, the floor and walls seemed far away and he found himself unsure of his balance. He had been pretty ill, he realized, when he came into the hospital. He had noticed a few psychotic patients whose behavior was odd and at first a little disturbing. After that, he got to feeling wonderfully well. Hadn't a worry in the world when Mrs. White came in. Then, abruptly, the idea got hold of him that he was with somebody else ... somebody else altogether!

"Why, it even flashed through my mind that maybe she'd suddenly lost her marbles—gone right off her rocker."

Mr. Smathers slowly shook his head. A wan smile reflected curosity and chagrin.

"That was a crazy notion for me to take. She didn't say anything irrational. Didn't do anything that would seem out of the ordinary in anybody but her. It just somehow shook me down when I couldn't get it straight about who it was, or just *what* might be happening. Then the thought hit me like a buggy whip: brother, it must be *you!* Maybe you've goofed off here, right when you thought you'd made it. It's the d.t.'s, brother. They got you after all!"

It was summer and a number of medical students who had completed their sophomore year were working as aides or attendants in the hospital, obtaining thus some practical experience with illness along with a modest but helpful remuneration. One of these, a young man perhaps more sensitive and introspective than his fellows, took up duties on the psychiatric section a few days before Eve White was dismissed. Having no full medical responsibilities, such students were not routinely informed about the history of each patient. In the psychiatric section particularly, every effort is made to preserve strict rules of privacy about personal matters, to prevent dissemination of things discussed in confidence.

This young man's hours of work began after supper when the section was usually quiet and medical activities minimal. He was thoughtful and sympathetic and liked to talk to the patients and help make the evening pleasant for them. Sometimes he joined a little group playing cards or checkers, or sat for a while with others who were watching television. Behind her timid formality, most people soon felt in quiet little Eve White, a receptivity and a need for friendliness. Nurses and interns found that she seemed to value any little attention, that she made them feel it had been well worthwhile to spend even a few minutes here and there in conversation with her. Anyone saw at once she was not a person who could readily pour out her troubles to another. She seemed also to need specifically the personal understanding, the support of more intimacy, the very things she knew not how to ask of another. Whether or not anything even remotely connected with her problems was discussed, the physician who offered her some of his time and interest always felt, despite her notable uneffusiveness and reserve, that she had found his attention most acceptable, that perhaps he had in some small way helped someone in genuine need.

The sensitive young medical student found his attention at once drawn to this thoughtful, obviously troubled, and delicately attractive young woman. Each evening he spent what time he could spare, talking quietly with her, sometimes mentioning briefly his own interests in the hope of sharing, and always seeking to project a token of warmth and understanding into the subtle isolation he knew, by his own experience, suffering can bring to those who are, in a special sense of the term, *unalterably inward*. He found that she was familiar with several poems and with some music that held for him a peculiar and personal significance. Unlike those who throw themselves forth glibly and volubly, she seemed to shrink from entrusting to words the untranslatable idiom of feeling. Despite her diffidence, or rather, he corrected himself, because of something implicit in her reticence and dignity, he came very soon to feel that he knew for sure some of the essential qualities of her character.

With such thoughts in mind, he was walking back to the nurses' station after checking on the condition of several patients in a small ward at the far end of the corridor. As he approached Eve White's room he scarcely noted that her light was on and the door ajar. She often read at this hour. A low, surreptitious whistle caught his attention. She was standing just inside the doorway. The rich slow voice that asked him for a cigarette made him suddenly tingle with surprise. Though Eve White had never smoked, it was not remarkable that she might decide to do so. She invited him to come in and talk for a moment.

Soon afterward he was at the telephone calling the resident physician. He could not precisely state what had happened, but asked if he could come and consult the resident at once. On his way across the hospital the bewildered young man wondered how to express himself. Mrs. White had made no complaint. She had neither said nor done anything in the least irrational. He had never seen her so happy or so energetic. What sort of fool would the busy young physician think him to be if he came to interrupt and make a disturbance because a patient showed evidence of robust health? But something extraordinary had come about. Of that he was sure. What this was, or how to speak of it, he knew not. His scalp seemed to prickle with the strangeness of what he had encountered, as he tried to frame for the resident his report of the profound impression that had come over him.

On learning of the incident we found ourselves able to sympathize with the young man's perturbation.

The more we saw of Eve Black the more it seemed evident that she was not a genuinely evil or vicious manifestation. But it soon became plain that she could not be relied upon to fulfill a promise and that, when it suited her, she would lie with easy equanimity. Her aims and activities seemed prankish rather than deliberately destructive. Her falsehoods were contrived not in cold treachery but in the reckless spirit of a child who almost feels that saying so may make it so. Though she often spoke harshly of Ralph White she seemed incapable of sustained hate. Her mockery of him and the indifference or disdain she often expressed for Eve White were never seriously vindictive. In frivolous pursuit of vanities and light pleasures, she occasionally carried out acts that brought brief and serious trouble to both husband and wife. But lacking concern for what most people regard as serious, she seemed to feel that her right to follow her own inclinations came first.

While Eve White was conscious and in control, Eve Black, though functionally absent, preserved subliminal awareness. Often she would become bored with the conventional routines of the housewife and mother and would occupy herself with plans, reminiscences, and fancies of her own, paying little attention to the life of the other. Invisibly present at some unmapped post of observation, she remained able when she chose to follow the actions and the thoughts of her spiritually antithetical twin. The hoydenish and devil-may-care Eve knew and could report accurately what the other did and thought and could even describe her feelings. These feelings, however, were not Eve Black's. She did not participate in them. The young wife's genuine and natural distress about her failing marriage was regarded by the detached observer as inconsequential and distinctly silly. The mother's love and deep concern for her little girl had little or no effect on Eve Black. She shared the factual data of Eve White's memory and verbally knew her thoughts, but she perceived her emotional reactions and values only as an outsider. And they were for this outsider something trite, bothersome, and insignificant. The devotion of Eve White to her child was entirely familiar to the lively and unworried Eve. Its substance and nature were, however, so clearly outside her personal experience that she could evaluate it and react to it only as "something pretty corny."

73

What dangers would be in store for our patient when she left the hospital and attempted to take up again the ordinary responsibilities of her life? There seemed little reason to believe that Eve Black would not continue to emerge from time to time. Despite the boldness and irresponsibility of this manifestation, we judged it unlikely that she would commit any felonious or very serious antisocial act. Such an inclination was apparently not among her caprices. Though she typically conducted herself in a way that would have profoundly mortified Eve White, and sometimes, apparently in fun or light-hearted mischief, involved her in situations that were difficult and embarrassing, she seemed, despite her reckless and hedonistic ways, able to evade really disastrous complications and consequences.

Though she was provocative and, in every nuance of voice and manner, flaunted sexual challenge and promise, she apparently had no real inclination to allow any of the adventures she took such joy in starting to conclude in real consummation. Not rare among women is the type that seeks excitement in the pseudo-romance of flirtation, begun with bravado and rich enticement, pursued with every innuendo of passionate anticipation, but always abandoned short of the presumable goal or of any reasonable degree of normal fulfillment. Some women no doubt feel a sense of mastery or perverse triumph by so exerting their attractions only to relish the disappointed hopes and frustrations of another. Our mischievous Eve was fundamentally too good-natured, and, in a limited but important sense, too innocent, to be so explained. With her, coquetry seemed to be only a small element of what she sought at dances or in night clubs. To dress conspicuously, to speak and move with discernibly erotic overtones, to seize the center of the stage by some slightly risqué, impulsive deed were, perhaps, not so much flirtatious as they were the naive expressions of a general exuberance. False allusions in the direction of wantonness and piquant but misleading hints of sensual passion were effective in attracting attention, in promoting for Eve Black the atmosphere of frolic and lively commotion she inevitably sought.

Like an imaginative little boy playing Davy Crockett, who dreams vividly of slaying bears and dying against odds in the Alamo, but who has no intention of inviting actual injury, this dramatically seductive and reckless girl's idea of jubilation seemed to include no sexual temptation for herself. As the study of her reactions continued through subsequent months, our conviction grew that this feminine manifestation, despite all her vitality and mischief and sensuous challenge, was limited by a deep and specific frigidity.

We had no assurance that Eve Black would not come out again or that she would fail to involve herself and Eve White in misdemeanors and indiscretions. On the other hand, there was hope that she might be restrained in her contest with the other for dominance by the common danger, by those elements of fate which they shared. In the complex equation between the two manifestations, there were apparently many factors we could not understand or accurately estimate. For all her bluster and assurance, the hedonistic Eve was by no means in control of what determined her emergence from limbo and her return thereto. Though unaware of what might constitute compliance, or of any voluntary means of restricting or influencing the rival for her consciousness, Eve White's status appeared to play a more and more important part in determining whether or not the invisible pixie would succeed in getting her times out for frolic. Our hope was to learn better how Eve Black might be mollified and indirectly persuaded toward cooperation by routes, however circuitous, through the responses of Eve White.

As she left the hospital with her husband, happy at the prospect of seeing Bonnie again, it seemed as if some ground had been gained. Ralph had come to the conclusion that his wife had not simply lied to him in saying she had no idea how the new clothes got in the closet, or in insisting that *she* had not bought them and had never seen them before. Believing, in a limited but really meaningful sense, that it was not she who had reviled him, defied and rejected him in Columbia, he could the more wholeheartedly do his part to help her. He felt that if strange, embarrassing, or damaging conduct should recur, he could better control his hitherto blind impulse to censure or punish his wife for what seemed so plainly to be unacceptable conduct. He was now able to modify the blame he had allocated to her in the past.

When Ralph had come in two weeks earlier to meet Eve Black in the office, after watching her for a while with spellbound eyes he had said:

"Why, that's exactly the way she looked—the way she was—when she threw those dishes at my head a few months ago. That's who it was!"

CHAPTER 9

For about two months improvement continued. Eve White returned from time to time for interviews. She was free from headaches and had suffered no more blackouts of which she was conscious. Occasionally there had been a lost lapse of time, brought to her attention by the clock, by the suddenly lengthened shadows, or by her husband's arrival for lunch when she was sure breakfast had been finished less than half an hour before. Such things indicated that her alternate had been in command. There had been no further sign of the "imaginary voice" and she seemed no longer greatly to fear its recurrence. No reports had come to her attention that suggested Eve Black might have committed conspicuous indiscretions.

Once she had found a small bottle of pungent perfume, a vivid red dress, and a few other small items of feminine apparel carefully hidden behind clothes put up for the season in a storage room. She winced at the thought of being seen in such a dress. Checking, she found that a relatively small amount of cash was missing from the drawer where she kept little sums saved from housekeeping expenses in a modest program to provide for extras or emergencies. Her first thought was to throw these things away at once. Remembering, that her counterpart had shown consideration (or caution) in limiting her purchases, she decided to leave everything as it was. If she did away with the dress and accessories, might it not provoke the other to replace them, —perhaps, out of vexation, even to go out and buy prodigally again, and so run up disastrous bills? Eve White decided that it would be worthwhile to compromise, to try cooperation to this degree in the hope that it might limit damages. Since the money had been taken from her own savings, she decided not to tell Ralph of the incident.

Usually the transitions occurred smoothly enough, for Eve Black seldom came out except when Mrs. White was alone or among strangers where no one would be likely to recognize the alteration. She reported also that the other had seemed more willing or better able to time her escapades with regard to the rights and convenience of both parties. Since leaving the hospital Eve White had seldom been interrupted by long lapses in the midst of pressing responsibilities, and now she was almost never left in unfamiliar surroundings or awkward and perplexing situations by Eve Black's inopportune withdrawal.

She told of one notable exception, however, when she had suddenly found herself on a busy street corner engaged in conversation with a young soldier whom she had never previously beheld. Wide awake and in possession of all her facultries, Eve White, despite profound embarrassment and consternation, had concluded immediately that the alternate must have come here, must have been talking for some time with this man. Had the power by which Eve Black maintained functional control failed her in the middle of her adventure? Or had she for some reason of her own deliberately chosen to retreat where she could not be followed?

Despite her belated arrival on the scene, Eve White soon caught the gist of what had been going on. For a moment the man was strongly persuasive, showing indeed a touch of indignation as if he considered himself unjustly misled. His new companion found it necessary to say very little. The contrast of her quiet dignity with the argument that must have been in progress seemed to affect him almost at once. His chagrin seemed to dissolve in bewilderment. Had she been aggressive as well as positive in her refusal, he might have chosen to argue further. Her very meekness and simplicity overthrew him, as if by some quick emotional judo sleight in which the strength of the assailant is, almost magically, turned against himself. Though wonder held him for a moment after she firmly repeated her unsmiling negation, he soon showed evidence of being no less eager than she for this interview to terminate. Then mumbling some final expression of courtesy, he turned and hurried off.

Despite these inconveniences and tribulations, Eve White felt encouraged. None of the things that had occurred since she left the hospital had caused Ralph serious trouble. He had been very patient in the small difficulties that came up and was nearly always considerate toward her. He seemed better able to express his affection. It was such a joy to see little Bonnie happy. It was characteristic of this considerate woman to be grateful even for small things. Generously she tended with real consistency to put the best possible interpretation upon the actions of others. She cherished every little item on which hope might be founded and tried to avoid complaints about what remained unfortunate. Though her physician was gratified to find matters this well for her, he still feared that, despite the efforts of both, this husband and wife had not made much real progress toward the sort of love and understanding necessary to make their marriage sound and happy.

Now that Eve White knew about the other manifestation it was no longer necessary to induce hypnosis in order to summon Eve Black. With her acquiescence, the other could be called out into activity just as Eve White herself was called back after Eve Black's initial appearance. This was done each time the patient came for an interview. Eve Black, too, was on the whole encouraging in her reports. The couple were getting along a little better, she thought, though by no means as well as Eve White tried to tell herself. She herself wouldn't put up for five minutes with Ralph or with any of his ways. It didn't trouble her too much for the other Eve to be living with him. As for her, she gave him little thought; she never came out in his presence, and so didn't "have to bother with the dumb muttonhead." She had not meant for the other Eve to find the few simple things she'd bought for herself. She insisted she had a right to some freedom, a little life of her own. She admitted that the money she took did not belong to her; but, with a shrug and a confident flash of her eyes, casually maintained that she had to get along somehow. When asked if she would like to get a job for herself and earn money that would be unquestionably her own, she replied in an amused playful tone:

"Now, Doc—you're always bringing up something like that. You know I don't want to settle down and waste my time on some old office or store. Life's too short for that. Sometimes you talk the way she thinks, Doc. Why in hell would I want to fret at some piddling job? That ain't living. Maybe it's to *her* taste. It'd bore me something awful. And besides I don't know how to do anything like that. I couldn't keep my mind on it five minutes."

The lighthearted Eve said she had been out briefly on a number of occasions that Eve White had never suspected.

"Sometime when she's downtown for the afternoon shoppin', I just happen to get out. Maybe she's looking at something she likes in the window of a store. When that happens I may just stroll around for about ten or fifteen minutes. Maybe I have a coke at Halley's where they got some pinball machines. After kidding a little with the soda jerker ᴏ some of the gang who hang out there, I may find my time running short. So I just wander back to the window where she was all lost in thought about that Sunday dress she'd been mooning over and wishing she could get for her precious little Bonnie. Then, when I got to go back, I leave her still looking at it, not having the least idea I've been out at all."

When asked about the soldier with whom Eve White had been confronted, Eve Black at first calmly professed ignorance. As if assuming the matter settled, she lightly turned to another subject. On being accused of lying, she was petulant, then with a warm smile said, "You can't believe just anything she tells you, Doc. She may try to act like a fancy little saint and tell herself she's going to be one. But you know she's human in her way, like the rest of us."

Finding that this explanation made no impression, she shifted her position in the chair. Crossing her legs, she gave her head a little toss and began to laugh softly. Without apology or excuse for her falsehood, she seemed amused as a child might who feels she has almost gotten away with an outlandish prank; though it had not quite worked this time, there was still fun in contemplating the possibilities.

"The poor scary thing couldn't have slept, I bet, if she hadn't told you about that," said the bold Eve with an air of superiority. "Of course, I know that fellow. Met him once before at a dance in Columbia. Just an excitable, crazy, mixed-up kid. Seemed to like my singing and the way I danced. When I ran into him the other day it seemed fun. Yeah, I told him I'd go out with him that night. Then he got a little tiresome. Wanted it to be just the two of us— and right then. He kind of lacks finesse," she confided with blended naiveté and quasiworldliness. "Tries to work too fast —you know the type, Doc."

Having a premonition that she would not be able to maintain control and "stay out" long enough to spend the evening with this acquaintance may have played some part in Eve Black's alleged decision to turn down the invitation. She denied lacking confidence that she could easily handle any situation that might have arisen. She had agreed at first to go with the young soldier to a restaurant or night club. Then, when he tried to get her to come right away, she realized that he had something more on his mind—something like parking in the woods or going to a motor court—and that he was likely to insist, and would perhaps become unpleasant.

"I wasn't born yesterday, Doc," she said with pert assurance, "and I don't aim to get laid by any such childish tricks as that. There's no profit in getting took like a sucker."

After the way she had challenged his feelings at first, the young man's hopes had apparently been high. Reluctant to abandon what he took as a promise, he continued to urge her, increasing the vehemence of his persuasion as she tauntingly evaded him. She might have had to make a little disturbance to settle the affair to her satisfaction, she admitted, with a kind of childish pride in the interest she had aroused:

"Yeah, I was just getting ready to tell off the headstrong coot, even if it took some shouting that might attract a crowd."

Then another and simpler solution occurred to Eve Black! Let Eve White do it! It would save a lot of bother and unpleasantness. Besides, there was something extremely amusing to this impish and irresponsible mind in the prospect of her prissy, righteous associate's having to handle the situation and terminate the argument. The temptation was like that which makes a school boy feel special relish in throwing his snowball at the top hat of some formal, imposing, and ordinarily imperturbable figure. Sometimes, but not regularly, she could fade away like this by choice and leave the other to face her problem. This time it had worked precisely. The unrepentant girl seemed more buoyant than ever. Her lively eyes shone with fresh delight as she boasted innocently of her achievement.

By now we had been sufficiently impressed with her untrustworthiness not to assume she necessarily had given a true account of this incident. After lying easily about some act which she presumed might cause censure, she would sometimes, on being unmistakably proved false, go on with further prevarication, exaggerating and embellishing what she had first denied, until she made of some mundane peccadillo an ingenious and glittering piece of mischief in which she could find both humor and pride.

Fortunately we were able to interview Eve White's parents several times during this period. When her husband had first attempted to describe their daughter's condition to them at the time she entered the hospital, they feared that he must either have become mad or that he might be instigating some outlandish stratagem through which to misrepresent his wife and thus exculpate himself as a preamble to deserting her. Having come promptly to the hospital, they were at first skeptical and a little distrustful of the physician. No amount of theorizing about dissociation, dual personality, or the unconscious, we felt, would be likely to help their feelings or enlist their cooperation. But after they had visited their daughter and, later, interviewed Eve Black, their point of view changed. Through them, through Eve White's sisters, her cousin Flo, and through other members of the family, we were able to obtain valuable historic detail of the patient's life.

We were both surprised and dubious when Eve Black told us she had enjoyed an independent life ever since Eve White's childhood. Feeling that she was probably a product of disruptive emotional stresses which the patient had suffered in recent years, we were inclined to feel that this was one of her boastful and expansive fabrications. She told us freely of episodes twenty or more years ago in which she had allegedly emerged, usually to engage in acts of mischief or disobedience. Familiar with the gratuitous fibs she told glibly and without compunction, we realized that her account alone could never be taken as reliable evidence. Since Eve White, whose word on any matter always proved good, had no access to the other's current awareness or her memory and, indeed, did not until recently even faintly suspect her existence, it was impossible through her to check directly and immediately on Eve Black's stories. Her memory did, however, afford considerable indirect evidence, because she was able to confirm reports of certain punishments she had received in childhood, of accusations made against her for deeds unknown to her but described to us by Eve Black.

Some of these stories were substantiated through the parents and other members of the family. Eve White's parents impressed us as sober, reliable people, conservative citizens of a small rural community. Throughout their daughter's long struggle to regain her health, they were faithfully cooperative and always loyal to her, even in situations which they must have found inexpressibly bewildering. The mother and father both clearly recalled several incidents that Eve Black had previously reported to us. They had had to punish their ordinarily good and conforming six-year-old daughter for having disobeyed their specific rule against wandering through the woods to play with the children of a tenant farmer whose house was approximately a half mile away.

They considered this expedition dangerous for so young a child and their daughter's unaccountable absence had caused them worry and distress. On her return Eve had received a hearty whipping despite her desperate and persistent denials of wrongdoing and disobedience.

In fact, these very denials only added to her punishment because the evidence of her little trip was well established and her plea of innocence was taken as a deliberate and bold-faced lie. Almost as surprising as disobedience and lying in such a good child was the daring with which she had wandered home through the darkening woods. Eve was timid and had for some time shown abnormal fear about going near the ditch under the bridge where a man had been found dead. This evening she had boldly loitered there as well as in the thicket beyond.

Eve Black had previously described this incident to us in some detail, expressing satisfaction and amusement about having "come out" to engage in and thoroughly enjoy the forbidden adventure, and particularly in having been able to withdraw and leave the other Eve, bewildered and sincerely protesting her innocence, to appreciate the sensations of the whipping. Though Eve Black, when absent or "in," preserved a considerable degree of indirect awareness of the outer world through Eve White's thoughts and perceptions she insisted that she was totally immune from any physical pain suffered by the latter and from any other sensations she experienced. The adult Eve White recalled this and several other punishments which she had had no way of understanding and which had sometimes deeply confused her in her relations with her parents. She was never able to gain memory of the experiences of Eve Black for which she was punished, though extensive efforts were made, both with hypnosis and without, to bring this material to awareness. After being told in detail what had occurred, she still was unable to establish any shadowy contact with it through memory. It remained extraneous to personal experience.

When for the first time we encountered Eve Black directly, we asked ourselves at once how such a manifestation could have emerged in the past and gone unrecognized for even a minute by the husband or by the parents, or, indeed, by anyone even casually acquainted with Eve White. How had she succeeded in concealing her identity not only from the other Eve but also from relatives and intimates thoroughly familiar with the quiet figure her every word, gesture, and expression so vividly belied? She had occasionally come out in the presence of these people but had not been discovered until she agreed to reveal herself to them in the physician's office and in the hospital.

Though she chose to emerge when no one who knew Eve White well was present, she had occasionally found herself thrust involuntarily into the presence of Ralph White whom she detested, or into the presence of the parents to whom she owned no relation, and into other situations where any striking change in Eve White would be at once noted. At such times she had usually been able to restrain her natural impulses and to mimic shrewdly her alternate's deportment in its superficial aspects, until she could find some way of removing herself to more congenial surroundings. More rarely, on reckless impulse, she had purposely precipitated herself into the family circle to quarrel suddenly with Ralph, scold Bonnie, indulge in a tantrum, or mystify the parents and a few other relatives with bits of behavior for which no adequate explanation was ever devised. On such occasions she quickly subsided, often being extinguished as an objective manifestation by inner forces which she could not successfully resist or ever clearly describe.

These small uncharacteristic episodes, scattered widely over the smooth expanse of Eve White's steady and gentle career, became as time passed relatively inconspicuous in the distance against the prevalent background which tended at last to absorb them. In retrospect the husband and parents had been forced, for the want of any other explanation, to think of those odd or wayward moments, those flashes of ill will and caprice, those strange spells when the docile Eve was not quite herself, as fits of temper, rare quirks of mood in a woman habitually self-effacing and considerate.

During her longer periods "out," when she expressed herself more freely in behavior incompatible with that of Eve White, Eve Black regularly avoided the family and close friends and sought only the company of strangers or of those insufficiently acquainted with her alternate to evaluate accurately the stupendous transformation.

Once we had seen and spoken with Eve Black, it seemed to us at first scarcely possible that, even in the same body as her alternate, she could for so long have concealed her separate identity from others. Yet, who among those acquainted with her would be likely to suspect, however unlike herself Eve appeared at times to be, such a situation as that voluntarily revealed to us by the patient? No matter how many clues one is given, no matter how obvious the clues, he will not be led to a conclusion that for him is inconceivable. He will keep on seeking explanations for the problem only among hypotheses that are available.

Having in mind no trace of the only concept in which successive details of perception will fit, even a very astute man may observe a thousand separate features of something his imagination has never shaped without grasping the gestalt, without being able to put into a recognizable whole the details he has so clearly discerned. Only our previous familiarity with three-dimensional space enables us to see the representation of depth in a picture. What is for us still unconceived can give us a thousand hints, boldly flaunt its grossest features, and still remain undelineated, formless, and uncomprehended as an entity.

Astonishingly incompatible gestures, expressions, attitudes, mannerisms, and behavior, occasionally displayed before intimates by Eve, provoked thought and wonder and demanded explanation. But who in the position of these people would be likely to find or create in his mind the hypothesis that forms a recognizable image? Let us not forget that Eve Black, until she voluntarily named herself to the therapist, took pains to remain unrecognized. At our request she demonstrated her skill in acting so as to pass herself off as Eve White, imitating the other's habitual tone of voice, her gestures, and attitudes. She seemed to take a childish pride in this accomplishment. Would it not, after all, require a sledgehammer blow from the obvious to drive into an unsuspecting acquaintance the only hypothesis that would lead to her recognition?

CHAPTER 10

The relatively tranquil period subsequent to Eve White's hospitalization did not last. Troubles too numerous and complicated to recount here in detail began to accumulate. The husband's role in this situation was undeniably difficult. Though he tried with patience and understanding to make the marriage a happy one, he could find little true intimacy at home, nothing that seemed like a warm lively response from his wife. It is doubtful if any ordinary man could have successfully solved the problems that confronted him. Like a poorly rooted plant, the basic relationship between Mr. and Mrs. White seemed to wither steadily. Even when no overt disagreement marred the day, little or no positive feeling was exchanged. When sitting together in the same room they could offer each other only the lifeless shadow of companionship. As Ralph's frustration and discouragement progressively increased, and he began to spend more time seeking some little fragments of pleasure or diversion away from home, Eve, as if helplessly borne away by an ebbing tide, involuntarily became more remote. The direction of her incentive and the form of her determination to preserve the marriage, did not alter. The sources within her from which the marriage demanded sustenance seemed to suffer from attrition. As with a stunned boxer who still struggles, unflinchingly but feebly, to keep his feet and continue, her stricken endeavor steadily weakened.

Manifestations of Eve Black grew more troublesome. She took over on several occasions and absented herself from the house during periods when Bonnie had counted on being with her mother. The little girl had been carefully instructed to go next door and stay with the neighbors if she found herself alone. Usually no great difficulty arose on this score, but Bonnie was found there safe and reasonably content either by her father or by Eve White if she regained her identity in time to return before her husband. Neither parent found it possible to explain satisfactorily to the neighbors why they could not give regular notice or warning of when Bonnie was to come. Nor could they make so young a child understand why her mother should sometimes disappear without letting her know, and after promising to read to her or cut out paper dolls. The child was told, of course, that Moms had spells of sickness, but that she would get better, and everything would be all right. But the nature of the illness, just how and why certain things happened that frightened and bewildered the little girl—who could explain this?

Several months earlier, in the beginning of Eve White's treatment and while Eve Black was still unsuspected as an entity, a threatening situation had developed. After the episode Ralph had brought his wife at once to the physician, insisting that the night before she had threatened to kill Bonnie. She had, he explained with unsteady voice, actually put the cord of a Venetian blind around her child's throat and had seemed to be trying to strangle her. He had stopped her with his own hands. He regretted having struck her lightly in the ensuing quarrel. But who could be sure of controlling himself under such circumstances? Eve White's denial in no way suggested the denial of one who was aware she had done this thing. Though shaken with distress and bitterly hurt, with level eyes moist, she firmly maintained she had not done such a thing.

It seemed preposterous to consider that Ralph, out of nothing, would arrantly produce such an accusation about such a matter, and in such a way. He impressed us as a reliable and kind person, doing his best to help in a painful and serious situation. To the physician it seemed, perhaps, even more difficult to conceive, more unjust to believe that this woman was lying or that she would ever under any circumstance do ill to her child. There are many people, to be sure, who can unflinchingly look another in the eye and with candid countenance lie foully and treacherously about momentous matters in voices that sound as if the sustaining hand of the Almighty lay over the speaker's heart. The physician knew this well. Despite the evidence, his judgment rebelled at the possibility of Eve White's being such a person. He must, he decided, seek elsewhere for what might bring sense to this paradox.

Even in psychosis it was difficult to conceive of this mother turning upon her child. Perhaps in the diapason of psychosis resides the possibility of any act by anybody. But he could not believe that Eve White was, in such a sense, psychotic, or that she had been so. Could the husband, in all the stress and perplexity under which he labored, have honestly misjudged his perception? What other and actual scene, however distorted or exaggerated by the witness's emotion, could leave this man with his present conviction? The physician could find no satisfactory answer. In temporary confusion, in hysterical episodes, many varieties of incompatible or spectacular behavior may emerge. Could this mother in a hysterical alteration of consciousness really try to harm her daughter? He could not believe it. Unable to account to himself for what confronted him, he had to wait for a satisfactory answer.

Sometime after Eve Black had revealed herself, she was questioned about this episode and at first denied any such act against Bonnie. She insisted that Ralph was a liar and that this accusation was a measure of his worth. Some days later, however, during another interview when confronted firmly with

86

her implausibility, her volatile mood had changed and she told a different story:

"Sure, Doc. I tried to tone down the little varment just a bit. She got to bawling and fretting. And I was busy. Hadn't been out in a long time. I was working out some plans, and if the kid wasn't quiet it might mess me up."

Unabashed by the admission, she talked at some length about the plans Bonnie had disturbed before casually saying that she would not have actually harmed the child. Judging not by the reliability of her word but the absence of serious malice or cruelty in the scamplike human entity, we were prepared to believe her on this point. She had, we concluded, in a petulant but transient outburst of jejune vexation meant to threaten dramatically and punish a little.

With this incident in the background, both Mr. and Mrs. White were especially apprehensive about any intrusion on the part of Eve Black into the life of their daughter. In such a complex situation it is difficult to estimate which of the two felt more insecure, more vulnerable, or more preplexed. The emotional strain on both was constant and sapping. Once when Bonnie had been left alone the neighbors were not at home. Frightened by the approach of dark she had run wildly back toward the empty house. Tripping, she had fallen and skinned a knee. Ten minutes later Ralph came in from work. Worn down by the sterility and stress of his present life, he had stopped to take a few highballs downtown before coming back to a grim and cheerless home. How long had this little girl been crying in her helplessness? How seriously was she injured? It was only a superficial skin abrasion but Ralph, in distress and growing indignation, could not accurately estimate its gravity. A little later when his wife appeared, still clad in the flashy red dress Eve Black had put on earlier that afternoon, and still reeking of her cheap perfume, he had lost the last secure hold he had on himself and was swept willy-nilly into a turbulent tide-run of honest wrath.

Large and small troubles continued to accumulate. Eve Black seemed to be steadily waxing. She gained control more often and flaunted her freedom with increasing boldness. On rare occasions she emerged deliberately before Ralph White to taunt and deride him. During interviews the physician found her less conciliatory, more openly determined to have her own way at any cost. After no word had come from the Whites for a longer period than usual, a short note was received by the physician. It was signed with the initials E.B. In a careless scrawl was written:

Doc,
I think I ought to let you know. E. W. is quite sick. She tried to kill herself this morning. I was able to stop her. Ralph don't know about it. She promised herself that nobody must ever know. I know you should. I'm not sure she won't try it again.

A telephone call was made. Eve White agreed to come for another interview without delay. She denied all knowledge of the note but admitted that she had been desperately unhappy. It was true that she had thought of suicide. But because of Bonnie and because of her religious convictions, she felt that she would never take such a step. Then with painful reluctance she said that she had at last reached a decision to leave her husband. She did not want a divorce. The only hope she could see for the marriage might lie in temporary separation. Most of all, her fears about Bonnie had brought her to this decision. She could not, she had been forced to realize, look after her little girl adequately until she got better. And although Eve White spoke calmly of getting better, it seemed plain that she had little real hope of this. The reserved young mother had decided to give up her child, forever if necessary, in order to protect her—protect her from something threatening and dreadful that eluded sharp definition.

So it was arranged for Bonnie to go and live with Mrs. White's mother and father, who still lived in the distant rural home where she herself had been born. Eve herself would find a job and work to support Bonnie. Her parents could afford no additional expense. Ralph was going to a city in another state with the intention of starting over in his business. He had been through trials that no normal man could have borne with equanimity. His wife felt that a temporary separation offered the best chance for their marriage to survive. The prospect for him was not pleasant, but he was determined to cooperate in every step that might eventually lead to a satisfactory solution. Since living expenses would be increased by these moves, Eve strongly felt that it should be her responsibility to provide for the major needs of herself and her daughter. It seemed to her that she must prove herself strong enough to carry out this mission before she could hope for further progress.

After the interview with Eve White, the other Eve was summoned. She first expressed pleasure in the plans for separation. "Maybe the poor old gal will get some sense in her yet," she said half-interestedly and with an easy smile. No, she had not exaggerated what she wrote about in her note. She had been aware of her alternate's thoughts as they progressed and accumulated to the awful resolution.

"She must have been half dazed, I guess," this Eve said, now a little more intent than usual. "She started into the bathroom and was so worked up she could hardly find her way. She seemed to be trying to act before she could think enough to stop herself. All sorts of crazy notions were batting through her brain. I could tell she was going after the razor and was going to cut the blood vessels in her wrist. Not just a little cut, like I might do if I really wanted to carry on. She was going to kill herself. Whether she remembered it or not, *I* knew nobody'd be back for an hour or two to do anything about it. She'd be dead by then." Pausing now, as she shifted a little in the chair, her body taking the familiar posture of obscurely voluptuous ease, she added wistfully, "And that would have meant I'd be dead too."

During the struggle to "get out," Eve Black said, it had seemed for a while that she might fail. "Something awful was on her mind, something I never was up against before." Shaking and uncoordinated but with unswerving resolution, Eve White had banged open the medicine chest and seized the stiff single-edged razor blade. Apparently wild with haste, she had lost hold of the blade. The other hand, fumbling to regain possession, knocked it to the floor beyond a clothesbasket.

"She'd already grabbed it again and was about to cut when I finally got out," Eve Black said. "I think she meant business, Doc."

During our earlier interviews, Eve Black had told us that Eve White's memory was sometimes disturbed during short periods when she was still in control but struggling against her alternate in an unusually difficult, and for the time being indeterminate, contest for consciousness. She had also claimed the occasional but not regular ability to rub out or absorb some small items of Eve White's own personal memory. This procedure, she said, took some unpleasant effort on her part and she seldom attempted it. When asked how such a feat, or alleged feat, was accomplished she was not too explicit:

"I just think as hard as I can about what's in her mind and keep on until she stops. It'll only work sometimes, and then I have to get right up close against her. Like when I'm coming out and she's going in, or the other way around."

Approximately a week later, the household having been disbanded, Eve White began work with a large corporation located only about fifteen miles from our offices. She had found a better-than-average opening there. Since she would in any case be separated from her husband and child, it had seemed desirable for her to live close enough to be seen by the therapist more often than before. Little difficulty now stood in the way of her coming for daily interviews when necessary. There had been no employment available to her in the small village near her parents' home. She could not be with or near Bonnie unless she gave up her resolution to work for her child's support and security. According to report she had been a diligent and conscientious employee before her marriage and until Bonnnie was born had continued to work in order to contribute to the household budget. Behind her lay considerable experience in typing and bookkeeping, and for a short time in her teens she had operated a small telephone switchboard. She found a room in a modest boardinghouse which she planned to share with another girl, and thus Eve White set out quietly to secure the little income so necessary for Bonnie and for herself.

Was such a move as this merely progress from the frying pan into the fire? In her present condition would she be able to hold this job? Or any job? Freed from whatever restraining influence the Whites' home may have imposed upon her, what would Eve Black now do? Was it folly for Eve White to attempt a life of independence among strangers with her unusual handicap, her all but unutterable secret?

Nothing yet had even suggested that she was developing a schizoid disorder. But for weeks she had been steadily losing initiative. Her vitality seemed to be fading perceptibly. Was it possible that such a manifestation as Eve Black might come out to stay? If Eve White were permanently extinguished, what would such a being as Eve Black set out to do? Directed by passing whims only, she was apparently incapable of any long-range plan. For all her bravura and childish air of confidence, one could not conceive of her being able to support herself. No more than an embryo whose life would terminate almost at once if cut off from the maternal oxygen, or some helpless and immobile parasite that must cling to its host for sustenance, could she be expected to maintain herself by her own devices. Like a fledgling that dares short flights from the nest, she had often sallied forth with bravado on her excursions into the active world; but how long would those wings sustain her if there were no longer the haven to which she returned? A bright, unworried butterfly fluttering for brief days with no fear of the morrow would no more certainly perish.

On the other hand, it seemed possible that Eve Black might become more cooperative. Despite the evanescence and inconsistency of her attitudes, she had regularly expressed scorn and dislike for Ralph White, and distaste for the sedate and conventional routines of Eve White's life as a conscientious wife and mother. Was the manifestation who called herself Eve Black a product or representative of unrecognized tendencies and attitudes in the other? Was Eve Black a hidden, unconscious, or subconscious side of the whole person, long denied expression by the other side and disowned by its prevailing awareness? This, perhaps, was too simple an answer. When we try to reduce complicated actualities to logical verbal statements, we often distort or falsify reality to achieve a neat and superficially impressive explanation. Let us merely say that this may be to some extent, or in part, or something like, what Eve Black was. If so, might not changes in Eve White's routine, some harmless modification of her strict viewpoints, reasonable expansion of her scope, freer expression of her emotion all tend to assuage the hypothetical forces invisibly rebellious far within her complicated being? Perhaps.

Let us remember, however, that we conceive of the personality, Eve White, as already ill. The problems she faced had all but overwhelmed her. It would now require her utmost effort to maintain integration. Would such readjustments as those just mentioned impose upon her added stress? Was it not dangerous for an insecure person to attempt modification of the familiar basic principles and framework of his living? The observer might agree that it would not be wise to attempt changes in what is basic and still advise an extensive liberalization or expansion of outlook and behavior. But what is an absurdity or an inconsequential conventionality for one person, may for another be the cornerstone on which the values and meanings of his life are founded. Even to question what one has acted on as sacred principle or as true propriety can be extremely disturbing to serious people.

To be told or to discover that the rules by which one has been faithfully abiding are false or inadequate has been known to shake even the most confident and robust minds.

If Eve White should try to modify her viewpoint and way of living in what might be roughly considered a compromise with Eve Black, would this weaken her position in the conflict? Would appeasement lessen the rebellious drive or would it serve chiefly to incite it? Would Eve Black, encouraged and emboldened, merrily cry havoc and loose at once the dogs of total and relentless war?

CHAPTER 11

During the next year we kept these two personalities under close observation. The patient usually came twice a week for an hour's interview with her therapist. Sometimes she was seen more often and there were interviews occasionally that lasted throughout a whole afternoon. With the permission of both ladies, tape recordings were made of each as she worked with the physician through many hours of therapy. Tape recordings were also made when her parents gave the extensive history of her early life. Eve White and Eve Black each took the Rorschach and other psychological tests. Electroencephalograms were made of them separately. Their handwritings were studied and compared by a well-qualified expert. Each consented to our making moving pictures. Our first pictures were on silent film but we later obtained a study with sound. By this means they were for the first time, one might say, able to see each other.

Eve Black because of her access to the other's thought while latent had, of course, an approximate idea of her alternate, of how she would speak and move and bear herself. Watching the film with obvious amusement, she commented from time to time when Eve White expressed an opinion or straightened herself in the chair, "Wouldn't she, now!" When the film showed Eve White get up and walk across the room, the disdainful observer murmured, "Mincing!"

Eve White, on the other hand, studied the film with solemn gravity. When it ended she sat still and tense in her chair. Embarrassment showed in the faint pink spots on her cheeks, in the withdrawal of her eyes. She sat silent for a few moments as if seeking her customary outward poise. We had never heard Eve White speak unkindly of another. Not in sarcasm, but humbly and in the truest spirit of charity, she at last found herself able to say in a low serious voice, "I suppose...I mean one could say there's a lot about her that seems fresh and...really...right attractive. She does seem so young."

Eve White according to her employers was able and industrious at her job; serious, methodical, and unfailingly courteous, she made an excellent impression. During her interviews with the therapist she tried to veil with her quiet reserve the sorrow and fear that, under the circumstances, another might have readily and fully exhibited. Without a whimper she endured the loneliness, the frustration, and grief of separation from her beloved daughter. Though she was never prone to make a display of her feeling, it was not difficult to see that Bonnie was the primary, almost the sole, object of her life and feelings. She seemed to find in her child a sole incentive, a last resource that sustained her in the cheerless routine of her present situation. As months passed she seemed no nearer a real foundation for the hope that somehow she might eventually have Bonnie with her. She could afford to make the expensive journey to her parents' home only at long intervals. It looked as if the little girl would grow up apart from her, and she feared that as years passed, her child would come to regard her as little more than a stranger.

The routine of Eve White's days were seldom varied. During working hours she kept her mind on the task before her. Preoccupied with her responsibilities, she seemed unable to avail herself of the little breaks by which others in the office found relief from the pressure of steady concentration. She often smiled at jokes that circulated from desk to desk, but never seemed to join freely in the laughter and the banter that punctuated and seasoned the long hours of occupation for nearly everyone else. After work was over, she spent much of the remaining time in her room. Skillful and assiduous at needlework, she made all of Bonnie's clothes and many of her own. She carefully pressed her few dresses and blouses, caring for them so meticulously that she always appeared more neat and orderly than any other woman in the office. Each day she wrote a letter to Bonnie, seeking in her unextravagant, modestly formal idiom to convey a mother's steady devotion.

She sometimes took a walk in the little park near the

boardinghouse, alone or with one of the other girls. At night she often read until bedtime or occasionally played cards with the group downstairs. She attended church regularly, taking an inconspicuous part in its activities. In her religious beliefs and attitudes she was never ostentatious, sanctimonious, or fanatical. Over this year of close observation Eve White showed no important change in her essential personality characteristics. Her new environment, the responsibilities of work, freedom from the routines of housekeeping, the attractions and diversions of a city much larger than any in which she had previously lived seemed to alter her habits and attitudes very little if at all. She showed no spontaneous tendency to develop new interests. The little satisfactions or pleasures that came her way she accepted quietly. Outer evidence of enthusiasm or vigorous initiative was never displayed, though her industry and persistence bespoke a deeply felt purpose in providing for her child.

Vulnerable, uningenious, and delicately feminine, she preserved a quiet dignity about personal sorrow, a dignity unpretentiously stoic. Under hypnosis she was sometimes able to bring out, not in freely released emotion, but a little more intimately, reticent comments on the lonely despair she habitually felt it her task not to display. Even then no frantic weeping occurred, no outcries of protest or self-pity. Unlike Morton Prince's celebrated Miss Beauchamp, she did not change fundamentally under hypnosis; she did not take on any new attitudes or characteristics that would suggest that she became another personality. Though hypnosis was often used to facilitate the expression of emotion, Eve White in this state was almost clearly recognizable as herself.

It has been presumed for many years that so-called dual personalities arise through the dissociation of an originally integrated entity of functioning and experience. Everyone, no doubt, becomes aware at times of traits and tendencies within himself that are somewhat inconsistent with his general aims and habitual standards. The ordinary person endeavors throughout life to suppress impulses that prompt him toward behavior he has learned to regard as unacceptable. So, too, he attempts with varying degrees of success to disown or cast off various habits, mannerisms, and other personal features that he feels alien to a desirable concept of himself. The degree of homogeneity or consistency achieved varies noticeably among people regarded as normal. The subject's recognition of success or failure in these aims also appears to vary. The familiar term *hypocrite* is often used to designate those whose claims or pretensions are grossly belied by their practice. Some people are even said to "lead a double life." There is reason to believe that some inclinations, attitudes, and qualities rejected and shut off from awareness maintain an existence or a potentiality not suspected by their possessor. The development of a secondary personality has been explained by some observers as coming about through the mobilization, organization, and eventually the emergence of what has been thus discarded or dissociated from consciousness.

In view of this concept, it seemed natural to believe that therapeutic effort should be directed along lines that might promote reciprocal recognition and eventual reintegration. Over many months the attempt was made with each Eve to work back step by step into early childhood. Hypnosis was occasionally used with Eve White in the hope it might help her regain memory of forgotten or repressed events, as aspects or fragments of emotional components of experience. We sought for some link or bridge between the two consciousnesses on which additional contact or coalition could grow or be built.

Under hypnosis Eve White occasionally showed the effects of considerable emotion in recalling and discussing some events of her childhood. At these times she never abandoned restraint or freely gave way to any open manifestation of her feelings. But against the still unbreached walls of her reserve, the impact of severe stresses could be discerned.

As already mentioned, we never succeeded in hypnotizing Eve Black. About all matters past and present her emotions were utterly free. Amusement, saucy vexation, eager anticipation, a fresh, childlike delight in trivialities, fleeting anger, naive vanity, all flashed in her volatile face, rippled through the lively tones of her abundant speech. It seemed impossible for his capricious manifestation to react seriously to any serious matter. She owned no attachments, accepted no responsibilities, and brightly dismissed any discussion of life's major issues as tedious. She was vibrant with superficial warmth and vitality, but her emotional range was evidently restricted to the shallowest fringes of human experience. Free of care and sorrow, she impulsively disported herself there in those fringes like a young kitten with a spool of thread. All attempts to advise her about the conduct of life were met with such insouciance as a gilded queen of the stage at the Folies Bergère might show to some mad and tattered fanatic who shouted arrogant damnation against her taste for diamonds and mink. The somber and historic zeal of Savonarola would have faded before the invincible levity of her smile.

Despite her access to Eve White's thoughts and her technical knowledge of this mother's grief in the separation from her child, the playful Eve showed little or no real compassion for her. Nor did she bear the other any ill will. Not in any important sense could she be defined as actively or purposefully cruel. Fundamentally good-natured, the scope of her feeling was confined to minor notes. Neutral or immune to major affective events in human relations, an unparticipating onlooker, she was apparently as free of hatefulness, or of mercy, or of comprehension, as a bright-feathered, innocent parakeet who chirps its little song undisturbed while watching a child strangle to death.

Relatively early in the course of treatment, a few weeks after the first recognized appearance of Eve Black, in fact, an effort was made, perhaps a too naive effort, to promote some sort of blending, or at least a better working liason between the two, by calling out both personalities at once. With deepening emotional relations between the patient and physician and with repetition of the procedure, the process of summoning or calling out the absent personality had progressively become simpler and more reliable. To Eve White the therapist proposed that, instead of invoking Eve Black alone, the name of each be called at the same time. As usual she was agreeable. But to this attempt Eve White reacted with violent headache and emotional distress so severe that it was not considered wise to continue. When the experiment was reversed, with the apparently invulnerable Eve Black manifest, much less agitation was observed. After one unsuccessful trial, however, she bluntly refused to go further. In explanation she could only say that it gave her "such a funny, queer mixed-up kind of feeling" and that she would not lend herself again to such an effort.

In contrast with the fairly recent case reported by Erickson and Kubie, Eve Black has not shown a regular and dependable desire to help the other with her problems.[11] The considerably submerged and obscure dissociated manifestation, regarded as a secondary personality by Erickson and Kubie and referred to by them as *Miss Brown*, apparently expressed itself only through the medium of automatic writing. And this writing was so verbally imperfect and abstruse that considerable interpretation or translation was necessary to promote even limited communication. Nevertheless, whatever the influence designated by the term *Miss Brown* may represent, it consistently worked to aid the accessible personality, Miss Damon. It was a therapeutic influence.

Efforts to interest Eve Black in taking a similar role met with grim obstacles. Many of these, as can be imagined, were not unlike what impedes and frustrates the psychiatrist who tries to help a typical psychopath deal more constructively with his own problems, to find real goals, and to develop normal evaluations. New toys or games can sometimes briefly arouse the interest of a capricious child. So, too, the therapist occasionally was able to enlist Eve Black's support in some remedial aim directed toward the problems of her body's coinhabitant. Sometimes attaining in her even an attitude of neutrality was of great value. What helpful acts of abstentions she could be induced to contribute, however, were evidently prompted only by fleeting, casual curiosity or the playful redirection of a whim toward some pretty novelty. Often by ingenious lies she misled the therapist to believe that she was cooperating when her behavior was particularly detrimental to Eve White's progress.

No reliable constructive or persistently sympathetic motivation was induced in the irresponsible Eve, but one valuable means of influencing her remained in the hands of the therapist. Her ability to display Eve White's consciousness and emerge to take control did not noticeably increase during the year after she left her husband. Sometimes the adventurous Eve could "get out" and sometimes not. Since Eve White had learned during treatment of the other's existence, it had become plain to us that her willingness to step aside and, so to speak, to release the imp played an important part in this alternate's ability to appear and express herself directly. But Eve White could not keep the other suppressed permanently or count with certainty on doing this for any given period. Her influence, and indirectly that of the therapist, were, however, still sufficiently strong to use for bargaining with Eve Black for better cooperation. When she avoided serious interruptions of Eve White's work and other responsibilities and refrained from pranks that caused the other deep embarrassment or other difficulties, she was rewarded with more time out.

Despite occasional brief eruptions of her alternate during

the hours of work, Eve White held her first job for approximately two months. Perhaps Eve Black was influenced more than she admitted by recognition of the necessity that her sober partner retain her position. In this strange symbiosis, it was obvious that Eve White must maintain a source of livelihood in order for Eve Black to subsist. Usually the adventurous one restricted her longer excursions into the outside world to weekends or to evenings when Eve White's absence would not be particularly conspicuous or evoke inquiry. Apparently incapable of holding steadily to any course, and only transiently motivated by any course, the lighthearted Eve slipped out every now and then in the office, during the lunch hour, and on other inappropriate occasions.

When urged by the physician on the grounds of fair play and personal expediency to use discretion, Eve Black would usually promise readily to mend her ways. But her excuses for intruding upon office hours suggested that even the lightest whim might lead her to involve the other in considerable difficulties. A couple of weeks after Eve White began her first job, the other out of curiosity decided to visit the office briefly. "I just thought I'd like to see for myself what it was like there," she explained with a tranquil smile. Lacking her associate's skill with the typewriter she soon made a series of mistakes; then, vexed or bored with what she considered a silly task, she awkwardly spelled out the words of a risqué joke. Amused at the incongruity of this offering in a serious business report, she tried her hand at filing, carelessly rather than purposely misplacing some important documents, and leaving a good deal of confusion for the other Eve to deal with. Having no incentive for work and finding the situation tedious, she seldom interrupted her colleague very long. But even when present for only a few minutes in the office, she sometimes created strange impressions, coming out spontaneously with some wisecrack or loud jest that was in astonishing contrast with everyone's concept of the sober Mrs. White.

More rarely, estimating that she would be able to hold the stage for a considerable period of time, she would leave the office to seek a more congenial environment where she could unguardedly express her inclinations. When this occurred she sometimes offered the excuse of headache or of a gastrointestinal disturbance, but by no means always.

Once the employee known as Mrs. White was observed to disappear from her post without giving notice during a busy afternoon. A few hours later the manager of the corporation she worked for was passing by a small moving-picture theater. The attention of this dignified executive was suddenly arrested by a jovial shout in which he was hailed by name. Though he was not thrown in close contact with Mrs. White at work and knew her only casually, this bold, vigorous girl, now about fifteen feet away and strolling out of the lobby of the theater, somehow brought her to his mind. There was an intense awareness of paradox in his mind that a woman so different could suggest the quiet little clerk.

"Glad to see you out getting a little fresh air, boy—might do you good," the astonishing apparition called to him in a loud enthusiastic voice. Her eyes flashed straight into his face for a moment and she gave him a warm smile. Then she turned and was lost in the crowd. Pausing for a moment, the manager wondered if his senses had interpreted correctly the details of this strange and rather embarrassing little incident.

On several subsequent occasions Mrs. White was left with the uncomfortable task of accounting for her peremptory and unannounced departure. The real employee felt that she could in truth say that illness was responsible, but she found it difficult to explain what the trouble might be and was left wondering in embarrassment what others might be thinking. Except for these peculiar episodes, she was so consistent and conscientious that Eve Black's occasional pranks were tolerated by her employers for a long time before their cumulative effect or some egregious and spectacular performance caused Mrs. White to lose the job. Sometimes she herself resigned, after learning by indirection (often by inference from odd remarks or conjecture based on surprising questions), of some exploit of her alternate that left her too humiliated or abashed to remain.

During the year since she began work she moved several times, finding it less difficult to seek a new boardinghouse or a new roommate than to attempt excuses or explanations. If she went about trying to describe her true difficulty, would not most people assume that such a story proved her bereft of reason?

Into the rapidly growing community, a metropolitan area inhabited by almost a quarter of a million people, many transients and strangers from all over the United States had been drawn by new industries, by general business expansion, vast Federal projects and important military installations. In such a community Eve White found it possible to obtain new jobs and to make fresh starts in neighborhoods far from the scenes she fled so repeatedly because of Eve Black's escapades.

CHAPTER 12

Except for relatively brief periods just after losing or giving up a job, Mrs. White remained steadily employed. In her basic aim to provide support for Bonnie by her own efforts, she was on the whole successful during this period of approximately a year. It was difficult for her to advance in her work because the activities of her counterpart eventually emerged in each new situation, making it necessary for her to leave positions in which there was promise of better remuneration soon. Again and again she was forced to start over somewhere else at a minimum salary. She had, one might say, held her own against the tide of her troubles without getting discernibly nearer an ultimate goal.

The other Eve's frequent manifestations made it still appear as strongly inadvisable now for her to take up the direct task of raising Bonnie as when she first separated in desperation from her husband. Though she still held to her purpose of going back to Ralph, it seemed increasingly plain that this resolution was sustained by what she accepted as duty rather than by any realistic hope that the marriage might ever afford her happiness. In it seemed to lie the only practicable opportunity of regaining her daughter.

The therapist often wondered during those eventful months how long this precarious balance could be maintained. Like some nimble juggler who keeps half a dozen balls whirling aloft while barely maintaining himself with one foot on a tightrope stretched high in the air, these incongruous mates, so strangely yoked in a common destiny, tottered repeatedly toward disaster, startlingly averted the fatal crash, only to proceed along the same incompatibly zigzagging, perilous course. Surely this career, with its stubbornly irreconcilable aims, could not continue indefinitely.

Eve White found herself severely handicapped in establishing simple friendships with others who worked with her in the various jobs she held and lost. It was difficult, too, for her to participate in little plans for diversion or ordinary social life that other girls at the boardinghouse suggested.

She soon found that she must keep each new acquaintance at arm's length in order to avoid as much as possible, and for as long as possible, their discovering the unpredictable instrusions of the other manifestation. These intrusions, even when Eve Black was relatively cooperative and undramatic, left anyone who had become acquainted with Eve White tingling in bewilderment. Vagaries of mood and manner are, to be sure, not uncommon; but in such a consistently sweet and unobtrusive person as Eve White, even a brief manifestation of Eve Black's brash voice and impish exuberance, or one hint of her typical attitudes, confounded the observer and elicited wonder. A rare glimpse of what seemed like such formidable eccentricity often made acquaintances withdraw.

Limited both by her natural retiring inclinations and her complicated situation, the sober little working girl dearly cherished what companionship she found available without undue risk. Having recently moved to a new boardinghouse ten miles from the one she left, Eve White often sat on the porch for a while after supper with her landlady and a few older couples who desultorily talked together there before going up to their bedrooms. In this little group were an elderly, retired high school teacher and his wife who showed her many pleasant little attentions. Kind and sensitive people, they both seemed more aware than the others of the unexpressed sadness in this quiet girl, and of the timidity that made it difficult for her to take an active part in the conversation.

This thoughtful gentleman, who had formerly taught English for many years, noticed occasionally in his comings and goings that Eve White sat alone reading in the hall or living room on Sunday afternoon. Seeing that the book she held was an anthology of poetry, he felt a new interest in this sweet, diffident little acquaintance. He was not the sort of man to come up at once and comment on her reading or announce forthwith his own devoted preoccupation with English verse. Though articulate and cordial, his old-fashioned courtesy bade him put aside his immediate impulse. Subsequently finding himself on the porch with Eve White, he mentioned the anthology and spoke of his own interest in its contents. Here, it seemed to this considerate man, was common ground, an area in which he could offer friendliness and perhaps something of his experience to this lonely, circumspect girl.

She was at once responsive. Though enthusiasm never

showed markedly in her face or voice, her intent eyes and her occasional laconic comment made him sure she was glad whenever he mentioned a sonnet familiar to them both or lightly quoted a few lines from Wordsworth or Keats to spice some little observation. At length Eve spoke a little to him, in her guarded manner, about the poems she liked best. At her timid request he finally read aloud to her from her favorite volume one Sunday afternoon when he found her alone with it on the boardinghouse porch. He found in these occasional opportunities to talk with Eve White a genuine stimulus and satisfaction.

She had expressed to the therapist her pleasure in finding these two older people and particularly her gratitude and respect for the former teacher who took pains to bring something like the warmth of an understanding uncle into the semi-isolation to which she was confined. When she spoke with regret of a change in this gentleman's attitude, she as well as the therapist had little difficulty in surmising that her alternate must have encountered him and behaved in such a way as to disconcert him seriously.

Though eventually Eve Black discussed this meeting, there seemed no good reason to bring it up again with Eve White and go into the painful details. At that time, after slowly reestablishing a friendly relation with her, this man and his wife had moved to their small house on the outskirts of town which was being built during their period in the boardinghouse and where they meant to spend their remaining years. Some weeks after denying any personal traffic with the former teacher or any knowledge of what might have affected his attitude toward Eve White, Eve Black with twinkling eyes told this story.

Having got out one evening just before supper she lost no time in taking off the simple dress her alternate was wearing. Getting out her own clothes from the closet where they remained untouched during her periods of absence, she wriggled into them with animation. Seating herself before the mirror she archly lined her eyebrows and put mascara on her lashes. With her own vivid lipstick she made over her mouth. Satisfied with her work she then decided to stroll over to a drugstore haunted at this hour by teen-agers and usually by some older men as well. There she thought she might find a male acquaintance who would suggest that she go with him to a dance. She hurried downstairs. Tripping through the front door, she paused at the cordial greeting offered her by the elderly gentleman who rose from his chair. Though she knew something about him, she had not, as she put it, been sufficiently interested in what he and Eve White discussed to pay much attention or have in mind any clear idea about him and his conversations with the other. After a nod and a spirited toss of her head, she would probably have gone on her way had not her childlike vanity been arrested by the attention he plainly offered. Surprise and pleasure grew in his eyes. He assumed at once that his melancholy and demure little friend must have been touched by a happy miracle. Only this could account for her being so gaily bedecked, so obviously and radiantly free of her habitual care, so boldy vibrant in her step and every motion.

"Why, dear child," he murmured, "you are lovely this evening." The freshness of her smile, the careless vigor of this body as she turned toward him, sank further into his awareness. "Why . . . why, you are lovely, indeed," he repeated, a little at a loss for words, but with added emphasis. Distractible as a kitten, alertly responsive to any admiring glance, Eve Black came over and sat on the porch railing near the chair from which he had risen. Hooking the toe of one high-heeled slipper around a supporting bar under the railing, she threw back her head and shoulders in a little gesture of simple exuberance. Her dark, tossed hair rippled as the overbalanced body, secured against falling only by her toe's hold on the thin upright bar, confidently righted itself in a quick, sinous wriggle. "Oops!" she gasped, flashing a playful glance at him as she carelessly smoothed the heavily ruffled dress and slip which had rustlingly flurried about her knees.

After one or two perfunctory remarks her companion fell silent.

"Nice evening now . . . wouldn't you say?" she asked in a low unfamiliar tone, her bright, curious eyes staring for a moment full in his face.

Trying to balance himself in these new impressions, he caught at the memory of his last conversation with Eve White. They had both tried to recall those lines about the Toyokuni color print. Subsequently the forgotten words had come back into his memory. He had reminded himself to repeat them to her. Now, seeking a path to familiar territory, he mentioned their last meeting and said aloud in his grave, well-trained voice:

> A blue canal, the lake's blue bound
> Breaks at the bamboo bridge; and lo!
> Touched with the sundown's spirit and glow,
> I see you turn, with flirted fan,
> Against the plum-tree's bloomy snow ....

With a sweeping roll of her eyes and a soft exclamation of laughter, Eve Black rocked over the banister, clapping her hands together once in pleasure. Though she had not paid close attention to the words, she took them as a direct and personal compliment to her own good looks. Realigning herself with a brisk, supple twist, she cried out:

"Now Pops, I do think that's right cute." Ready to join in any game, she arched her brows for a moment of concentration. In a voice lively with accomplishment, she added, "I know one too that ain't bad! Listen, Pops, I bet you goin' to like it." After one or two false starts during which she broke off, laughing at the inexactness of her recollection, she finally recited:

> They call him a lovin' man;
> He sure ain't got cold feet.
> He can make you warm inside,
> And your heart do the boogie beat.

She swung herself off the porch railing with a brave swirl of ruffles, touched her immobile companion cordially on the shoulder, and was away with quick, buoyant gait toward the stairway to the street. Energy overflowed in the unstudied and piquant rhythm of her walk.

When she reached the sidewalk, Eve Black turned, waved cordially, and with a smile, called out, "Nite-tee—now!"

CHAPTER 13

Perhaps the reader will grant that we were justified in our fears of what might happen to such a creature as Eve Black during her nocturnal adventures about the city and its environs. Not long ago this was a sleepy and conventional town; but its old streets were now choked with thousands of soldiers from the adjacent Army camp and with more thousands who had migrated to work at the hydrogen-bomb project a few miles down the river. The suddenly energized and crowded city spilled over in all directions, running into many miles of suburbia where new growth pressed into every road and lane. An immense dam up the Savannah River had been completed, furnishing a clear lake with shorelines that wound for over a thousand miles. New shopping and business sections sprouted like equatorial vegetation at outlying points a dozen miles apart. Trailer camps, some packed with as many as a thousand families, dotted the landscape.

Along with the migratory workers and other newcomers from afar, entertainers, gamblers, operators of night clubs, perverts, con men, strip-teasers, shrewd opportunists, well-schooled criminals, bawdy adventurers, narcotic peddlers, enterprising pimps, and strangely sophisticated Sicilian entrepreneurs had drifted into the area like a tidal fringe. Small cabarets sprang up in abandoned warehouses by the river and in former haylofts far out in the country. Where shady country roads used to meander toward the quiet city, miles of neon signs now flared in the night, and through their pink and gaudy efflorescence beat incessantly the sound of juke boxes, tinny pianos, and hot saxophones. Here in these once bucolic hillsides were all, or nearly all, the opportunities for the kind of iniquitous folly offered by Montmartre or by the harbor front at Port Said. Dark little bars, pretentious restaurants, versatilely equipped gambling houses, motor courts, and dance halls with extraordinary facilities, all catered to the restless, unrooted horde of workers whose Saturday pay was lavish in comparison with the traditional wages of the community.

When one thought of the provocative and heedless Eve Black out on her own until all hours of the night in such an environment, it was not easy to feel confident about her safety. We often discussed the dangers our patient was likely to incur and what might be done to minimize them. We could conceive of no way to control Eve Black directly except by sending Eve White to the State Hospital. As weeks passed and we saw that the venturesome Eve repeatedly extricated herself from crisis after crisis, many of which she herself had precipitated, we began to feel that beneath her naive recklessness there must exist a real shrewdness, perhaps some reflex pattern of action by which she unfailingly saved herself when danger became acute. She responded to the glitter of bright lights automatically, as a trout rises to a flashing spinner. The major considerations of ordinary life never curbed her irresponsibility; but she seemed immune to the strong urges toward serious misconduct that sometimes spring from a genuine personal attachment or, fleetingly, from the simpler, bare sexual impulse. Giddy and outlandish as was her demeanor in sober surroundings, she apparently remained free from the customary temptations that sometimes lure even conscientious people into disaster.

As time passed it became steadily clearer to us that she was attracted not by sin or depravity but rather by the trappings with which they are so often garnished. One would suppose she might be likely overnight to end up as a captive in some regimented white-slave racket, or perhaps be found with her throat cut from ear to ear beside some lonely swamp. But whatever led to the final fatal step in such directions apparently had no meaning for her. She was totally disinterested in what others found serious, be it good or evil; she thrilled to the spirit of light, loud, and essentially purposeless frolic and mischief, seeking it particularly in the bright fringes of actual danger.

The reader has perhaps watched a half-grown squirrel taunt and tempt a fox terrier in the dog's own yard. Climbing down from the safety of his tree such a squirrel often deliberately exposes himself to the swift foe, who, with one shake of the head, could immediately extinguish his life. The squirrel repeatedly invites destruction, often delaying his flight until escape seems quite impossible. The immense peril of his situation seems not to perturb the small frisky adventurer. He must sense something of his danger, however. He is plainly exhilarated by the game, and perhaps some vague realization of the fate he flirts with contributes to his sharp delight. There is no goal or purpose for the squirrel, but sport and frolic. Yet the game holds for him a thrilling fascination.

Eve Black, as a manifestation of personality, as a functional entity, seemed to be without the emotional components of full, normal, human response to any major issue. With no serious goals to distract her, it seemed only natural to romp and play. Free of personal attachments, entirely without the conscious experience of any profound emotion, she apparently evaluated possible consequences and risks in her career with little more sober foresight and apprehension than the squirrel in his game with the terrier. Like the squirrel, she too exhibited nimble and, so far, unfailing instinctive facilities to escape destruction. A scamplike zeal, an untroubled insouciance, possessed both figures.

Though Eve Black got into many small difficulties and sometimes was apparently in or near dangerous situations, she had throughout these twelve months of adventure always escaped dire consequences. From time to time the newspaper headlines told of a knifing at some honky-tonk she occasionally visited, or of a police raid on the night club where only a week before she had aroused general enthusiasm with her repartee, her spontaneous pranks, and her lusty singing. Prompted by applause, she had finally joined in there one night as an amateur with the late floor show. Though often conspicuous in small suburban pleasure spots such as the Club Agentine, the Neapolitan Restaurant, and the Red Casino, and occasionally the center of livelier-than-average groups in larger dine-and-dance establishments, no information came to us of grave misconduct on her part in these surroundings or of any serious ill fortune that overtook her.

One day when the hour of Eve White's appointment arrived, the physician was surprised to find that Eve Black had come in her place. After some discussion she agreed to cooperate in the process of eliciting her alternate, but maintained that, according to the demands of fair play, she should be recalled before the interview ended and restored to the original position of functional ascendancy, or liberation, in which she came to the office. This was agreed upon and after the interview with Eve White, who also admitted that the arrangement was just, Eve Black was called out again and allowed to go on her way.

Aside from the basic question of fairness in such a complicated situation, there were additional important reasons for not interfering with the balance of power these two had worked out between themselves. Should Eve Black be deprived of the period of freedom she had by chance or through her own efforts somehow obtained, she would be unlikely to fill another appointment if she were in control at the time. Would she not, in fact, be likely to assert herself by some act of unusual recklessness? Her tendencies toward cooperation would almost surely be discouraged. Perhaps she would be provoked into extremely rebellious or retaliatory behavior. There was, it seemed, reason to fear Eve Black's ill will and opposition, whether expressed outwardly in damaging behavior during her freedom or from within by the methods which had once caused Eve White's headaches and blackouts, and perhaps had contributed to her extreme anxiety.

From this time on it was occasionally the second Eve who came to fill the appointment Eve White had made. This she did of her own volition without the need of persuasion. In the waiting room she at once made herself happily at ease, quickly became acquainted with other patients who sat there and with their accompanying relatives. Talkative and irrepressible, she soon engaged everyone in a conversation spiced with little jokes and drolleries. Her camaraderie was immediate and pervasive. Though much of her speech consisted of clichés or unoriginal slang phrases her own fresh and superficial feelings bubbled so gaily through even the most desiccated words that they often took on an April flavor.

Usually when Eve Black came to the office she wore, not Eve White's conservative clothes, but her own. They never failed to catch the eye, to flash with some bright note that harmonized with her inimitably lively spirit. Eve White usually sat inert, patiently waiting her turn, reading a book or busy with some delicate piece of needlework. Soon there was no question in the secretary's mind about which patient to announce to the physician. Even on occasions when she had not had time, after getting out, to take off Eve White's clothes and dress in those of her own choice, it was seldom difficult to recognize her at some distance, from her bouncy gait, confident carriage, and general air of well-being and energy.

On one occasion she attracted, and welcomed, particular attention in the waiting room and in the corridors of the office building. These quarters were shared by a dozen physicians; and their secretaries, having encountered Eve Black casually, still talked months later about the remarkable impression she had made. It was the eve of St. Valentine's Day. Eve Black, before coming in to fill the other's appointment, had decided to take some pains in decking herself out appropriately for the occasion; she wanted to achieve some fine and specific decorative note that would harmonize with the ancient traditions of the holiday.

She appeared in a striking dress. It was indeed lovely and elaborate, rich with ruffles and lace, enticingly cut and fitted; even a plain woman wearing it would not fail to stir interest and, no doubt, elicit a few whistles. With all the pride and anticipation of a six-year-old child who has brought off some spectacular little triumph (that is sure to be discovered, and so to which she need not directly call attention) Eve tripped quietly into the waiting room, silent for the moment; but her eyes were eager and jubilant in anticipation of the applause she was sure would be forthcoming.

There was about her an air of rare embellishment, a quietly euphoric expectancy. Into her luxuriant dark hair that now hung free at shoulder length, she had woven dozens of small red roses, carefully forming a vivid heart-shaped figure, an elaborate and resplendent floral valentine. With the aplomb of a happily self-conscious Primavera, or of some Ionian love goddess aware of all her exotic charms, she took her chair, smiling graciously into the various faces that had automatically turned toward her in quiet fascination.

The physician decided it would be inadvisable to call out Eve White and thus inflict upon her the vision of herself in such extravagant display. Eve Black evidently retained these decorations until displaced, holding on to her finery until all strength was exhausted and, only then, allowing Eve White to emerge at home, to discover herself in such adornment that her senses reeled. Commenting later on the episode Eve White said with quiet dignity, "Even an actress, a woman accustomed to playing parts on the stage, wouldn't have gone out on the streets looking like that."

The Rorschach and other projective tests that had been made revealed nothing important about either Eve White or Eve Black that was not already known. From any patient's responses in such tests one can, if he likes, theorize indefinitely, and by the manipulation of the currently popular dynamic concepts, work out explanations of dubious validity along any line he might choose. Such explanations, however, often depend upon arbitrary assumptions about contents of the unconscious that are never demonstrated, rather than on what is recognized as evidence. Speculations of this sort offered little or no assistance in understanding or in dealing with our problem.

It is, however, interesting to note that the Rorschach record of Miss Black was interpreted by the clinical psychologist as "by far healthier than the one of Mrs. White." He felt that Miss Black's record indicated a predominant hysterical tendency and that Mrs. White's showed "constriction, anxiety, and obsessive-compulsive traits." On the Wechsler-Bellevue intelligence scale Mrs. White's I.Q. was estimated as six points higher than that of her alternate. Of each, however, the psychologist reported:

There is evidence that the native intellectual endowment is well within the bright normal group . . . ; in Mrs. White's case anxiety and tenseness interfere, in Miss Black's superficiality and slight indifference as to achievement are responsible for the lower score.*[14]

These technical tests threw little or no light on the important questions that still confronted us. They did not bring us any understanding of how or why the manifestation called Eve Black had emerged; nor could we find in them anything that helped explain how Eve Black had access to Eve White's thoughts and memory while Eve White remained unconscious of the other's entire experience. Was this professed unconsciousness real and complete? So indeed it appeared. Despite her disavowal and apparent disregard of them, was it possible that some of Eve White's principles and viewpoints at times exerted an indirectly restraining influence on the irresponsible Eve Black? Did something of what she knew only as "the other Eve" unconsciously play an invisible part in her behavior, perhaps serving sometimes to prevent her from taking a final step into dangerous situations?

Often enough the daring Eve retreated, leaving her sober and cautious sister to deal with problems that she found too difficult to face. Perhaps even when absent, the conservative Eve's qualities and judgment came into the equation whenever matters became critically serious for the other. Both Eves denied awareness of any such interaction. During the many months of observation no blending or mingling of their characteristic traits was even momentarily observed. Each, with remarkable consistency, played her own role, denying any direct participation in the aims and goals or personal experiences of the other. After all this time each remained unalterably herself.

Differences between the two manifestations became, in fact, more impressive as the months passed. The better we get to know a friend, the more sharply he stands out as himself with innumerable small as well as important features that distinguish him from all other men. Abstract terms and

* For the full report and interpretation of these examinations see Appendix B, page 308

descriptive words do not convey much of what one experiences directly of another human being, of his specific personal entity. Nor could any list of ten thousand such items be even near complete. Let us, nevertheless, set down for what they are worth a few points of contrast between the two Eves:

EVE WHITE	EVE BLACK
Demure, retiring, in some respects almost saintly.	Obviously a party girl. Shrewd, childishly vain, and egocentric.
Face suggests a quiet sweetness; the expression in repose is predominantly one of contained sadness.	Face is pixielike; eyes dance with mischief as if Puck peered through the pupils. Expression rapidly shifts in a light cascade of fun-loving willfulness. The eyes are as inconstant as the wind. This face has not known and will never know sadness. Often it reflects a misleading and only half-true naiveté.
Voice always softly modulated, always influenced by a specifically feminine restraint.	Voice a little coarsened; "discultured"; has echoes or implications of mirth and teasing. Speech richly vernacular, liberally seasoned with spontaneous rowdy wit.
Clothes: simple, conservative, neat and inconspicuously attractive. Posture: tendency to a barely discernible stoop or slump. Movements careful and dignified.	Dress is becoming and a little provocative. Posture and gait suggest lightheartedness, play, a challenge to some sort of frolic.
Almost all who know her express admiration and affection for her. She does not provoke envy. Her strength of character is more passive than active; steadfast on de-	Immediately likable and attractive. A touch of sexiness seasons every word and gesture. Ready for any little irresponsible adventure.

fense but lacking in intiative and boldness to formulate strategy of attack.

An industrious and able worker; also a competent housekeeper and a skillful cook. Not colorful or glamorous. Limited in spontaneity. Reads poetry and likes to compose verse herself.

A devotee of pranks. Her repeated irresponsibilities have cruel results on others. More heedless and unthinking, however, than deeply malicious. Enjoys taunting and mocking the alternate.

Consistently uncritical of others; tries not to blame husband for marital troubles. Nothing suggests pretense or hypocrisy in this charitable attitude.

All attitudes and passions whimlike and momentary. Quick and vivid flares of many light feelings, all ephemeral.

Though not stiffly prudish and never self-righteous, she is seldom lively or playful and not inclined to tease or tell a joke. Seldom animated. Her presence reflects her unexpressed devotion to her child. Every act, every gesture, and the demonstrated sacrifice of personal aims to work hard for her little girl are consistent with this love.

Never contemplative; to be serious is for her to be tedious or absurd. She is immediately amusing and likable. Meets the little details of experience with a relish that is catching. Strangely "secure from the contagion of the world's slow stain," and from all inner aspects of grief and tragedy.

Cornered by bitter circumstances, threatened with tragedy, her endeavors to sustain herself and defend her child are impressive. This role is one essentially so meek and fragile that it embodies an unspoken pathos. One feels somehow that she is doomed to be overcome in her present situation.

No allergy to nylon has been reported.

Reports that her skin often reacts to nylon with urticaria. Usually does not wear stockings when she is "out" for long periods.

CHAPTER 14

The responsibility of helping Eve White with her own personal problems, as well as trying to extricate first one Eve then the other from various adversities, mishaps, and impending calamities that were brought upon each in turn by Eve Black's heedless and irresponsible caprices, became an increasingly difficult task for the therapist. It was occasionally necessary for him to intercede for Eve White in regard to the difficulties that arose in her work through the alternate's activity. Eve Black, from time to time, would call from some night club, disturbing his sleep with childlike requests for advice or for succor when she had worked herself into situations that threatened to become serious. More rarely she called at some late hour on an impulse to share with him a little of the festivity she was enjoying, or to sing over the telephone a bar or two of some song with which she was enlivening her surroundings.

From the two Eves a great deal of biographical information was steadily accumulated. This was repeatedly checked with her parents. Though, as already mentioned, Eve Black or some nuclear fragment of this manifestation evidently emerged during the patient's early childhood on scattered occasions, it seemed more and more likely that the division between the two functional entities must have been much less sharp at that time, the contrast less consistent and less spectacular that what we were now observing.

We have mentioned that in early childhood Eve White was punished for visiting the children of a tenant farmer, thus disobeying her parents' orders against wandering in the woods. There were other punishments for deeds she could not recall for which Eve Black took credit. The parents confirmed Eve Black's account of these.

Though Eve White recalled no unkindness on her part toward her younger twin sisters, she had been punished several times for cruelty to them during their infancy; but Eve Black admitted to having felt annoyance with them which she once expressed by biting their toes hard enough to cause considerable pain and wild yelling. She remained unrepentant, however, and still seemed to take pride in having asserted herself in this as a child.

When our patient was five or six years old, her cousin and

113

close companion, Flo, was given for Christmas a doll which seemed to Eve a thing of inexpressible loveliness. As an adult Eve White recalled in detail her feelings about the doll, her longing for it, and a peculiar sense of emptiness or of rejection in finding not herself but Flo in possession of this cherished creature which her warm fantasy had half endowed with life. Her cousin had been thus blessed, while her own parents had left her, it seemed then, deprived and desolate, with no equivalent to which she could give the tender feeling, the ardent yearning, this doll had awakened in her.

When her reserve had been lessened under hypnosis, Eve White sometimes spoke at length about this early experience, giving in detail the subtle and complicated essence of this emotion from the remote past. Once or twice her eyes brimmed with tears that finally ran down her cheeks. Revival of these memories seemed to coalesce with her present grief about the separation from Bonnie; the old longing for this doll was a clue that could open and expose her present devotion to her actual child, an emotion she usually found it difficult to express freely.

Once after such a discussion Eve Black was called out while Eve White's cheeks were still moist with tears. After a quick, bold glance to orient herself, the carefree Eve seemed to notice something distracting or unfamiliar. Putting a hand to her cheek, with a motion as casual as when one brushed off a fly, she recognized the tears. With disdain for such foolishness she said, "So! She must've been bawlin' again . . . . She does it about just anything."

When the doll belonging to Flo was found broken, violently smashed to bits, strong circumstantial evidence pointed to Eve as the culprit. Though she denied guilt, she was punished. As for other similar childhood incidents already mentioned, the adult Eve White denied any recollection of breaking Flo's doll. Again Eve Black took credit, saying that at the time (and still) she saw no reason why the cousin should have such a doll while she was denied. With arbitrary and childish simplicity she thus justified herself, evincing pride in the directness of her solution.

Looking back over the entire history, it seemed to us likely that these sporadic disturbances were brief and rare during childhood and adolescence. It has been mentioned that they ceased entirely with Eve White's marriage and did not recur until after the miscarriage several years later, about the time her headaches and blackout spells began.

During the same interview discussing events of her early childhood, Eve White mentioned a blue china cup. Her interest seemed to sharpen as she spoke of this cup. She remembered herself playing with it in the company of her cousin Flo, when she was about five years old. The incident seemed to hold some definite significance, for she kept coming back to it. She could recall nothing of importance that had occurred in connection with the cup, but the circumscribed spot of memory in which it had reappeared evidently held for her some sharp flavor of the past. An unaccustomed animation came into her voice as she talked on, trying to find some association that would bring recollection of surrounding events. Despite continued attempts nothing further emerged, and at last she turned to other subjects. Discussion of the china doll belonging to Flo had apparently suggested the china cup, though there was, as far as she could recall, no close proximity in time between her contact with these two objects. Eve Black denied any memory of the cup.

Not through either Eve or through the husband or parents, but from a relative unavailable to us sooner, we learned, some weeks after Eve White had separated from her husband and began working, of a period about two years before her marriage during which she had seemed distinctly unlike herself. While working in a town far from her parents' home, this informant reported, the patient had behaved very peculiarly for several weeks. There was much about the episode that he did not understand. Most of what he could tell us had come to him indirectly. Evidently Eve had deviated greatly at that time from her customary ways. It was concluded that she had suffered some emotional disturbance or "nervous illness."

There were rumors that she had suddenly married. Several conflicting stories had reached the relative about this, and some of them indicated that violent quarreling and abuse had occurred at once between the bride and groom. The relative who discussed this with us said he had never reached a clear understanding of what actually occurred. At the end of these mysterious weeks, Eve, apparently well and quite herself again, had returned to her parents' home.

Both Eve White and Eve Black denied such an episode. The Eve we always found truthful never gained any recollection of such an episode in her life, though she did remember being ill, and perhaps, delirious, while working in this town long ago. After the subject had been brought up many times with Eve Black, she finally brought forth an elaborate story some of which, but by no means all, coincided with the information obtained from the relative and from other sources.

The unreliable Eve finally told this story. She had come out during the period mentioned. That was not, of course, her initial active manifestation. It was, however, the only interval of real freedom lasting more than a few minutes that she had obtained in several years. Furthermore it seemed very different from the brief excursions into the outer world that she had made in the past. For the first time she felt confident of her control, assumed that she could prevail indefinitely, and determined to set out on her own course of life.

She promptly decided to go to a dance. There she met a man who, evidently in his cups after a night of merriment, brought up, perhaps half in jest, the proposal that they marry. His attitude seemed to imply that this might be a good plan, if for no other reason—well, then—just for the hell of it. It is not unlikely that to Eve Black such a proposal on such grounds might have had immediate appeal.

Once she had admitted any knowledge at all of the incident, she insisted that a marriage had been performed; but she denied that she had had any sexual relations with this man either before or after the ceremony which she said took place. She never altered this denial. "Now wouldn't that have been a stupid thing to do!" she said, as if referring to something entirely without fascination and somehow preposterous.

During several months of questioning she recounted many details of outlandish strife and turbulence in the few weeks she considered herself as having been legally wed. During this time she had apparently enjoyed her longest period of uninterrupted sway. She maintained that she was predominantly in control, almost constantly present. She confessed that she had enjoyed frustrating the alleged husband by denying herself to him after allowing him to think she was ready for consummation of the relation. As in many stories about other matters, some of which will be mentioned later, it became ever more plain that Eve Black was often lying to us, not merely in an effort to evade, but in her enthusiasm to produce an impressive and remarkable account. After considerable investigation we reached the opinion that during this period Eve White had very probably been in a state of altered consciousness, in a fugue or somnambulism of undetermined degree, and that the alternate, or some less complete form of her full manifestation, had dominated the situation. In fact, Eve White's amnesia always seemed complete for the events Eve Black described as her own adventures. A thorough search of the legal records showed no evidence that a marriage had occurred.

Despite occasional minor interruptions by Eve Black, Eve White had held her present job for a longer period than usual. After a year of employment she had gained ground in some respects. At present she was working efficiently in the best position she had yet obtained. A raise in salary and her careful management had enabled her to save a little money recently. The headaches and blackout spells had not troubled her for many months. The prospect of returning to her husband and of working out a bearable relation was still blocked by serious obstacles; but, having achieved a small measure of personal security and financial independence, she had become a little more hopeful of eventually reaching some acceptable solution. Though sadly missing the presence of her child, she found some comfort in her successful efforts to provide for her. She had made a few friends in the once strange city and with them, despite many worries and responsibilities, occasionally enjoyed simple recreations.

Meanwhile Eve Black, though less actively resisted in emerging, had in general been causing less trouble. Being bored with all regular work, she seldom "came out" to make careless and costly errors or to indulge in complicating pranks while the breadwinner was on her job. Though in leisure hours she often got in bad company, picked up dates, and indulged in boisterous amusement and idle flirtations, her demure and conventional counterpart, lacking knowledge of these deeds, was spared the humiliation and distress some of this conduct would otherwise have caused her.

CHAPTER 15

At this point the situation changed for the worse. Eve White's headaches suddenly returned. They grew more severe and more frequent. With them also returned the blackouts. Since the earlier headaches had been related to, perhaps caused by, the other Eve's efforts to gain control, and the blackouts had often represented this alternate's emergence into periods of activity after a severe inner struggle, she was suspected and questioned. She denied having any part or influence in the new development. She did not experience the headaches, but, surprisingly, seemed now to participate in the blackouts and could give no account of what occurred during them. Apparently curious and a little uneasy about these experiences she said, "I don't know where we go, but go we do."

Two or three times the patient was found by her roommate lying unconscious on the floor. This, so far as we could learn, had not occurred during the previous episodes reported by Eve White as blackouts. It became difficult for her to work effectively. Her hard-won gains in serenity and confidence disappeared. During interviews she became less accessible, while showing indications of increasing stress. The therapist began to fear again that a psychosis might be impending. Though this fear was not, of course expressed to Eve White, it was mentioned to her reckless and invulnerable counterpart. Again the fact was emphasized that, should it be necessary to send Eve White to an institution, the other, too, would suffer the same restrictions and confinement. Perhaps, the therapist hoped, this fact would curtail her in any unadmitted mischief she might now be working.

Sometime after the return of the headaches and blackouts, with Eve White's maladjustment still growing worse generally, a very early recollection was being discussed with her. The incident focused about a painful injury she had sustained when scalded by water from a washpot. As she spoke her eyes closed sleepily. Her words soon ceased; her head dropped back on the chair. After remaining in this sleep, or trance, for perhaps two minutes, her eyes opened. Blankly but calmly she stared about the room, looking at the furniture and the pictures as if trying methodically to orient herself. Continuing their apparently bewildered survey, her eyes finally met those of the therapist, and stopped. Slowly, with an unknown but curiously impressive voice and with immeasurable poise, she said, "Who are you?"

For the first moment it was vividly apparent that this was neither Eve White nor Eve Black. She did not need to tell us that. The thousands of points distinguishing the two Eves had become more clear and convincing as we acquired additional experience with each. This new woman showed herself ever more plainly and in all respects to be another entity. Only in a superficial way could she be described as any sort of compromise between the two. She showed no evidence of Eve Black's obvious faults and inadequacies. She also impressed us as being far more mature, more vivid, more boldly capable, and more interesting than Eve White. It was not difficult to sense in her a capacity for accomplishment and fulfillment far beyond that of the sweet and retiring Eve White. Beside this genuinely impressive newcomer, Eve White appeared colorless and limited. In her were indications of initiative and powerful resources never shown by the other.

This third personality called herself Jane, for no particular reason she could give. In her early appeared the potential or the promise of something far more of woman and of life than might be expected from the two Eves with their faults and weaknesses eliminated and all assets combined.

Some weeks after Jane emerged, thus making a group of three patients, electroencephalographic studies were conducted.

REPORT OF ELECTROENCEPHALOGRAM

This tracing consists of 33 minutes of continuous recording including uninterrupted intervals of 5 minutes or more of each personality as well as several transpositions. The record was made with a Grass Model 111 EEG machine (8 channels) under conditions standard for this laboratory.

Each personality shows intervals of alpha rhythm interspersed with periods of diffuse low-voltage fast activity. Intervals of L.V.F.A. are presumably associated with periods of mental tenseness, which the patient admitted experiencing. Although it is possible that these periods occurred at random, tenseness is most pronounced in Eve Black, next in Eve White, and least of all in Jane. Several EEGs would be needed to show this to be a constant relationship.

When alpha rhythm occurs (relaxation), it is teadily maintained at 10½ cycles per second by Eve White and by Jane. Eve Black's alpha is increased in rate of 12 or 13 cycles per second—generally at 12½. This increase is significant and falls at the upper border of normal limits approaching an F1 category. It is interesting to note that F1 records are fairly common in psychopathic personality although no consistent correlation has yet been demonstrated. In addition to the increased rate, there is evidence of restlessness and generalized muscle tension during Eve Black's tracings which are not observed in the other two personalities.

Transportation is effected within a few seconds. It is usually accompanied by artifact from eye movements and slight body movements. Alpha rhythm is frequently blocked for several seconds during the following transposition. Alpha blocking was not pronounced in passing from Eve White to Eve Black. It did not occur at all in transposition from Eve Black to Eve White. This might possibly suggest that transportation from Eve Black to Eve White is easier to effect. However, only two such transpositions are recorded.

No spikes, abnormal slow waves, or amplitude asymmetries are recognized.

SUMMARY

All three personalities show alternate periods of alpha rhythm and low-voltage fast activity, presumably due to alternate periods of mental relaxation and mental tenseness. The greatest amount of tenseness is shown by Eve Black; Eve White is next and Jane least. Eve Black shows a basic alpha rate of 12½ cycles per second as compared with 11 cycles per second for Eve White and Jane. This places Eve Black's tracing on the border line between normal and slightly fast (F1). Slightly fast records are sometimes (but not consistently) associated with psychopathic personality. Eve Black's record also shows evidence of restlessness and muscle tension. Eve Black's EEG is defiinitely distinguished from the other two and could be classified as borderline normal. Eve White's EEG probably cannot be distinguished from Jane's; both are clearly normal.

J. Manter, M.D.

EEG Laboratory
Medical College of Georgia.
Jan. 5th, 1953.[14]

Many months followed during which there were three patients to interview and work with. Jane showed awareness of what both Eves did and thought, but had little or no direct access to their stores of knowledge and their memories prior to her emergence upon the scene. If either recalled an event from the past she gained some knowledge of it, but had no recognition of its being her own experience. Through

120

her reports the therapist could often determine when Eve Black was lying. Jane at first felt herself personally free from Eve White's responsibilities and attachments, and in no way identified with her in the role of wife and mother. From the beginning she seemed capable of warmth, and probably of devotion and valid love. She cooperated with sincerity and with judgment and originality beyond that of the others. Though it took her a while to learn what was quite new to her, she soon took over many of Eve White's tasks at work and at home in efforts to relieve and assist her. Her feelings toward Eve's little girl appeared to be those of a wise and richly compassionate woman toward the child of a family not her own, but still a child in emotional privation.

Her warm impulses to take a more active role with this little girl were complicated by the deep conviction that she must not in any way act so as to come between the distressed mother and her only child. During the first few months of her separate existence Jane became stronger and more active. Despite her fine intelligence she began without experience or at least without full access to the experience of an adult. As time passed Jane stayed "out" more and more. She could emerge only through Eve White, not finding it possible to displace Eve Black or to communicate through her. Almost any observer would, we thought after several months of study, find it obvious that Jane, and she only of the three, might solve the deepest problems that had brought the patient we call Eve White to us for treatment. If Jane could remain in full possession of that integrated human functioning we call *personality*, our patient would probably, it appeared, regain full health, eventually adjust satisfactorily, perhaps at a distinctly superior level, and find her way to a happy life.

Should this occur, it seemed then very unlikely that Ralph White's wife would ever return to him. On the other hand it was little more likely that Eve White, even if she became free of all that she had known as symptoms, could or would ever take up her role again as wife in that marriage. Should she try to do so, it was difficult to foresee much happiness for her or the husband. The probability of deep and painful conflict was apparent, also the real danger of psychosis.

Were we impersonal arbiters in such a matter, it would have been easy to see, and to say, that the only practical or rational solution to this astonishing problem was for Jane to survive, and Jane only. A steadily prevailing Eve Black would indeed be a travesty of woman. The surface was indeed appealing, but this insouciant and likable hoyden, though apparently too shallow, too incomplete, and too good-natured to plan or do deeds of willful malice, would, if unrestrained, forever carry disaster lightly in each hand.

The sense of duty, the willingness for self-sacrifice, so strong and so beautiful in Eve White, might bring her back repeatedly into this marital situation which she lacked the emotional vigor to deal with, and in which it was not likely she could survive. Jane, whose integrity and potential goodness seemed not less than that of Eve White, held rich promise of the power to survive, even to triumph against odds.

We did not judge ourselves wise enough to make active decisions or exert personal influence in shaping what seemed to impend. It is plain that, even if we had this wisdom, the responsibility was not ours. Would any physician order euthanasia for the heedlessly merry and amoral but nevertheless unique Eve Black? If so, it is our belief, it could not be a physician who had directly known and talked for hours with her, not one who had felt the inimitable identity of her capricious being.

A surviving Jane would provide for Eve White's half-lost little girl a maternal figure of superb resources. Perhaps in time she could give the child a love as real and deep as that of the mother herself. Perhaps. But would those feelings be the actual and unique feelings that sustained the frail and tormented Eve White in her long, pathetic, and steadfast struggle to give the child a chance for happiness? It may be said that this is foolish and tedious quibbling, that Jane after all, *was* the little girl's real mother. Was not the child born of her body? All awareness of her as a daughter ever experienced by Eve White was, to be sure, recorded in the electrochemical patterns of Jane's brain. True indeed. But *was* she her mother? Those who had known Eve White personally would find it hard to accept simple affirmation as the whole truth. What this whole truth is can be better sensed in direct feeling than conveyed by explanation.

The psychotherapist's responsibility in such a complex matter is not always easy to determine. Morton Prince has been accused by some, particularly by McDougall, of taking too active a part in "squeezing out" Sally. Our experience made us feel very keenly the wish not to exert pressures arbitrarily and perhaps play a part in the extinction of qualities possibly of real value if they could be integrated into more responsible patterns of behavior. We believed there was some choice open to the psychiatrist as to which personality he should try to reinforce, but that he must be tentative and work along with developments within the patient (or patients?) rather than make full and final judgments.

We felt that therapy had played a part in the emergence of Jane, but we did not consider her merely our creation. Our influence seemed to have been more catalytic than causal. Psychotherapy had not been directed according to an arbitrary plan. Although we persistently investigated early experiences through all three manifestations of our patient and encouraged emotional reaction to them, we sought to avoid insistence on any of the popular theoretical forms of interpretation.

Jane continued to grow in influence, to be out more and more. Through Eve White's exercise of memory she (Jane) established contact with some events in the early life of the other, and seemed to become more rooted in a past. We could not predict with any great confidence the outcome, but we became hopeful that some reasonably good adjustment might work out through the capacities contributed by Jane.

At a distance bridged only by printed or spoken words these "beings" may appear as merely fictitious abstractions. In the flesh, though it was the flesh of a single body, one found it more difficult so to dismiss them. Final decisions or choices in the course of involuntary developments must, we decided, be offered freely to something within our patient, perhaps to something beyond any levels of contact we had reached with Eve Black, with Eve White, or with Jane.

Jane, who appeared to have some not quite articulate understanding or grasp of this whole matter, not available to either of the Eves, shared our sharp reluctance about participating in any act that might contribute to Eve White's extinction. Unlike Eve Black, Jane soon gained profound and compassionate realization of Eve White's relation to her child. The possibility, the danger of a permanent loss of all touch with reality had occurred to Eve White. Through this we found a better appreciation of her feelings as a mother. Too restrained ordinarily by modesty to speak freely about such a matter, after hypnosis she offered, in quiet tones of immeasurable conviction, to accept this extinction if it might win for Bonnie Jane's presence in the role she felt that she herself had not succeeded in filling adequately for her child.

It has been said that a man must first lay down his life if he is to find it. Was it possible, we wondered, that this mother might, through her very renunciation, somehow survive and find a way back to the one and dearest thing she was ready to leave forever? That we did not know. Long and intimate personal relations with this patient had brought us to wonder if in her we had blindly felt biologic forces and processes still invisible to us, still uncomprehended and not quite imaginable.

Several months after the appearance of Jane, Eve White, anything but a physically bold or instinctively active person, was challenged suddenly by an event which for her was momentous. Of this Jane, deeply moved, wrote to the therapist:

Today she did something that made me know and appreciate her as I had not been able to do before. I wish I could tell her what I feel but I can't reach her. She must not die yet. There's so much I must know, and so very much I must learn from her. She is the substance of, *This above all, to thine own self be true.* In her, too, *the quality of mercy is not strained.* I want her to live—not me!

She saved the life of a little boy today. Everybody thought him to be her child, because she darted out in front of a car to pick him up and take him to safety. But instead of putting him down again, the moment his baby arms went around her neck, he became her baby—and she continued to walk down the street carrying him in her arms.

I have never been thus affected by anything in my four months of life. There seemed only one solution to prevent her possible arrest for kidnapping. That was for me to come out and find the child's mother. In the end I had to give him to a policeman. Later tonight when she had come back out, she was searching for her own baby. She had her baby again for a short while this afternoon; and I'm so happy for that. I still can't feel Eve Black. I can't believe she's just given up. *I feel inexpressibly humble.*

CHAPTER 16

Let us go back a few months to the time of Jane's first appearance. After her initial question to the therapist, when she asked, "Who are you?" she had quietly continued her survey of the surroundings. Her calm face showed neither fright nor obvious bewilderment. She did not hasten to ask questions.

After a few minutes the therapist, already impressed by the air of maturity and competence in this new figure, saw fit to inquire, "What is your name?" Looking at him gravely, her face seemed very thoughtful. After a moment, with no evidence of embarrassment, she replied, "I don't know."

For a while she said nothing more, apparently pondering on her situation. Then she asked, "How long have I been here?" As the physician gave her briefly some information about what had preceded, she occasionally asked other pertinent questions. She had the manner of someone who needs time to absorb each new item of experience and who intends to meditate before committing herself to speech. She denied even the slightest knowledge of any such person as Eve White (or Eve Black) and at first appeared to find what the physician told her of her relationship to them scarcely more remarkable than any other item that came under discussion. Everything, she admitted, was to her new and utterly unfamiliar. She denied consciousness of any life or experience prior to the moment she had opened her calm, steady eyes a few minutes ago. After considerable conversation, she was again questioned about her identity, and said, "My name is Jane." Of how she knew this, or why she made such a choice, she could tell nothing.

Except for her impressive command of language, which far surpassed that of the two Eves combined, her mind during this first interview suggested the *tabula rasa* of John Locke, the empty sheet upon which experience is to write but which now is blank and without content. If this manifestation was indeed without previous cognizance of the world or of self, whence had come this bearing of dignity and confident poise, these implications of a maturity and strength never suggested by either of the other two? By what subterranean channels did she draw on the store of words acquired by the other consciousnesses and now use these words so differently? Her idiom no more suggested the pinched, laconic reserve of Eve White than it suggested the ebullient slang of Eve Black. As the interview proceeded the physician sometimes felt that here was an enigmatic paradox: a woman, or the foreshadowing of a woman, hitherto unknown, who evinced truly adult judgment and power without a vestige of the human experience out of which, and out of which alone, such capacities can be formed.

Jane looked no more like circumspect Eve White than like that shallow, boisterous scamp, her willful, provocative, and ever-coquettish alternate. One did not have to ask questions or put to any test this clearly civilized and unaffected feminine apparition to know that the trivialities and loud capers of Eve Black would hold for her no attraction. Though these eyes never flashed with the vivacity characteristic of Eve Black, they seemed to reflect a disciplined vitality, an ease, and a range of feeling beyond the reach of Eve White's utterly genuine but circumscribed reactions. Jane's face had its own alert and thoughtful expression. Unlike Eve White she could laugh, and her smile was fresh and lovely. She had the face of a woman whose interests might extend far beyond anything known to the other two. Her posture in the chair suggested neither Eve White's tense decorum nor her alternate's semiadolescent, almost lascivious repose. Just as Eve Black gave the illusory but vivid impression of being richer-blooded, better-fleshed, and more rounded than Eve White, so Jane seemed a little taller when she stood, more lightly erect, more capable of command. Her gait and movements were her own, unobtrusively eurythmic and perfectly feminine.

Mrs. White was little more likely than a sweet Sister of Charity to draw boldly inquisitive glances from men on street corners. Everything about Eve Black seemed designed specifically to attract such attention. Though many polite eyes were likely to note with appreciation Jane's progress along any sidewalk, even a fool would automatically restrain his impulse to whistle. There was about her no flaunting whatsoever of erotic charm, but dull indeed would be the man who would not on second glance surmise that here was an authentic potentiality for what is naturally sensuous.

It was a matter of considerable interest to the therapist that neither Eve knew that a third manifestation had emerged. Even a few days after her initial appearance Jane, however, had many observations to make on each of the others. Since then she had enjoyed access to each of the other's consciousnesses during its periods of prevalence. Within a week she had, as an unparticipating spectator, so to speak, accompanied Eve Black to the dance halls. She had also attended Eve White at work and followed sympathetically this mother's longing thoughts about her daughter; she had appreciated, without sharing personally, her loneliness, her gentle courage, and her deep background of insecurity and fear, and her sense of impending doom.

Jane seemed to meet each item of this indirect or vicarious experience with genuine interest. She soon learned a good many details of Eve White's work. This did not bore her as it did Eve Black. And she reported with utter detachment, but with civilized amusement, various pot-valiant remarks, rowdy witticisms, and lusty incidents that emerged among the groups Eve Black encountered when she was out for the evening.

"You know, Doctor," she said seriously, "I'm beginning to think that girl actually has a sort of talent. There's no one at the places she visits who can stir up so much fun all around. It's true I haven't had long to observe, but it seems to me that people in night clubs, no matter how much noise they make, are bored and worried and often can't find the pleasure they've come to seek. I understand Eve Black very little, but she must have a real enthusiasm that comes out in play, or teasing, or in any childlike antic. It isn't that she has, or needs, such a good voice. She puts a contagious excitement and hilarity into any little song, or joke, or bit of horseplay. Soon other people forget their own moods and seem also to be having more fun."

The therapist wondered at first if Eva Black had knowledge, or at least some suspicion of this new presence. It would not be unlike her to withhold such information either for purposes of evasion or for the simple amusement she might derive from seeing the doctor hoodwinked. But in time it seemed plain that she, like Eve White, was unaware of the intruder. After considerable acquaintance with Jane had impressed him with her qualities and viewpoints, the therapist decided to make her existence known to Eve White. Jane agreed to do what she could to communicate with the other, to try, by whatever complex or ambiguous means might be available, to convey a sense of her friendly presence. It was decided that Jane make this effort at the moment when the physician decided to inform Eve White about her new invisible sister.

Jane was accurately described to Eve White as a capable and intelligent functional entity, as a sympathetic and understanding possible resource, as one in whom she might find a powerful ally. Not through hallucination or by direct access to the other's thought, but apparently in some less tangible and less familiar brief expansion of awareness, Eve White seemed to obtain some convincing realization of Jane—not as part of her own being, but as a proximate entity, unperceived but for the moment somehow intimate and of profound significance. Before the wonder and astonishment had faded from her pale face, before the tentative voice of Eve White could make its first comment on the experience, the tone sharply changed and Eve Black burst out suddenly and unbidden.

With a vehement and disdainful toss of her head she sprang from the chair and strode across the room. With her back to the physician she stood for a moment with a hand on each hip. Turning she approached him, wrath and indignation on her face, her eyes flashing now not in jest or coquetry.

"What in almighty hell's this all about?" she shouted. "I might've knowed you and she'd cook up somethin' fishy. . . . You and her and all your fine honorable airs!" In her hot vexation she turned her head and emphatically mimicked the act of spitting in a gesture of contempt. The peak of her anger passed quickly. Taking a seat on the arm of her chair she faced the physician, still with the air of one unjustly aggrieved but with a little of her habitual cajolery now returning.

"All right now, give me the straight of it," she demanded. "What about this Jane business? What about it, Doc? I've got the right to know!"

Though she became somewhat mollified as her questions were answered, it was plain that she disliked the new situation. Accustomed to full privacy from within during her personal adventures, and confident in her ability to discern the thoughts and plans of Eve White, she was unprepared and unwilling to share her habitat with another presence whom she could not detect but who had means of observing her own career. Though her disgruntlement did not altogether subside, it was difficult for Eve Black to remain serious about any matter for very long. After childishly insisting that the physician bend every effort toward eliminating or at least suppressing the newcomer, she finally became able to make a few jests and quips about the situation. As a person whose ways and capacities she well knew, Eve White was a rival with whom Eve Black felt she could easily cope. This stranger, whose thought and action lay well outside the scope of her awareness, was another matter.

During the eleven months in which all three carried out their separate careers, Eve Black was never able to displace Jane's consciousness, nor could Jane be called out by the physician when Eve Black was present. Jane soon found herself spontaneously alternating with Eve White. At first without volition or forewarning, she came forth for brief periods during the times when the gentle Eve was in control. A little later she often found it possible to come out intentionally. By then she had learned enough about the other's office work and other responsibilities to carry on successfully whatever Eve White had been doing. Although Jane did not find it possible ordinarily to emerge at her own behest when Eve Black was in control, on one or two occasions she apparently did accomplish this. Eve White, however, may have momentarily replaced Eve Black's dominance to provide the means of outlet for her.

Jane's knowledge expanded rapidly. At first she reported only the immediate thought and reactions of that Eve who was conscious and available to her. When they recalled and thought upon incidents in the past, Jane also was made aware of these incidents. She soon gained considerable scattered and unrelated information in this way about events that occurred before her recent birth into selfhood. Though unable to summon or command the memory of either, and by this means make unrestricted explorations of her own, she nevertheless collected carefully the data that cumulatively became available and used it skillfully to orient herself. Neither the present nor the past experience of either Eve impressed her in any way as belonging to herself. She steadily developed an increasing affection and compassion for Eve White, and finally what seemed to be a devoted but onesided intimacy; but she was seldom intolerant toward Eve Black or vigorously critical of her frivolous conduct.

Despite her unfailing poise and maturity of judgment, Jane, particularly in the early weeks of her career, often showed a specific naiveté quite her own. Her reactions suggested that all experience was so new and fresh that even the most commonplace matters glowed with a novelty and charm invisible to the ordinary adult. Her rapid acquisition of knowledge suggested that beyond or beneath the limits of her awareness lay considerable resources not yet her own but which bit by bit would become more available. Small items of direct experience, like keys that unlock secret doors, seemed to give her access to additional material that correctly aligned or shaped itself about isolated factual fragments as she consciously acquired them.

Though at first George Washington's name held no significance for her, a few sentences of information about this historic figure brought within her grasp a good deal more about the American Revolution and its chief figures. In some respects she seemed like a person who fifteen years ago in college had mastered differential equations or Latin but who since that time had never thought of calculus or seen a Latin word. Such a person if called upon again to exercise his thoroughly atrophied faculties, would reacquire the lost knowledge with a facility and acceleration impossible to a true beginner. In some respects such an example suggests what we encountered in Jane, but not in all respects.

Some features of her status can perhaps be further illustrated by the description of a hypothetical person born in Munich, who in early childhood spoke fluent German as his native tongue, but who at seven or eight years of age removed to a rural area in Nevada. Let us assume that such a person never again heard, read, or otherwise used the German language and that, in addition, an intractable amnesia obliterated all recollection of his childhood in Bavaria. Let us go further with our hypothesis and postulate that even the existence of such a language as German had been kept entirely from our immigrant, who would naturally assume without question that he was born in the Rockies and had never lived elsewhere. If suddenly transposed as an adult to Berlin, such a person might indeed find, in his efforts to orient himself linguistically, some startling and inexplicable resources from within. We do not offer this analogy as a complete, precise, or even an approximately close representation of what we encountered in this third personality manifestation. It may, nevertheless, bring out some aspects of her condition.

Information that Jane acquired was often of the sort that could have been furnished by the two Eves. Other material seemed to emerge at the stimulus of some clue from resources not available to either of them. Jane's interests, her viewpoints and attitudes, her tastes and inclinations, all her personal reactions, consistently indicated a disparate entity, another being whose experience remained apart from that of the others. All her behavior was constructive and socially acceptable. In contrast with Eve White she displayed ingenuity, humor, and confidence. In her active cooperation she sometimes wrote down comments on the situation and sent them to the physician. A couple of months after what she occasionally referred to as her "birth," he received a note from which these excerpts are taken:

Considering all angles I think things look a little better. I have learned from Eve White that ambition alone isn't quite enough to carry things through to a desired success. It requires an increase of knowledge and a quality of effort pertaining to the interest at hand.

She never gives up! If she falls short due to a lack of knowledge, she's on a constant search for it until it's acquired. I have begun to understand her ability to carry out well all she undertakes... Facing all her conflicts she searches for the happy medium. I like this simple unhappy girl. ... She loves baby Bonnie to distraction. I've noticed also that the things of culture in which she delights are to Eve Black the quintessence of dullness. They leave her cold in the literal sense as well as the spiritual. Nothing of what Eve White reaches for makes sense to Eve Black.

I think that [in Eve White] the mind must be adjusted to carry so much weight. What precipitates the crisis may be a mere trifle. ... I've seen Eve White survive some of the most severe blows a person could be expected to bear. ... Most people in her situation would have given up long ago. Somewhere there's a breaking point. The times that Eve White has been nearest to it have often followed incidents of little real importance. There was the occasion when Eve Black went out with that man. She [Eve White] couldn't help that so why should she take the blame for it? Perhaps it is because Eve Black has placed her in so many unpleasant situations and left her to take the responsibility. At present that is the only way I can account for it. It may seem that I am defending Eve Black in this statement. Believe me I am not. I chiefly wish to say that I do not feel guilt because of what she did. So why should Eve White? I agree entirely with Eve White that what Eve Black did was wrong.

In the therapist's office Jane spoke of the new and interesting things each day brought. Limited as her scope of activities might be judged by an ordinary adult, she showed no impatience or ennui. She seemed grateful for the opportunity to absorb and contemplate the smallest details of daily routine. At times she expressed a thoughtful uncertainty about the role she might play in her unusual relation with Eve White and Eve Black.

"I'd like to do whatever you think is best, Doctor," she said on several occasions, "but I don't want to get in trouble with either one of them."

A few months after her first manifestation, Jane, coming out on Christmas Day when Eve White was at the home of her parents, set down on paper these reflections.

MY FIRST CHRISTMAS

I think I have missed much, not having had a childhood period. Bonnie Baby is a very happy little girl today and is so fortunate to have a mother like Eve White who devotes her all to the happiness of one little person. Her baby must never know the sorrow and insecurity suffered by her wonderful mother. Eve White is once again her natural, clear self. She has been able to maintain the right attitude during this holiday. I know I could not be big enough to give so much so freely, to deprive myself of what I might desire for a family that had neglected me as she must have been neglected as a child. This has caused her to develop an illness from which she may never recover.

Her eagerness to offer gifts to those she loves brings a reward: a joy and happiness to her in knowing they are pleased. They, perhaps for the first time, have given serious thought to buying gifts for her. I wonder if they have ever done this before. I doubt it, because she cried so humbly this morning. Has no one ever loved her, or deeply cared if she was happy? It takes so little to make her happy—a smile or a kind word from either of her parents.

I feel depressed and unhappy. I don't know how to live. I understand almost nothing of the meaning of love and security. I know I must have both to be happy. I have little idea of my purpose, of what I may be searching for. I can never feel satisfied, for there seems to be some further point, some goal . . . where?

Sometime later she wrote:

When I first met Eve White I felt that her selflessness was a purely neurotic trait. I got the impression that she meant to keep the favor of her family and friends by doing anything they requested of her. This, I now find, is not entirely true. There is no doubt that she is ill; but she does not have personal gain in view when she does her best for her loved ones and associates. Her sacrifice for the happiness of another is the only way in which she can respond. I know I cannot be like that.

*   *   *   *

I was surprised to find that I have a quick temper. In attempts to control it I sometimes repeat to myself, "This is a discussion, not a quarrel." If this doesn't help I peel off nail polish. I refuse to make scenes like those I've seen Eve Black make. I also refuse not to get mad ever, as Eve White does. . . .

*   *   *   *

Loneliness is what I must learn to conquer. Eve White finds a wonderful peace in praying. This does not work for me. She really lives every day according to the religion she believes. She seldom prays for herself. . . .

I have decided that religion cannot be used just as a tonic. It must be something that comes from inside. . . .

*   *   *   *

Eve Black soothes her feelings by dating or getting high. I have no desire to drink like that. I would merely be foolish and silly. I don't, like Eve White, believe it is wrong to take even one highball. But so far I've never had anything at all of that sort. . . .

*   *   *   *

A feeling of loneliness possesses me completely. . . . I hope I can somehow be helpful to Eve White. Perhaps I have only a short time to live my curious fragment of life.

One might easily see or read into the character Jane some fusion of, or even a mere compromise between, the diverse tendencies of the two Eves. On her first appearance this expectation naturally arose. But it immediately became difficult for us to fit or even to force her into such a concept. As time passed she appeared to us with increasing clarity and emphasis to be another entity. If she had, indeed, been formed of their substance, it was still difficult for us to assume that the process was merely additive. If all her elements were derived from the other two, this union, we decided, like that of hydrogen and oxygen to make water, must have resulted in a product genuinely different from any of the ingredients from which it was formed.

CHAPTER 17

After approximately seven months of experience with Jane and more than a year and a half with the two Eves, we prepared our report of this case for the American Psychiatric Association meeting, and also a longer article, published later in the *Journal of Abnormal and Social Psychology*.[14] What, we asked ourselves, was the meaning of these events we had observed? Many laymen are inclined to believe that most claims of amnesia are simply pretense or fraud by which the claimant hopes to evade responsibility for some objectionable or antisocial act. When our newspapers carry an account of some man who has been missing for a week and, returning, tells his wife he had no memory of what occurred, the reader will often grin and wonder to himself if it were a blond or a brunette with whom this husband slipped off.

There is no doubt that the claim of amnesia is often spurious. A large percentage of all persons charged with serious criminal acts whom we have examined over the last twenty years have grasped at this ancient excuse. Most police officers consider it a corny ruse. In only a very few of the many claimants is there reasonable evidence of a true disturbance of consciousness.

The concept of multiple personality at once arouses similar suspicions. If Eve White is an unhappy wife sharply curtailed in her activities, restricted by her moral standards from seeking various pleasures and frivolities, what could be nicer for her than to simulate a dual personality? By so doing she can, the casual observer may say, have her cake and eat it too. By assuming the role of Eve Black she can evade her responsibilities and all or any prohibitions of her moral code. She can live it up as Eve Black and then return to her status as the innocent wife and mother without troubling her conscience. Who would not find such an arrangement remarkably convenient? Could undiluted hypocrisy ever reach greater depths?

Fugues and other states of amnesia not caused by epilepsy or by definitely organic brain disorder are usually classified as forms of *hysterical dissociation*. Hysterical manifestations, though formerly respected as major afflictions and interpreted with awe in terms of devil possession and witchcraft, have come to be regarded by many as imaginary illnesses, or as little more than dramatic and deceitful "putting on." Medicine emphasizes a clear distinction between *malingering*, the conscious and deliberate simulation of illness, and *hysteria*, in which the symptoms or signs of illness are generally believed to be a result of unconscious emotional or psychologic forces within the patient. Some popular but rigidly held beliefs about the contents and functions of the *unconscious*, often claim or imply a detailed, extensive, and scientific knowledge of this area. But much of this alleged body of knowledge depends for support at many crucial points more on fantasy, arbitrary theories, and mere assumptions than on anything that can honestly be called *evidence*. So much has been said and written about unconscious processes and motivations that many of us have been led to neglect or to minimize the almost infinitely varying scale of *awareness* manifested by the human organism.

Between the utter black of absolute unconsciousness and the untinged white of man's full and sharpest sensibility lie manifold shades of percipience, ever-changing levels of recognition, reaction, understanding, appreciation, and realization. The patient in an emergency room who to the intern seems to be deliberately pitching a tantrum may not only be *either* hysterical *or* pretending; he may indeed be both. Some cases of hysterical anesthesia wince at a sudden pinprick; others not only preserve their calm but maintain immobile relaxation while needles are forced into the quick of the nail bed. During this process some have no pupillary dilatation, which, being quite involuntary, even the most fabulous Spartan would not be able to restrain if such pain were actually felt. A relatively small unpleasant stimulus, such as the inhalation of aromatic spirits of ammonia, or some simple suggestive measure may immediately relieve one patient's paralysis. In another the disability may be more serious. We have occasionally seen a hand, clenched years before in a typical conversion reaction, that remained useless, the joints ankylosed, with severe calcification shown by

X-ray. What psychiatrist has not seen patients come into the hospital showing unmistakable, and apparently superficial, hysterical manifestations, who several days later had progressed into waxy flexibility, the profound disintegration, the full psychotic chaos of catatonic schizophrenia?

How real, we repeatedly asked ourselves, was the separation between Eve White and Eve Black? Could it be that Eve White was merely pretending that she did not know what the other manifestation thought and did? If her consciousness was altered during Eve Black's activities, to what degree did it subside? Did her specific functional entity disappear into something like sleep, or like profound hypnosis, when her counterpart was dominant? If so, how deep a sleep? The person who in ordinary hysteria is said to lose consciousness seldom hurts himself and usually seems to retain some, perhaps infraconscious but real, perceptive contact with his surroundings. But we have seen striking exceptions to this rule. One of our most classic examples of this disorder plunged down a flight of stairs, split her scalp to the bone, without awakening or in any way emerging from her fugue.

We were at first, despite the astonishing effects of the transition between the two Eves, predominantly skeptical. After experiencing a sense of wonder, sometimes touched with awe, during an interview with these ladies, we would tell ourselves and each other that surely what we had beheld could not have been quite so remarkable as it seemed. We kept looking for some mask to fall, for the distinctions that seemed so sharp to blur, for the play, if it was some sort of deliberate or unconsciously motivated pantomime, to serve its purpose and at last be done.

It has been said that no one takes seriously or believes in such a thing as multiple personality except the naive and those who have directly dealt with such a manifestation. Was there, we wondered, something so intriguing and spectacular about what we seemed to have come upon, that we involuntarily acted to preserve the illusion? Many who think they have seen a ghost, or obtained evidence of telekinesis, or been a party to anything so uncommon as to be considered miraculous, refuse to accept common-sense explanations and rationalize away obvious points that might compromise the magic quality of their experience.

Before the dawn of our century Bernheim gravely warned that "when a physician employs hypnosis with a patient it is wise always to be aware of who may be hypnotizing whom." If these three personalities were something less remarkable than our impression of them, what part had we ourselves contributed to the exaggeration or to the illusion? If learned people in our own time can gather and, through the nonsensical rites of dianetics, work themselves into the conviction that they have recaptured memories from previous existences before the birth of Christ, how could we be confident that our own interest and enthusiasm had not contributed a great deal to what we seemed to be observing?[15] Our most respected medical journals today sometimes carry reports in which psychiatrists and psychologists confidently prove (for themselves and for many readers) that the dream of an adult reveals specific misfortunes he has, as an embryo, suffered in the womb from such experiences as being frightened by his father's penis during the sexual intercourse of those who were to become his parents.[16] Surely, we told ourselves, let us not through our interest in this matter add further to the elements of pseudo science that are already invading the psychiatric literature and threatening to comprise its status as an honest and properly modest, branch of medicine.

It seemed of some importance to us to learn how other observers would react to what we had so long been studying. All three of the ladies with whom we were dealing agreed readily to appear before the Dugas Journal Club, a group of approximately forty physicians, psychologists, physiologists, chemists, and allied workers from the faculty of the Medical College of Georgia, the staff of the University Hospital, and the local Veterans Administration Psychiatric Hospital. It was Eve White who was presented first at this gathering. She gave a synopsis of her medical history and replied to questions asked by many serious students of the biologic sciences. Then Eve Black was produced in the swift metamorphosis now familiar to us, but which brought, with audible intake of the breath, this group to vivid attention. Jane was presented later and similarly examined. It was our hope that from this circle of our colleagues, men of experience in a wide range of scientific inquiry, light could be thrown on some aspects of this case to which we might have remained insensitive.

For approximately two hours the three ladies answered questions and participated in a discussion with the group, each displaying the characteristics and idiosyncrasies so distinctly her own. It was our wish that these exacting observers attempt to discover any artifice we might have overlooked, that they press and percuss and test in every possible way the manifestations that had impressed us so much. In this sober setting, where it had long been the custom to weigh dispassionately grave biologic questions, a sense of drama steadily grew. All three of the characters remained unchanged during the prolonged cross-questioning. Not one of them could be thrown off balance by any stratagem or sudden ruse. From none emerged a word, act, or gesture inconsistent with her separate identity. One experienced clinician who asked Jane about an event that occurred almost a year previously received this reply, "But, Doctor, you forget that I am only seven months old!"

Another physician, speaking with Eve Black, asked some questions about Eve White's reactions that implied they must after all be her own. When this was denied he said, "But surely you share some of her feelings. You are, in a sense, twins, aren't you?"

With a quick snap of her eyes, she replied emphatically, "But not *identical* twins."

The wish and the obligation to avoid, in so far as we could, overestimating or misconstruing what had so strongly impressed us, led at length to a decision that it would be worthwhile to present this patient personally at the American Psychiatric Association meeting in Los Angeles. Both Eves and Jane agreed to make the journey of almost three thousand miles and to appear before small or large groups of psychiatrists. A written or an oral account, however detailed and extensive, would, we felt, give only a pale and insubstantial impression of an observer's direct experience with the subject of our study. Though our moving-picture films* and tape recordings offered something additional, we felt that only the presence of this patient could adequately convey the nature and the degree of her strange disorder.

After some deliberation those in charge of the program decided against having her appear in person. Though every precaution possible would have been taken to conceal Eve White's real identity, it seems to us now in retrospect that serious dangers of unpleasant publicity might have been en-

---

* Available for professional use to educational institutions and medical groups only. Psychological Cinema Register, The Pennsylvania State University, University Park, Pennsylvania.

countered despite all efforts to avoid it. We had no way of knowing how long this tripartite status would prevail. We believed that witnessing the completeness of the personality manifestations and their persistent separateness would be a rare and potentially enlightening experience for the serious observer, and we still feel that an important opportunity was lost. This multiple personality does not now exist. Despite our regret over not having been able to demonstrate at first hand to such an appropriate group what we had observed with wonder and astonishment, we are convinced that, for the reason mentioned above, the Program Committee's decision was wise and correct.

Of those who read our report, some, no doubt, will conclude that we were thoroughly hoodwinked by a skillful actress. It seems possible that such an actress after assiduous study and long training might indeed master three such roles and play them in a way that would defy detection. The roles might be so played for an hour, perhaps for several hours. But we wonder if any person consciously dissimulating could over a period of months avoid even one telltale error or imperfection. Though this does not seem likely, we do not assume it to be impossible. Let us remember, too, that in plays the actors are given their lines, their roles are limited to representation of various characters only in circumscribed and familiar episodes of the portrayed person's life. The actor also has costume and makeup to help him maintain the illusion.

Were we, others may ask, taken in by what was no more than superficial hysterical tomfoolery? We do not argue that the psychopathology we encountered had nothing in common with ordinary hysterical conversions and dissociations; but we do believe that there was also something more and something different. If one chooses to regard these three manifestations of personality as products of disintegration, could such a presumed disintegration be schizophrenic, or perhaps incompletely schizoid? If the process was akin to the processes of schizophrenia, it must still be noted that none of the three products, not one of the three personalities showed anything suggesting the presence of that disorder. Are we justified in postulating a once unified whole from which our three performers were split off? Or is it possible that the functional elements composing each, as we encountered them for so long, were never in the past really or completely unified?

The developmental integration of what we call *personality* appears to be a complex process of growth or evolution, a not-too-well comprehended unfolding of germinal potentialities. Let us compare such a process with the zygote's course from microscopic unicellular entity to adult human being. Retracing the biologic course of identical twins, we come at length to cellular unity in the single zygote. It seems reasonable to assume in the multiple personalities at least a primordial functional unity. If so, is it possible that some division might have begun far back in the stage of mere potentialities, at preconscious levels of growth not accessible to us except in surmise or theory? If so, what chance, we asked ourselves, was there for an adequate integration to occur?

In our many hours of enthusiastic work with this patient, did we gradually lose ourselves and our judgment in an overdramatization of the subject? Are we able to report what is objective or merely the *verbal forms* of our surmises and speculations? It is not for us to give the final answer to these questions. We are aware that the only terms available to indicate what we think validly carry also many connotations that we do not assume or believe to be supported by fact.

Obviously the differing manifestations we observed in one woman's physical organism do not, in all senses of the term, indicate three quite separate people. Our words referring to the possible disappearance of permanent extinction of one of the personality manifestations perhaps imply that we regarded this as an equivalent, or at least an approximation, of death. Are we guilty of a misleading exaggeration? No heart would stop beating should this occur. No eyes would permanently close. No flesh would undergo corruption. Such an extinction would not fulfill the criteria by which death is defined. Yet, we ask, would his immediate replacement by an identical twin invalidate for a bereaved widow the death of her husband? This analogy is not precise. In some respects it is misleading. It does not give us an answer to the questions we raise. Perhaps it may, nevertheless, accurately reflect some of our own perplexity.

For these and for many other questions that confronted us in this study, we obtained no full or certain answers. We frequently asked ourselves what we meant by referring to the manifestations we observed by such a term as *multiple personality*. Immediately we found ourselves facing the more fundamental question: what is the real referent of this familiar word *personality?* In ordinary use we all encounter dozens of unidentical referents, perhaps hundreds of overlapping concepts, all with vague and elusive areas extending indefinitely, vaguely fading out into limitless implications.

Any day we may hear that John Doe has become a *new man* since he quit liquor three years ago. Perhaps we tell ourselves that Harvard actually made a *different person* of that boy across the street who used to aggravate the neighbors with his mischievous depredations. Many religious people describe the experience of being *converted* or *born again* in terms that to the skeptical often seem fantastic.

With a good deal of truth perhaps it may be stated that after her marriage Mary Blank *changed,* that she became *another woman.* So, too, when a man's old friends say that since the war he has not been the *same fellow* they used to know, the statement, however inaccurate, may indicate something real. John Brown may be said, perhaps with considerable validity, to be his own worst enemy. We hear that an acquaintance when drinking the other night was *not himself.* Another man, we are told, *found himself* after his father lost all that money. Every now and then it is said that a certain woman's absorption in her home and children has resulted in her losing her *entire personality.* Though such sayings as these are never taken literally, there is often good reason for them to be taken seriously.

Are they not, these exaggerations or distortions, used to indicate very imperfectly what is by no means totally untrue but what cannot be put precisely or fully into words? The real meaning of such familiar statements, however significant, helps only a little in explaining what we think we encountered in the case reported. Some relation seems likely, as one might say there is some relation betwen ordinary vocal memory or fantasy and true auditory hallucination.

Though often distinguished from each of the other terms, the word *personality* is sometimes used more or less as a synonym or approximation for *mind, character, disposition, soul, spirit, self ego, integrate of human functioning, identity,* et cetera. In common speech it may be said that John has a good mind but no personality, or that Jim has a wonderful personality but no character. Often this protean word narrows (or broadens) in use to indicate chiefly the attractiveness or unattractiveness of some woman or man. Our newspaper columnists have occasionally used it playfully to signify the extraordinarily attractive mammary equipment of certain Hollywood actresses. In psychiatry its most specific function today is perhaps that of implying a unified total, of indicating more than *intelligence* or *character*, more than any of the several terms referring with various degrees to exactness to various qualities, activities, responses, capacities, or aspects of the human being. In the dictionaries, among other definitions, one finds *individuality* defined as "the quality or state of being a person; personal existence or identity."

There is, apparently, no distinct, or whole, or commonly understood referent for our word *personality*. But the term is useful to us in psychiatry despite its elasticity, and often *because of* its elasticity. If they are to be helpful, all such elastic terms must be used tentatively. Otherwise they may lead us into violent and confused disagreement about what are likely to be imaginary questions, mere conflicts of arbitrary definition. Bearing this in mind, we felt, and still feel it proper to speak of Eve Black, Eve White, and of Jane, as three personalities. Perhaps there is a better term available to indicate the manifestations of this patient. If so we are indeed prepared to welcome it with enthusiasm and with relief.

Our study raised many questions. Even for us it had settled few, if any. The relatively slight or inconclusive differences between the personalities of our patient, noted electroencephalographically and those shown in psychometric and projective tests, were not particularly impressive beside the profound and consistent differences felt subjectively in personal and clinical relations. A qualified expert examined for us the handwriting of each Eve. Though considerably impressed by consistent and significant differences between the two productions, it was his opinion that those with adequate professional training could establish sufficient evidence to show both were done by the same human hand. After a detailed investigation our consultant expressed this conclusion:

As a conclusion of the opinions derived from analysis of the various handwritings of this multiple personality patient, it is believed that the handwriting does not undergo complete subordination to each marked change of personality, even though each group exhibits evidence of emotional instabilities. It readily appears the handwriting of each personality is of a different person. Such apparent or discernible variations may lead the untrained observer to believe that the handwriting of each personality is completely foreign to the other. However, extensive investigation of these handwriting materials establishes beyond any doubt that they have been written by one and the same individual. Nothing was found to indicate a willful and conscious intent to disguise writings executed within a personality or between the first and second personalities.

Ward S. Atherton, Captain, Military Police Corps, U.S.A., Chief, Questioned Document Section, Army Provost Marshal General's Criminal Investigation Laboratory,

Camp Gordon, Georgia.[14]

Though unable at the time we presented our study to the American Psychiatric Association to add anything significant to the hypotheses offered in the past by those who had worked with similar patients, we found ourselves singularly stimulated by our direct experience with this case. If we had not so far devised final or even fresh answers, we had at least been prompted to ask ourselves a number of questions. A few of these, even when put in verbal forms outwardly familiar, we found to our surprise had somehow become new to us and peculiarly provocative of thought.

CHAPTER 18

It was still impossible for us to foresee or to estimate with any confidence what would next befall our engrossing patient. The ultimate prognosis was entirely beyond our prediction. Though long acquainted with the general content of Morton Prince's celebrated studies, we both for several months after the emergence of Eve Black deliberately refrained from reading his *The Dissociation of a Personality*[3] and *Clinical and Experimental Studies in Personality*.[17] We hoped thus to avoid unduly projecting the conclusions and conceptions of another into what we encountered. But later, after carefully reviewing these books and all other available material on multiple personality, we felt that Dr. Prince's Miss Beauchamp, far more than any other patient reported, resembled our own. Miss Beauchamp, after years of treatment, at last became sufficiently well integrated to make a satisfactory adjustment. In this we sometimes found encouragement when Eve White's condition was worsening and her future looked particularly ominous.

The arrival of Jane brought us considerable hope. Here, we thought, was an ally whose strength might be added to Eve White's apparently dwindling resources. Here too, it seemed to us, were potentialities of a broader understanding and response to life through which perhaps might occur some reconciliation of the opposing diversities and conflict between the two Eves. Since Jane had vastly more capacity for fun and humor than Eve White, might not the shallow hedonistic impulses of Eve Black find through Jane more acceptable outlets and more mature goals? The situation did improve for several months; then again for some time there was no substantial progress.

After the disturbance at the suburban corporation (described in chap. 19) Eve Black for a while was less ambitious in her exploits. Minor incidents continued, however, to indicate her activity. One morning Eve White telephoned the therapist from the department store where she had been working successfully. Her voice showed unaccustomed agitation as she complained:

"What's wrong with her? She goes around telling lie after lie. Doctor, it's so embarrassing I can hardly stand it. I'm confused. The stories she tells are so unnecessary. She's been telling customers that this and that piece of merchandise will be in the next day when she must know we don't even carry those things. I've tried to believe she isn't really bad— maybe in some respects a nice person-but I don't see how she can be anything but hateful." She sobbed over the telephone.

Such a loss of patience and quiet discipline was not characteristic. Eve White usually succeeded in restraining her tears even when large misfortunes befell her or when tragic events portended. Perhaps the never-ending repetition of exasperating petty annoyances would eventually undermine her docile but remarkable self-control. If this defensive barricade could not be kept intact, would Eve White rapidly deteriorate? Or was it possible that she might become less constrained, more adequately articulate, and eventually better able to survive?

During this period she wrote:

Dear Doctor:
Meditation is the only word that comes to my mind at this time. I am told to write down my thoughts as they

144

appear. Perhaps this word is in my thoughts because it carries with it the implication of relaxed tensions, and a great desire to understand the truth of this illness. It has me in a state of confusion. It seems enormous. Out of it I may try to find some way of happiness for my child and for all those I love. To be able to give happiness to others is the greatest satisfaction one can experience.

• • • •

Why I made such a scene sometime ago in your office over the china doll Flo had as a child is beyond me. Actually it was very childlike of me. I hope that outburst will be forgiven. You wanted me to bring back all I could remember of it. My memory is quite short; but as well as I recall it was a china doll with golden hair and blue eyes. It was lovely.

Perhaps I envied her having it. I guess I was selfish to the extent that I wanted it for myself. When I look back on the incident I remember I loved that little thing of beauty. I enjoyed just looking at it as she held it in her arms and rocked it as one does a baby. When it was broken it hurt me as much as it did Flo, because I had bound so much joy into just seeing it. To the best of my knowledge mother punished me because for some reason she thought I had broken it. It's been a long time, but I'm certain I didn't. That's all I can remember of it. I hope it is what you wanted to know.

Sincerely yours,
Eve White

Before this letter was mailed Eve Black, during a brief period out, found it. On another sheet of paper she typed a comment of her own which she sent with the other:

Hi Doc,
Our brain child has a way with them big words, huh? This blessed machine don't work so hot for me, as you can see. You know, of course, I broke the china doll, and I am not sorry a tap. I'd do it again. They thought Flo was so much, and she ain't no better than me or nobody else. You should have seen her flaunting her pretty doll in my face. Sure I broke it and if I had gotten the tanning for it, which I didn't, I'd still be glad I broke it. I can't type so fancy and all like Eve White, but hunt and peck and what have you, I can type too. If I said I was grateful for the patience you shown with me you'd sure as fire faint, so I

won't say it. You know you're cute, remind me to tell you. Guess I'd better sign this thing one way or another, heck, I'll do it like madame.

Sincerely yours,
Eve Black

Jane seldom wrote letters in the ordinary sense. On separate sheets she set down, almost every time she was out for any length of time, a sort of diary of her thoughts. These are a few of her reflections during the weeks when Eve White was employed in the large department store:

How horribly frightened Eve White must have been when she first realized how ill she actually was. (For Eve Black there was no surprise, since she was in a position to know about the things that were so disturbing.) Sometimes now I ask myself, "How can I stand this any longer?" Then I realize that this is no time for doubts and fears. If that brave girl has been able to find hope over such a long period of time . . . and still display . . .. an honorable and kindly personality, I feel that I must exert a little harder effort to become rightly confident, and give ample forethought to each task . . . I'd like to be able to overcome disturbing setbacks as graciously as she. How can she bear so much without complaining . . . ? The effort she exerts to control the understandable fear brought about by Eve Black's behavior would give the average person cause to mistrust the entire human race. . . . I am surprised that she [Eve White] hasn't turned to narcotics or drink to find relief from her problems. . . . Eve White and Eve Black are two individuals, separate and vastly different. Yet there is something binding us all together in some remote fashion. None of us can be eliminated it seems without fatally damaging the other two. . . .

Eve White seems to think she is slowly dying. Did I call her weak once? What a poor judge of character I must be. She is constantly trying to arrange everything so it will be easier for her successor, whoever that may be, than it is now. . . . The doctor seems to feel that I will be the successor. There I differ with him. I think it will be Eve Black. But I do not know. If it should be me, I hope the day may come when Eve White will know the fulfillment of her desires, especially for Bonnie, through me. It confuses and depresses me to feel that if I am to live it must be through the "death" of one so fine. If there is any chance for her to survive I refuse to become a part of anything that would shorten her life as part of the Trio. Often this does not seem possible. She is too unhappy. In spite of the unhappiness I feel on her behalf we seem to be moving toward a climax, toward something I cannot foresee.... Drifting as we are is not building strength. It allows Eve Black to absorb even more.... No matter what troubles come, or what punishment she might receive, she is still determined to proceed with her evil desires.

●　　●　　●　　●

She must be able to see she's destroying Eve White, herself, and me. She seems to be effective about it.... I would not want a life where I would be in continuous struggle as Eve White is.... I do not need to say here that I'm frightened. I am scared to death.... Our future, I believe, depends on the support of the few who really love her. Is it possible that, had someone really loved her soon enough, there would have been no US?

At approximately this point in their careers our three personality manifestations were each for the first time given the semantic differential test, a relatively new exploratory device until then unfamiliar to us. Dr. J. McV. Hunt, editor of the *Journal of Abnormal and Social Psychology*, to whom we submitted our report, kindly suggested this step. He pointed out that it would be interesting, and possibly helpful, to have the results of such tests interpreted by psychologists unfamiliar with the case history, by workers with no information about the characteristics of Eve White, Eve Black, and Jane as they had appeared to us. We were, and are, most grateful to Dr. Hunt for this opportunity and also to Osgood and Luria who devised this test and carried out the blind analysis of the material we obtained separately from the three personalities.

The test contains fifteen significant concepts: LOVE, CHILD, MY DOCTOR, ME, MY JOB, MENTAL SICKNESS, MY MOTHER, PEACE OF MIND, FRAUD, MY SPOUSE, SELF-CONTROL, HATRED, MY FATHER, CONFUSION, SEX. The patient places each of these items in a scale indicating judgment between two contrasting evaluations such as *valuable—worthless, deep—shallow, tasty—distasteful, active—passive*, etc. The scale gives seven choices of degree for the estimate to be indicated between the two extremes as shown in this example:

MY FATHER active ———:———:———:———:———: X :———:
———: passive.

MY FATHER soft ———: X :———:———:———:———:
———: hard.

The fifteen concepts listed above are each checked on the scale between ten pairs of polar terms such as the two just listed. "In the test form itself," Osgood and Luria point out, "concepts are rotated against scales in such a way that each concept appears once with each scale, but with a maximum interval between successive appearances of both." This test, of course, requires no specific skill or experience on the part of the one who gives it. It is accurate to say that the procedure is self-administered after the person to be tested receives the forms and understands the simple mechanics of his task.

Osgood and Luria analyzed the results obtained on two occasions (with an interval of two months) from each of our three personalities. Aside from these results they had no clue to any characteristics of the disparate manifestations. Their only other information about the case is summarized in their report.

> ...We know that we are dealing with a case of triple personality, and these have been labeled for us (presumably by the therapists who collected the semantic data) "Eve White," "Eve Black," and "Jane." We suppose that "White" and "Black" have some connotative significance—certainly, as will be seen, the quantitative semantic data distinguish sharply between them. We also know, of course, that the patient is a woman, presumably participating in some kind of therapy; we do not know the stage of therapy or whether or not she is hospitalized. We considered it also fair to ask (from J. McV. Hunt) about the following items of sociological status, because they contribute to the meaningful interpretation of certain concepts: concept CHILD—does this woman have a child? Yes, she does. Concepts FATHER and MOTHER—are her parents alive? The mother is, but Hunt doesn't know about the father. Concept MY JOB—has this woman had a job outside of home-keeping? Yes, she has. This is the sum total of our external information about the case.[18]

We had no direct communication with our co-workers; and Dr. Hunt, through whom we sent the test material, gave them no further information to supplement the few

148

items mentioned above. Osgood and Luria did not know who was treating this patient or in what part of the country she was located until after their results were submitted for publication. Analysis of the material resulted in appraisals from which we quote these excerpts:

EVE WHITE

...*Eve White perceives "the world" in an essentially normal fashion, is well socialized, but has an unsatisfactory attitude toward herself.* Here the usual social *goods* are seen favorably. MY DOCTOR, MY FATHER, LOVE, SELF-CONTROL, PEACE OF MIND, and MY MOTHER are all *good* and *strong* whereas FRAUD, HATRED, and to some extent CONFUSION are *bad*. The chief evidence of disturbance in the personality is the fact that ME (the self concept) is considered a little *bad*, a little *passive*, and definitely *weak*. Substantiating evidence is the *weakness* of her CHILD, as she sees him (or her), and the essential meaninglessness to her of MY SPOUSE and SEX. Note also the wide evaluative separation between LOVE and SEX. In the interval between (the two tests) ME and SEX become more *bad* and *passive* and simultaneously become almost identical in meaning to her—and note that her conceptions of LOVE (a good, strong thing) and SEX (a bad, weak thing like herself) have moved still farther apart.

EVE BLACK

... The most general characterization here would be that *Eve Black has achieved a violent kind of adjustment in which she perceives herself as literally perfect, but to accomplish this break, her way of perceiving "the world" becomes completely disoriented from the norm.* The only exceptions to this dictrum are MY DOCTOR and PEACE OF MIND, which maintain their *good* and *strong* chacteristics, the latter, interestingly enough, also becoming *active* (on the second test). But If Eve Black perceives herself as being *good*, then she also has to accept HATRED and FRAUD as positive values, since (we assume) she has strong hatreds and is socially fraudulent. So we find a tight, but very unnormal, favorable cluster of ME, MY DOCTOR, PEACE OF MIND, HATRED, and FRAUD. What are positive values for most people—CHILD, MY SPOUSE, MY JOB, LOVE, and SEX—are completely rejected as *bad* and *passive*, and all of these except CHILD are also *weak* (this may be because CHILD was weak in Eve White and much of the change here is a simple flip-flop of meanings). Note that it is MOTHER in this personality that becomes relatively meaningless; FATHER, on the other hand, stays *good* but shifts completely from *strong* (in Eve White) to *weak*. . . . note also that in this personality LOVE and SEX are closely identified, both as *bad, weak, passive* things.

JANE

. . . The general characterization is that *Jane displays the most "healthy" meaning pattern, in which she accepts the usual evaluations of concepts by her society yet still maintains a satisfactory evaluation of herself.* MY FATHER, MY MOTHER, MY CHILD, and MY DOCTOR—most of the significant persons in her life—are seen as *good, strong,* and *active.* The major modes of behavior, PEACE OF MIND, LOVE, SELF-CONTROL, and MY JOB, are seen as equally *good* and *strong,* but *somewhat passive*—as if these ways of behaving and thinking were simply accepted without stress. The two socially agreed-upon evils, HATRED and FRAUD, are put in their proper places. The most significant characteristics of Jane's meaning system, however, are these: the self concept, ME, while still not *strong* (but not *weak,* either) is nearer the *good* and *active* directions of the semantic space; note also the close identification of ME and MENTAL SICKNESS, which here is not an unfavorable concept to her. Her attitude toward her husband, MY SPOUSE, is for the first time meaningful (unlike Eve White) and tending toward the *good, strong, active* directions, like the other significant persons (unlike Eve Black). And LOVE and SEX (quite unlike Eve White) are both favorable and quite closely identified. The changes from testings 1 to 11 are simply such as to strengthen the healthy pattern evident in the first view. ME becomes considerably more *good* and *active;* MY SPOUSE for the first time becomes completely identified connotatively with MY DOCTOR and MY FATHER (and loses its tie with CONFUSION); and LOVE and SEX become intimately identified with each other and close in meaning to SELF-CONTROL and PEACE OF MIND.[18]

Osgood and Luria apparently consider the differences reflected in the test material to be of interest. They say:

The thumbnail semantic sketches of each personality just given make it intuitively evident that the semantic differential does draw sharp distinctions between the three personalities inhabiting one nervous system. . . .

The first thing to note is that the correlation of each personality with itself (e.g. testing 1 and 11) is regularly much higher than the correlation of that personality with any other personality (with the single exception of Eve White 1 and Jane 1). This is quantitative justification for the statement that the semantic differential does differentiate between the several personalities of this woman. Whether it differentiates in a valid way is a matter that can be judged only by relating our analysis to the detailed case history material available elsewhere.

Another important thing to note above these correlations is that Eve White and Jane (the two "socialized" personalities) are fairly highly correlated whereas the correlations of Eve Black with the other two are definitely low, even negative. In other words, Eve Black is clearly the most deviant and disordered personality.[18]

The results of the test lead Osgood and Luria to estimate Jane and Eve White as "socialized" personalities. They differ chiefly from each other in their responses to the concepts ME, MY SPOUSE, and SEX—Eve White's reactions suggesting a negative critical attitude, Jane's suggesting their acceptance as positive values. "Eve Black," they report, "shows gross differences on almost all concepts."

In addition to the brief descriptive characterizations quoted above, Osgood and Luria tentatively offer further interpretive estimates. They feel that these, unlike the objective material already given, should be regarded as speculative. They infer from the tests that of the three, Eve White is "most in contact with social reality and under the greatest emotional stress." Her responses indicate awareness "both of the demands of society and her own inadequacies in meeting them." The tests also suggest in the blind analysis that Eve White "sees herself as a passive weakling and is also consciously aware of the discord in her sexual life, drawing increasingly sharp distinctions between LOVE as an idealized notion and SEX as a crude reality.." She is described also as showing "dominance of the super-ego," as "accepting the mores or values of others (particularly her mother) but continually criticizing and punishing herself." "If this case came to the psychotherapists with a voluntary, self-initiated plea for help," Osgood and Luria conclude, "then it seems likely that Eve White was dominant at the time."

Judged solely by the tests, Eve Black appears to be "clearly the most out of contact with social reality and simultaneously the most self-assured." She is described as accepting socially disapproved attitudes as "perfectly legitimate," as seeing "herself as a dominant, active wonder-woman," and as "in no way self-critical." Of Eve Black, Osgood and Luria also say, "Like a completely selfish infant, this personality is entirely oriented around the assumption of its own imperfection," and "personal perfection is apparently the demand acceded to rather than sexuality." They cannot tell whether or not our patient has been committed to an institution, but, if so, they find it "likely that this personality was the reason for commitment."[18]

To our surprise, interpretation of the test indicated Jane as "the 'original' personality, in the sense of being most characteristic of the woman her friends and relatives knew...." She also appeared to be "the most puzzling of the three personalities." She is described as "superficially...a very healthy personality: 'all's well with the world and I'm getting better and better.'" There are indications that she finds the chief people in her life admirable and effective and reacts to "all socially approved modes of action as *good*, *strong*, and *passive*." The analysis of her test suggests that Jane may be "an essentially strong, healthy, and improving ego-dominated personality," but some points indicate that through self-deception she may have "woven a web of repression as to the state of reality," that the promising features in her performance may be misleading. Two possible interpretations of Jane, according to the test, become possible, one offering much hope, the other strongly suggesting that what is most encouraging about her may be quite insubstantial. "In any case," they conclude, "we doubt if Jane would have either come for therapy or have been institutionalized—as such."[18]

If we keep in mind the fact that Osgood and Luria had no information at all about this patient except the few items mentioned above, some of these estimates, based solely on what each of the personalities scored in the test, seem remarkably accurate. To be sure, they have been informed that she is a woman, that her disorder is that of multiple personality, that there is a husband and a child, that her mother is living, and that she had a job outside the home. Nothing else about the patient, who lives almost a thousand miles away, was accessible to them. They knew nothing about Eve White's reserved manner, her circumspect behavior, her separation from her husband, her conscientious industry in her work. They had heard nothing about her aims and objectives. Nor did they have any hint, except from her responses to the test, of Eve Black's boisterous air of well-being, of her idle frolics in night clubs, or of her irresponsibility. They were not aware that she, as well as Jane, considered themselves unmarried, or that neither accepted motherhood as a personal experience, despite their sharply contrasting attitudes toward Eve White's role as a mother and toward her child. They had no way of realizing that, while the reactions of Eve White in the test to such items as HUSBAND, CHILD, and SEX were based on her own experience, those of Jane and Eve Black were, consciously, *not* to MY CHILD or to MY HUSBAND. Nor did they have any clue to the fact that in registering their responses to SEX and LOVE, these two regarded themselves as virgins.

It is interesting to note that the tests indicate Jane as the "original personality," in the sense of being "most characteristic of the woman her friends and relatives knew." Osgood and Luria, of course, were not aware that she considered herself as having been in existence only about six months when the first test was made, only about eight months at the second. They did not know that Eve White was the personality who originally consulted us or that she was the one familiar to friends and family, or that Eve Black had enjoyed only rare, sporadic, and usually brief appearances until a few months before we first saw Eve White. So far as we were able to learn, no one had ever encountered any manifestation of Jane until she emerged full-grown, as Pallas Athene at birth, suddenly in the office. She denied all personal memories of experience prior to that moment. Many of Jane's qualities that we cannot successfully formulate in words had impressed us from the first. Perhaps from some of these came the reactions in the test that suggested her as the original personality.

The work of Osgood and Luria was not completed and their impressions formulated until several months after the three personalities were tested. Great changes and unforeseen developments in the case had meanwhile occurred. They worked, however, let us again emphasize this point, with no additional information about the course of the disorder. The uncertainty about Jane and her potentialities, which the test results bring up, is a point of great significance. Is she, despite her superficial promise, a figment too good to be true? Are her healthiness and her apparent capacity for a full life little more than thin formalities, something less than real? Are her socially correct attitudes, her apparently rich responses to the manifold stimuli and opportunities of existence, her humor, her theoretically wise choices, chiefly the unfelt, or inadequately felt but mechanically perfect, gestures of a manikin, or a semimanikin? Will the qualities we have surmised in this manifestation, after all, prove to be little more than a blind mimicry of life? Osgood and Luria do not say that this is so. Their interpretation of the tests, however, made us wonder if Jane was as sound as she appeared to us.

If we are wrong about Jane, the prognosis for our patient becomes poor indeed. Or is the alternative (second) estimate of Jane, offered tentatively from the test results, more likely to prove correct? Is Jane merely a two-dimensional mirage of the true and fine feminine image that emerged and convinced us of its incipient reality? Or can this likeness be indeed another and a stranger Galatea?

CHAPTER 19

A small business transaction involving Eve White and several members of her family brought to our attention interesting questions concerning her legal status. On our advice she sought the services of a distinguished attorney. In discussing the case with us her counsel brought out a number of important points that illustrated the many nuances and complexities running through the entire situation. The law of our state, he explained, does not officially recognize multiple personality or afford precedent to indicate what should be done if one such identity should object to commitments made by either or both of the others. After being introduced to all three of his clients, our learned consultant, impressed by the multitudinous and intricate hypothetical issues and subtle potentialties in the rare situation, sagaciously suggested that all three of the personalities sign any important legal paper.

There seemed no reason to doubt that Jane would be agreeable to anything that might be beneficial for Eve White or Bonnie. If the manifestation of Eve Black should gain complete and permanent control, this good-natured scamp would scarcely be prone to think seriously about business transactions or to attack the validity of agreements made by a party with whom she steadfastly denied identity, in behalf of a child she emphatically maintained was not her own. Nevertheless, the careful jurist felt there were substantial grounds for drawing up an official document for the signature of all three of the personalities. The following excerpts are taken from a recorded agreement signed by the group, pseudonyms being substituted, of course, for the actual names of those involved.

WHEREAS, there has appeared for treatment as a patient of ... and of ... a certain person who possesses the outward appearance and physical endowments of a white female sui juris and competent to bind herself by contractual obligations, but, who, upon investigation and examination, by the said ... and ... appears to have what is spoken of as a multiple personality, there being in this one physical person three separate personalities, each of whom possesses a full name by which she considers herself indentified, so that any contractural obligation binding upon one of such personalities, for the purpose of identification, would require execution in the name by which such personality is identified; and

WHEREAS, the three personalities are identified as above described by the names Evelyn Black, Evelyn White, and Jane Black, respectively; and

WHEREAS, the personality identified by the name Evelyn White is married to one Ralph White and by him is the mother of a five-year-old girl, Bonnie White; and

WHEREAS, by reason of the exceptionally unusual phenomenon of such multiple personality, the said ...

NOW, THEREFORE, in consideration of the premises, and in consideration of ... to each of the said three personalities known as Evelyn Black, Evelyn White, and Jane Black, and to Ralph White, the receipt and sufficiency of which are hereby acknowledged, and in further consideration of the agreement ... the abnormality which has resulted in such triune personality, which agreement by the said ... by their acceptance of these presents and their acting in reliance upon the obligations set forth herein, the undersigned, Evelyn Black, Evelyn White, Jane Black, and Ralph White, hereby ... and the undersigned release and discharge, and each will release and discharge, the said ... from all liability for ... and they jointly and severally agree to indemnify and save harmless the said ... from any loss or damage which they or either of them may suffer or sustain by reason of any claim or demand made by or on behalf of the said Bonnie White or any other relative of the undersigned for damages alleged to arise, directly or indirectly, for any reason whatsoever.

IN WITNESS WHEREOF, the undersigned have hereunto set their hands and seals, this —— day of May, 1953.

Evelyn B. White	(L.S.)
Evelyn Black	(L.S.)
Jane Black	(L.S.)

Our legal consultant, after several interviews in which he carefully discussed details of the transaction with each of the personalities, soon became quite familiar with them all and found himself urbanely at ease with whichever lady was present. On one occasion at his office the need arose for an additional witness to a paper. Stepping across the hall, he called in an earnest young attorney who had often expressed deep respect and admiration for his older colleague's sound judgment and unerring practicality. Not disclosing to the other man anything that would lead him to suspect than an experience unusual in routine legal procedures lay ahead, he anticipated with gentle but lively humor the reactions of the obliging friend. After Eve White signed, Eve Black was called forth. In order to obtain the third party, Eve White had first to appear again, since only through her could Jane emerge. Maintaining an air that implied that all this was to him commonplace and undeserving of explanation, the experienced attorney unobtrusively watched the young colleague struggling with his consternation. By a masterly effort of professional poise he curbed his immediate strong impulses to seek enlightenment at once about this perplexing matter, to ask for some clue by which he might sanely orient himself in a scene as curious and unlikely as the illogical sequences of a vivid but chaotic dream. Nonchalantly concealing his amusement, the senior attorney proceeded gravely with the technicalities at hand.

Jane, with her eager interest in absorbing all she could in a world still very new to her, found substantial satisfaction in meeting people and establishing pleasant social relations. Neither loquacious like Eve Black, nor, like Eve White, passive and shut in by taciturn reserve, she was easily and intelligently articulate, a stimulating and adroit conversationalist, who could tactfully draw from another valuable reflections of his own experience.

156

Though usually cheerful Jane had periods of discouragement. During one of these she wrote as follows:

Often I've wondered what happens during the period of time between changes of the personalities.

It's the strangest feeling for Eve White to be "out" and have the doctor call to me. I know in advance that he's going to call me out, because he always asks her if he can talk with me; but it's still an unusual feeling when he calls my name. I can hear him but it sounds as if he were far, far away; and the sound of his voice is almost like a beacon to guide me for the first few seconds.

His voice is the first sound I can recall. How afraid I was; but that fear has vanished, and a new fear has been born. Then I didn't know why I was afraid. Now I do—sometimes.

Every day that passes I become more afraid, in spite of Dr. Thigpen's encouragement.

He says I will live, but I'm not even sure I'd like to. Some day, he insists, I can find happiness. But how can I hope for the normal happiness that other girls look forward to? No man would consider marriage to a girl who has been ill in the manner that I have, and who could blame him? Perhaps it is hereditary, or if not that, it might recur. Therefore marriage is definitely out. That's why I feel it's best for Eve White and Ralph to get a divorce. One child involved in this is enough.

I know, facing facts, that we will never have a normal life, but it's wonderful to hope.

I despise pretending to be Eve White, but socially and in business this is a necessity. I want to be myself.

Eve White prayed once to be like other people. What a wonderful, far-fetched thought, for if we do get well, we won't be like other people, because those who know of our illness will refuse to forget.

Wish I could write poetry, too. It eases some of the ache.

Though Eve White still maintained consciousness most of the time and retained her position as the usual and chief representative to the outer world of the complex and diverse trinity of forces within, Jane, as months passed, emerged with increasing regularity to relieve her at work and, particularly, to deal with difficult situations that called for an assertiveness and decisiveness that her timid sister lacked. When Eve Black obtained control, Jane still could not in any way exert an influence either directly or through

Eve White, who was sometimes and in some way within reach of her wordless counsel or support. Eve Black then had to go her way unchecked until, by choice or by chance, she lost dominance and faded from the outer scene.

After working for almost two months in the office of a new and thriving suburban business concerned primarily with the sale, repair, and provisioning of boats and automobiles, but also including a drive-in restaurant, bowling alley, motel, and liquor store, Eve White found herself again in difficulty. With no antecedent recollection except that of being peacefully at her job, she awoke with all the surprise of one suddenly emerging from sound sleep to find herself in the midst of a raucous and bitter altercation. She could not at first grasp the nature of the conflict. The head of the business organization was ordering off the premises an oily-haired stranger whose isolence at once proclaimed all that the two-carat-diamond ring on his finger, the garishly checked sport coat and lavender shirt seemed to confirm. As the circumspect Mrs. White in silence was still unsuccessfully trying to unravel the threads of abuse and argument that roared about her, she was further confused when both men turned upon her with oaths and incredible accusations. Despite her intense embarrassment she clearly heard these words, but she could not yet formulate even a theoretical background that might have evoked them. Without any pattern in mind of the basic situation in which she found herself playing a central role, she could only maintain silence.

The head of the enterprise for which she worked was a squat behemoth who ordinarily spoke a rapid, slightly broken English with undertones of Italian accent. Ordinarily he was not difficult to understand. Now, jet-propelled by vociferous passion, his tirade was becoming ever more incoherent. Behind his current prosperity lay years of economic strife in the slum areas of a distant metropolis. His present operations were well within the law. He was usually friendly and essentially courteous behind the rough outer manner in which he conducted ordinary transactions. Having come recently to this section, he had already brushed several times with the thieves, sharpers, and racketeers who abounded in the swollen population. Though he prided himself on being a fair and peaceable man, the boss when unjustly dealt with, could rise and rend the air with the vehemence of his brawling youth.

As the two irate men shouted at each other, and from

time to time at her, Eve White made out some incongruous fragments of the subject they seemed to be tearing apart between them.

A trip to Miami.... Stories about fabulous jewels in a vault at the bank.... Jewels brought from France by ancestors of noble blood.... Claims by the slick-haired insolent stranger to concessions or an interest in the business.... Bawdy leers in her direction with further references to Miami.... Money missing from the cash register ... or from somewhere.... The bookkeeping "all in de messa terribile...." What about the case of liquor—gone, gone...? Indecent words.... Hard-lipped accusations by the arrogant man with the flashing diamond ring ... about presents.... Presents ...! From him—to her ...! Further mention of Miami, with more than innuendoes of shocking insult.... Wild cries of "liar—liar—liar ...! Contessa be God-damned.... Deesa china dolla types—so mucha lady.... CHEE-SUS ...!" Then came a fearful oath.

Eve White, trembling with fright and mortification, realized that Eve Black had been at work. But just what had she done? Coming into the complex and bizarre scene at this advanced stage she found it difficult to distinguish between what might have already occurred and what had been merely planned or promised. Had Eve Black actually carried out serious acts of intimacy with this detestable figure of fraud and false elegance? The incomprehensible talk of jewels and of vaults at the bank: had felonies been already perpetrated? With a chill that seemed to settle in the marrow of her bones, she confronted the possibility that, if her alternate had ... and with this man ..., then she herself might be pregnant. She did not know what to deny, what to protest. These men were too angry, too far advanced in the matters over which they wrangled to heed her questions.

Finally as the two voices began to subside a little in tone, Jane emerged and Eve White faded from the unhappy scene. Unlike her departed associate, she had some clues to guide her. She placed the foppish quasigangster with oiled hair as an unpleasant nightclub companion of Eve Black's. Only part of the other's experience was accessible to her awareness and much of this was clouded in varying degrees of uncertainty. But she realized that the heedless Eve had taken pleasure in enticing the opportunistic and shady entrepreneur and she became aware that Eve had promised to do something crucial about the relationship this very evening.

Not all the details could be deciphered, but apparently this man had been convinced that she would go off with him at this time. The boastful Eve had also regaled him and others with fantastic lies about her family, had spun an elaborate and grandiose tale about her antecedents, describing them as Huguenots of noble birth who had come to Charleston long before the Revolution bringing jewels of great value. Jane could not penetrate the other's memory sufficiently to be certain whether Eve Black had, as usual, so far evaded the sexual transactions she so wantonly promised. This she decided, she must for the present assume on the strength of an unclear but helpful feeling which people sometimes call *intuition*. Now Jane was able to recall more clearly the tempestuous part played by her bawdy inner neighbor when the quarrel began.

It is doubtful if Eve Black had succeeded in convincing her recent admirer that she was of noble birth or that her family retained such heirlooms as she had described, but she apparently had convinced him that she was the idolized mistress of her employer. She had told him also that a partial ownership of the business had been made over to her in anticipation of a marriage, which, she confided to the man with the diamond ring, she did not intend to go through with. At first she had encouraged her self-seeking admirer to believe that she would get him cut in on her employer's enterprises and enter upon a clandestine relation *in situ*. He foresaw a possibility of introducing gambling machines and call-girls into the situation if he could count on her connivance. By opening up across the road on a small scale, he could, he felt, take advantage of the clientele already built up by Eve's employer through the restaurant and motel.

After much maneuvering and stalling, Eve Black had been confronted by the two men shortly before the end of working hours. Her employer had sought her out in alarm after finding his accounts in disorder and had collided with the bogus lover who had come for a showdown about his own interests. Enraged, but by no means daunted, the irresponsible Eve, in lieu of offering an explanation or defense, had lit into her two accusers with indignation and curses. She better than held her own with them until, more or less in triumph, she opportunely vanished from the uproar.

Exacerbated no little, the employer and the other man had begun to fling exaggerations about wildly when Eve White appeared. Jane found that Eve Black had actually received only a few shoddy and inexpensive gifts from her pretentious wooer. No evidence of stolen money could be found after tempers had cooled. The bookkeeping had been badly muddled by Eve Black and this had misled the employer. She had also, apparently, encouraged the darkhaired man to help himself to some whisky, perhaps to convince him of her boasted part-ownership. Jane was eventually able to bring the altercation to a close and settle the affair without legal action being taken by anyone. Eve White lost this position; but before long she found an opening in a large department store where she began work as a salesgirl.

CHAPTER 20

Eve White kept her job at the department store until several months after our study was reported at the meeting of the American Psychiatric Association. Eve Black took great interest in the news items that appeared in the press about the case of which she was a part. Indeed, she seemed to be fascinated by the anonymous fame she found for herself in these accounts. During her midnight revels she sometimes hinted to acquaintances of the evening that she was a woman of renown and, perhaps, a sort of genius. She let it be known that there was more to her than met the eye. Distorting the account in the news, she occasionally pictured herself at present as voluntarily disguised in the role of a carefree girl, more or less as a grand duke might affect incognito to avoid recognition when he seeks light amusement. She endeavored to give the impression that in real life she might be a great and glamorous personage, a movie actress, a poetess, a research scientist on the verge of discovering the cure for poliomyelitis, or, perhaps, an operatic contralto who had spurned contacts from La Scala. The innuendoes and fragments of stories varied with her mood. There is reason to suspect that at least once she convinced a tipsy dancing companion that she had achieved distinction in Seville as a female matador.

Eve White asked permission to leave her work early one afternoon because of a minor physical indisposition. Approximately an hour later the manager of the department store received a telephone call from someone who gave her name as that of a nationally known woman journalist connected with the *Chicago Tribune*. The manager was asked if Mrs.

Eve White was one of his employees. The alleged journalist explained that she had come to the city to see Mrs. White and write an account of her to be featured in Chicago and perhaps elsewhere. She briefly discussed with the busy executive some points about multiple personality, attempting to romanticize the disorder and implying that in some respects at least it was to be regarded as a rare gift or talent. The attitude of the inquirer soon convinced the department-store manager that he was the victim of some ruse or practical joke and he hung up the telephone. This led to inquiries about Mrs. White's work. Despite a generally good record of efficiency, her immediate superiors reported that, particularly during recent weeks, she had been extremely moody and temperamental. Often she had seemed listless and unhappy; then again she would be overconfident and careless, paying little or no attention to her job and chattering boisterously on irrelevant subjects. As time passed these erratic episodes became more troublesome and finally Eve White lost this position.

Before this action had been taken, Eve Black explained that during one of her occasional periods "out" at the store, she had been rebuked for carelessness. The sharpness of the criticism had been tempered by remarks about her usual high standard of work.

"It made me mad all over," she said unregretfully. "That washed-out snip! So goody-goody, and always so, so-oh right! I just thought I'd let 'em know what the score was. She's so smart. Let her get out of it," she concluded proudly. "But suppose she loses her job?" the therapist asked. "She'd get another one," she snapped, her eyes flashing. "She always does. That's her worry, anyhow—not mine."

Jane told us she felt that Eve Black had, in addition, been motivated in this prank by a heedless impulse for notoriety. Scorning any sober thought of the consequences, she followed the prompting of a whim to bring her in this way to the attention of the manager, and the man who had criticized her, the fact that she was a person who had stirred interest in places afar.

A few months earlier Jane had said, a little wistfully, "You know I'm looking forward to seeing what summer is like. I've seen winter and spring, but not summer. Isn't that curious?"

Though Jane, with increasing experience, was now able to relieve Eve White more often and more effectively at work and sometimes to emerge on critical occasions and deal successfully with complications caused by Eve Black, she had, so far, found no way to bring about any appreciable reconciliation or satisfactory compromise between the deeply conflicting aims of those two. Her support of Eve White was a palliative factor, but no changes had occurred that suggested truly curative influences at work.

Some months after the separation Ralph White had become distinctly attentive to his wife, coming often to see her on weekends and urging her to return to him. She had left him with the understanding that she was to live alone until she recovered or at least had improved sufficiently to make with confidence the decision to renew their relations. Until then they were not to live as man and wife. Only under these conditions did she feel she could go on with her plans. Ralph's attempts during this period to woo his wife back and to put pressure on her to rejoin him proved upsetting. On these visits he tried several times to persuade her to engage in sexual relations with him. Her stress and perplexity mounted until it became necessary for the therapist to intervene and reemphasize to Ralph White the terms of his agreement.

After a long period of apparent indifference, interrupted by occasional contacts that ended in setbacks for Eve White and in distress and misunderstanding for them both, he was now showing renewed interest in his estranged wife. Eve White's reserve and taciturnity made it difficult to determine adequately what changes may possibly have occurred in her attitude toward Ralph. It was plain that his presence, and particularly his efforts to hasten a reconciliation, caused conflict. Jane, who maintained an impersonal attitude toward Ralph spoke more freely than Eve White did about the situation. It was her opinion that the wife's attachment to her husband had steadily declined, that, without clearly realizing it or freely admitting it to herself, she was increasingly affected by a deep dread and repugnance at the prospect of returning to him. She tried to tell herself, according to Jane, that this reaction, or as much of it as she would recognize, must be a feature of her illness, something she could hope might eventually subside.

Some of Jane's written comments on the relationship between Eve White and her husband were puzzling to us. At times she would express a judgment that impressed us as naïvely oversimplified and unrealistic. Were these uncharac-

163

teristic statements to be explained by Jane's unique lack of direct experience? Or could they possibly be an imperfect and misleading expression of her reactions to attitudes of Eve White that remained subconscious or vaguely apprehended? Referring to her in her diary during the period we are now discussing Jane wrote:

> This simple girl possesses direct honesty, genuine religious faith and unfailing gentleness. What made her as she is? Sometimes I feel an impulse to attack what she stands for, not because it isn't good, but because it seems to be unreal. Still I know how very real and sincere she is. She could add much to social and religious organizations. It seems to me she would make an ideal wife and mother. Why then, I ask myself, was Ralph White not satisfied? Why was he not happy with this sweet girl as his wife? Are there ulterior motives behind his plea for her to come back? Or has he at last realized what he had? Is she too much for any man to live up to?
> Eve Black on the other hand is the life of any party. That little featherbrain never fails to sparkle. When I review all the things I've heard and seen about Ralph White, I wonder if perhaps Eve Black isn't the girl he fell in love with. They seem to have much in common, whereas he and Eve White have nothing. In a sense Eve Black makes people happy too. She is so full of life herself that it picks others up—just watching her. *Unless* she is angered! Then one may need a baseball bat and a good pair of handcuffs. Or maybe a hairbrush administered in the right place would help!

Now, after almost a year of separation, Ralph came to the city apparently determined to take more positive steps, to settle somehow an unhappy stalemate that had become for him progressively more unsatisfactory. Telling his wife that he was unable to see that *she* had made any progress, or that *they* had made any progress, he strongly urged her to give up her present plans and return with him to Jacksonville, Florida. He was now employed there temporarily. If they could be together for a while, perhaps improvement would begin. Maybe they could soon take Bonnie back to live with them.

Eve White firmly and repeatedly declined, saying that she felt this step was entirely beyond her ability at present. He then asked her to go away with him for the weekend, so they could spend a few days together and see if she

164

might find their relationship better than she remembered their life in the past. She continued to shake her head. In time Ralph's patience became exhausted. He grew irritable and Eve more and more withdrawn and unhappy. Finally he became angry and a serious quarrel broke out. After expressing his vexation frankly and making remarks that led his wife to fear he might be planning legal steps to gain custody of Bonnie, he returned sadly to his room at the hotel.

Sitting there in disappointment, remorse, and intense frustration, he took a highball hoping that this might afford some relief. He felt that he was at a miserable and bewildering impasse and needed desperately to find some new line of thought or action. After perhaps an hour of morose meditation, he decided to pack his bag and be off. At the knock on his door he swore inaudibly. He got up and opened it. There he beheld, with astonished eyes, the woman whom he had so recently left in bitterness and sorrow.

Or *was* it his wife? Eve for a moment tried to pretend that this was so, saying she had thought the matter over and had changed her mind. Though she had practiced such impersonation of her alternate before, Eve Black did not deceive Ralph. He made this known to her at once.

"All right," she said, "so what of it? She don't want to go with you, but maybe I do. She don't like you. But . . . well, I'm beginning to think you're right cute."

She came nearer and took him by the hand. Except for a few former instances that had occurred before he had any idea of her as a separate consciousness, when she was trying in every way to mimic Eve White to preserve her own secret, Eve Black had always confronted Ralph with scorn and derision. Her glance had flared with open hostility. She had regularly denounced and mocked him in scurrilous abuse. He had never before been personally aware of the good-natured friendliness and gaiety that she so freely dispensed to others. The provocative and inviting eyes that turned upon him now, apparently with warmth and excitement, must have stirred his feelings in a way by no means familiar.

Why, he soon began to ask himself, should he have found it absurd to think of being friendly when she first entered the room? How had he regarded this manifestation?—as that aspect of his wife, perhaps, that contained her worst qualities?—as the mobilization of all her reactions to him that were negative? Everyone, to be sure, has good and bad qualities. Is there a human being whose outlook does not vary profoundly in serious alterations of mood? Ralph did not doubt that his wife had a strange and serious psychologic illness. Through some process or disorder that no one understood very well, the two sides of her nature had apparently separated to a degree that was quite fantastic. When she was in that state in which she called herself Eve Black, he could not tolerate her. Now, so calling herself, she seemed different—friendly, warm, and as he had never seen her before.

Could this be the improvement everyone had been hoping and working for? If the organized portion of his wife's thought and feeling that had been causing all this trouble could change for the better, would this not be at least a step toward recovery? Responding to the flagrant charm of those bright eyes and to the tremendous vitality that contrasted so sharply with the wan figure he had left earlier in the evening, he could not help thinking that perhaps something wonderful indeed had occurred. As they sat talking, Eve Black crossed her legs. It is very reasonable to believe that Ralph found what had seemed wantonly flirtatious when directed toward another could be delectable and rich with thrilling promise when directed toward himself.

Against such thoughts and feelings, no doubt opposing suspicions and skeptical doubts arose. Surely, Ralph found that within himself, too, there was more than one homogeneous force of intention, that conflicting impulses of many sorts were exerting their influence. This new and sudden interest in him she now seemed to show could, of course, be fraudulent. What unpleasant designs might she now have in mind? Could a great and lasting change occur in any such fashion as this? Yet she had come to him after the quarrel; and she seemed ready to go with him to Jacksonville for the weekend. Even if no permanent improvement had come about, would it not be wise for them to try being together for a weekend? That was precisely what he had attempted to persuade his wife to do hardly more than an hour ago.

The more he looked at the woman before him, noting the fire in her glance, the stirring innuendo of those little quick motions, the more it must have seemed reasonable to feel that this change in her attitude should be welcomed. Behind the serious hopes and major intentions that shaped this man's thought there stirred, no doubt, human impulses more immediate. There could scarcely fail to be an exciting appeal in the prospect of spending the weekend with a girl who looked like this and seemed to be in such a mood. Having been rejected by the sad, unresponsive, and devitalized woman Ralph had tried to win back, the average man, suddenly confronted by this voluptuous and inviting apparition, might have found it difficult to avoid the fundamental reactions conveyed in the vernacular by such phrases as *this girl is really stacked, there's something about her that let's you feel she could be a mighty hot dish*. The amazing differences between this girl and the unhappy, frigid woman he had known as his wife must have made it impossible for him not to feel, however illogically, that the intimate relations she offered might constitute an act of marital infidelity. If anything like this became clear in his thought, would it not have been challenged by the absurdity that arose as he reminded himself that he was married to this woman and that, for the first time in so long, perhaps for the first time ever, she welcomed him fully and cordially as a mate?

Here, one might say, even if nothing more valuable or abiding came of it, beckoned an enticing adventure, something with all the allure of stolen fruit. And yet it remained free from penalty and from wrong. Enlivened by the transient enthusiasm she could so vividly display, Eve Black must have appeared now to be plainly a creature of such passion and erotic potentiality and inclination, that the immediate prospect of spending a night with her might well have stirred the imagination. Some men, after being bitterly disillusioned or icily rejected by what they regard as the sacredly good manifestation of femininity, have been known to fling themselves wildly into the arms of despised harlots.

There had for some time appeared to be a strong ambivalence in Ralph White's basic attitude toward his wife. He seemed sincere and remarkably patient in trying to help her to get well and in wanting to have her back with him. On the other hand it was impossible for him not to be plainly wearied by the prolonged stresses and uncertainties of his situation. He was puzzled by the nature of her illness, and it is easy to see how at times he must have wondered if there was not something spurious about her strange state. After this recent failure and rebuff, it is quite possible that some elements of feeling may have prompted him to be done with her and try to find some sort of happiness.

Impelled by a confluent pattern of motivations probably complex and manifold, Ralph soon found himself urging and coaxing Eve Black to go with him to Jacksonville. Flashily seductive, apparently surrendering, then coyly withdrawing, she played with gusto the elusive role of the nymph pursued. Stimulated by hopes and anticipations that grew ever more vivid and enticing, Ralph became more confident and expansive in his wooing. The event must be gala; there should be a celebration. He spoke of a corsage. She pointed out that she had at hand only the dress she wore. Why then, he would forthwith buy clothes, fine and fitting raiment for the splendid occasion. As he spoke of such matters, her eyes blazed with promise and her whole body became tense in its buoyancy.

A week later in the physician's office Eve Black denied as emphatically as ever that Ralph was her husband. Not with regret, but with pride she said she had found in the physical intimacy with him no pleasure but a good deal of petty annoyance. After the new dress, the hat, the shoes, and the handbag had been purchased in Jacksonville, she took few pains to conceal this from Ralph. Even after she began to express her distaste for him in vituperative language, he still endeavored for a while to win back in her the attitude she had shown when, for the first time, she had offered some promise and semblance of response to him. It was difficult for him to realize that this glowing simulation had been pure fraud. When efforts were exerted to make Eve Black consider the wisdom and ethics of her behavior in this episode, her eyes danced with mischief.

"I got the dress I wanted, didn't I?" she snapped triumphantly, dismissing all other aspects of the matter as irrelevant.

Eve White, after several days of complete subjugation, during which she remained invisible or absent, finally regained contact and control in Jacksonville. In these strange surroundings, with no clue to the circumstances until Ralph returned to the apartment, she was numb and helpless with fear. After learning from him enough of the story to orient herself, she found a coldness in herself toward her husband for which she had no words. In a despair more complete than any she had until now experienced, Eve White took the first available train out of Jacksonville and returned alone.

Before we learned that our patient had left the city a picture post card brought this news.

Hi Doc.

Having more fun. People believe anything!!!! Did you know I'm the latest thing from the West Coast? I'm singing at the Viennese Petticoat nightly at $50.00 a night. A bluff will soon wear off so I agreed to sing three nights. See you next week—

Eve B.

The fact that Ralph White had a night job in Jacksonville, she told us later, had played an important part in tempting her to spend the weekend there with him. The scheme to get new clothes was made much more attractive to her by this point. She was doubtful if she would have gone through with her plan had it been necessary to spend the evenings with Ralph. Since he did not get back from work until long after midnight, she devoted the preceding hours to visiting the liveliest spots in and about the city. At one of these places, along with other ingenious and elaborate falsehoods, she claimed to be a professional entertainer who had worked steadily during the last few years in sumptuous cabarets at Los Angeles. As a mere guest her impromptu banter and bouncy enthusiasm at once brought her considerable attention. The strongly contagious quality of her high spirits, the bold yet somehow childlike way she had of initiating playful contact with strangers at the bar or at various tables, and her facile readiness in improvising little jests and jokes, evidently led the management of this night club to believe her, or at least to wonder if the extensive experience as a singer, dancer, general enlivener, or comic actress, of which she boasted might not indeed be true. The Viennese Petticoat during recent months had not been quite living up to the gusty level of merriment proclaimed in its advertisement, which prominently displayed drawings of a well-fleshed girl kicking high in a cancan step. Some definite stimulus was needed to spark its none too zestful atmosphere.

After watching and listening to Eve Black, the manager finally decided to offer her a trial appearance without fee but with the understanding that remunerative performances might follow if she did well. It is difficult to conceive of a person better fitted than Eve Black to step into such a role without preparation. Entirely without self-consciousness, finding amusement herself in every trifle, she could give even the most banal or inane remark a little twist of novelty. A natural mimic, she spontaneously filled out any joke she told with small gestures and expressions that brought to it a new dimension of freshness. Though her voice was ordinary, the hints of erotic passion, the implicit spoofing of serious and solemn matters, the bright sunlight of her own excitement set people humming with her involuntarily on almost any tune. Unabashed and unstudied, she approached even the most forbidding figures with all the spontaneity of a cordial puppy. Every response she provoked was capped by repartee so euphoric that little real wit was needed. A person who finds interest that is genuine and intense in what has become commonplace or trivial to others can often transmit his enthusiasm in such a way that they, too, begin to feel a fresh response. When telling a threadbare anecdote she was able, with a flashing sweep of her eyes, to bring in almost any bystander as if by a personal and promising little attention.

Even if she had been possessed of sufficient perseverance to work regularly at such a job, it is unlikely that she could have sustained the effect of those few performances. Once accustomed to her gambit of antics, groups would perhaps soon have tired of her invincible ebullience and begun to notice the mediocrity of her voice and the familiarity of her little jokes and pantomimes. There is little doubt, however, that for those three nights, as she acrobatically danced the fine tightrope line that distinguishes the risqué from the ribald and suffused her irresponsible but unsynthetic jubilation on all sides, The Viennese Petticoat was indeed a club worth visiting.

Not long after the events just mentioned, Eve White made the decision to obtain a divorce from her husband. All doubt and vacillation seemed to have left her. She no longer felt any need to consider the matter further and without delay consulted her attorney. On learning that her husband had taken Eve Black to Jacksonville and spent the weekend with her, she knew that she would never go back to him, whether or not she eventually recovered from her illness. Her reactions indicated something even more complex than the hurt of a faithfully conventional wife who finds that her husband has spent the night with another woman who regarded him and the whole affair as a triviality. They reflected also deep horror in the awareness that her own person had, without her will or knowledge, been used in this pe-

170

culiarly treacherous transaction. Jane told us that she did not feel it would be right for her to exert any influence or take any responsibility in Eve White's decision. In her opinion, as a sympathetic bystander, the other woman had already made up her mind and probably could not be dissuaded. Eve Black was delighted with the decision but her reactions showed that she was very little concerned personally. She was pleased as one can be pleased about a relatively trivial matter.

"If she had good sense, and wasn't so finicky, she'd have got rid of the sorry lout years ago," was one of her comments.

Both Jane and Eve Black in discussions with the attorney agreed to support Eve White and to add their signatures to hers on legal documents whenever he felt this was desirable.

CHAPTER 21

A few months after Eve White obtained her divorce, Jane reported on a social experience of her own which seemed now to be growing in importance to her. It's development occupied an ever-increasing part of her attention as her diary reveals:

Initial meetings will always be significant to me. I think of how often valuable friendships are forfeited because of first impressions. The attentions of one who has come to mean much to me might have been lost by careless indifference on the part of Eve Black.

The frivolous Eve had gone to a dance and was now for the moment unoccupied. Jane in retrospect thus describes the incident:

"May I have this dance?" a good-looking, well-dressed young man asked. Without even a courteous glance in his direction, the bored, capricious girl answered, "I don't dance, sorry. My roommate dances well."
She then abruptly indicated a slim red-haired girl, dressed in black, standing beside her.
"But I want to dance with you," came the soft reply.
Oh, heavens, she thought, I may as well dance with him. That's the quickest way to get rid of this male pest.
It was then that by mere chance I emerged. And for the

first time in my life I danced. I did it very poorly, but nevertheless, I had fun the balance of the evening.

As he spoke of Kentucky, I stole a glance at the handsome, soft-spoken stranger who called himself Earl Lancaster. He was to bring much happiness into my lonely life.

I had turned a corner and suddenly found eyes of understanding in the face of a life and love unfolding out of the dust of complicated events that had so long directed my thoughts and mannerisms. Dr. Thigpen had told me one afternoon in his office, "Jane, the day will come when you will see things differently. You will want love, a husband, a home, and children. You have a lot of feeling somewhere there inside of you."

I thought he was wrong, of course. I was sure I would never need any of the things that two people with the same interests want. I thought I was a woman created to live alone.

I remember when I had to tell Earl about my illness. Many people had interpreted my story so narrowly that I feared telling him. But I knew I must. It would not be fair otherwise. I knew if someone else told him first, I would lose his respect. After I had told him all there was to tell, I asked him how he felt about dating me.

"The same as I did before," he said.

That's the kind of person Earl is. My appreciation for his patience and understanding cannot be expressed—nor my gratitude. . . . We know that if this love of ours has a happy ending it will indeed be a miracle. We are faced by the fact that Eve White or Eve Black may be the remaining personality, but he is willing to wait and see. Can anyone blame me for wanting to live? Our love has weathered many a bad storm, but nothing has yet severed the bonds of understanding between us.

Though much of Jane's diary now reflected her interest in this young man and the new aspects of feeling and living that were opening before her, she also turned often to reminiscence about her own brief career.

Restlessness dominates me so much at times. I keep going back to the first time I can recall, the day I found myself sitting in the doctor's office. I noticed first of all that he was dressed differently, and the realization came to me that he was a man. I then realized that I knew no basic facts about myself—such as where I lived, who I was, etc.

Later I was told that he was Dr. Thigpen. When he

asked me my name, I said Jane. And so I became Jane. I don't mind people calling me Eve, when I'm out, as I did at first.

I've begun to feel despondent much of the time. It seems to be a mood I can't shake. I wonder if confusion can contribute to one's gains.... My enthusiasm is often misinterpreted. I seek opportunity, but seem to make little or no progress.

I wonder if Eve White has experienced such periods when her powers of concentration were disturbed; perhaps *diverted* is a better word for it. My pattern of thought seems to reach a point then, for no good reason, break off. My imagination lacks the feeling of construction.... Actually I don't know what I'm like.

On another occasion, in describing her growing interest in Eve White's daughter, Jane wrote:

She is the first person I loved beside my doctor. For this tiny intelligent child I want to do things that a mother might do, even though I have never been a mother.... Where do I fit into the picture? Sometimes I feel I don't belong in it at all. But then how do I get out of it?

Perhaps one might accurately say that Jane now seemed to think more about experiences that were personal to herself. Earlier she had functioned largely as a commentator on the problems of the two Eves and had been more or less content in this role. At first she never spoke of despondency or of worries that were her own.

Eve White had made good improvement since the divorce. She did not show any evidence of regretting this step. Never as freely articulate as Jane, she wrote much less in her diary. She was doing well at her work and during medical interviews she was always clear and cogent. Her diary, however, sometimes recorded items such as these:

I suppose it was some two years ago when I got the bad headaches. Maybe it was longer or less. I seem to have lost all track of time. I don't even know what day this is and I can't find the calendar or a newspaper. Jane says it is Tues., Sept. 18th. Then it must be over two years since I first came to Dr. Thigpen for the headaches.

I remember the kind young doctor who sent me to him. He told me ... that I wasn't just imagining that I was sick.

I guess he thought he might hurt my feelings if he told me point blank that I was mentally ill. But he wouldn't, because I already knew. Of course I had no idea what was really wrong with me.

A note of resignation increasingly pervaded Eve White's writings. Her hope for a successful solution to her problems steadily diminished. Sometimes her attitude seemed plainly that of one who has accepted extinction as inevitable and is seeking to put her affairs in the best order possible. During this period she wrote:

The fact that I have an unusual disorder is something that I realized long ago I must accept, and try to make the best of the existing situation. My greatest worries lie in trying to look ahead to the future for my baby daughter. It would be foolish for me to say or even hope that this will not affect her little life. It already has. . . . She has no mother or father. What hurts me is for her to climb on my knee, touch my face with her tiny hands and ask, "Are you my Mommy or is it one of the others?"

What answer can I give my child?

The last time I remember talking with her, she told me that in another year she would begin school and asked if I were coming home to send her. You cannot tell a tiny child that her mother is never coming home, that someone who looks like Mommy but who, I am told, is different, will take charge of her future life.

I only hope that Jane will learn to love her as I do. If so, I will not fear. I don't mind dying; except I am afraid that Jane might not understand how very much little people need love and understanding. Especially my baby. She's so sensitive. . . . About my life, there's always been something missing. There still is. I don't know what it is; but I don't suppose it matters now.

Though Jane continued to be serene in manner and never showed any obvious signs of the stress and the haunting fear so familiar in Eve White, she began to report strange and disturbing feelings and unpleasant experiences entirely novel to her. For the first time in her brief span of being, she now complained of severe headaches, of weird and terrifying nightmares. She repeatedly expressed fear:

Double darkness must have covered Eve White's face as the distressing nature of her true illness became revealed to her. It must have pounded into her brain with the impact of terror.

I feel this because for the first time I am experiencing some of the really blinding pains of the headaches she has described. I am afraid . . . I know where they are coming from. I know what is wrong. How must she have felt, not knowing anything for so long, then to find that she must tell herself, "You have a dual personality"?

I am frightened beyond words when I awaken in the middle of the night with a headache so severe I cannot see. I fix a smile on my lips when I walk down the street to keep people from knowing I can't completely think half of the time anymore. I can understand how Eve White thought she was going insane. I, too, feel now that *I* am. Something has to give.

When I sleep I am not resting. I am dreaming weird, unbelievable dreams. These I am trying to record also. The doctor said it might help. I've tried to get in touch with him all week, but he doesn't seem to be there. He could help me I know. . . . I wonder if I'll live to see another sun. . . . I can't think.

Despite these new developments, work continued. Jane now sometimes spoke of the work as "our" job rather than "her" job. She emphasized increasingly the terror and horror caused by her dreams. Snakes continually appeared, often gruesomely, in the bizarre nocturnal scenes. From the records Jane made, let us quote a few scattered items (see also reproduction of a page of this letter and drawing, on the next page):

For the last few nights I have dreamed that various parts of my body were turning into snakes. Each night more of me is consumed by reptiles. It's getting hard for me even to try to sleep, because I am afraid. . . . Dreaming can become positively maddening. I awaken at night and feel as if all these horrible, unbelievable things are really happening to me. Often it takes some time to convince myself it is only a dream. . . .

In a dream I was going fishing and Ralph White was walking behind me. He kept repeating the same words, "Keep walking. Don't look back." But for some reason I turned and saw him standing there with a long black snake in his hand. . . . Just as I glanced at it bit him on the hand. It seemed almost as if he were trying to *protect me*.

A few nights later I was looking through the window

in an old deserted hut. In the center of the room was a snake pit. Lots of men were standing round it. All of them had scaly hands—like snakes. Into the room from a side door came Earl. They took him and threw him in the pit. When he emerged his feet and hands were black and they also looked like snakes. . . . Two nights later I dreamed the same dream, except this time the man forced into the pit was my doctor.

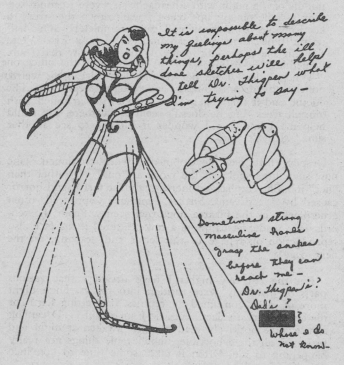

It is impossible to describe my feelings about many things, perhaps the ill done sketches will help tell Dr. Thigpen what I'm trying to say—

Sometimes strong masculine hands grasp the snakes before they can reach me—Dr. Thigpen's? Dad's? ▇▇▇? Whose I do not know—

Jane's description of her nightmares, in which her limbs seemed to turn into reptiles. Hours elapsed after she awoke before she could convince herself that her hands and feet were not snakes.

Many nights I have dreamed that parts of my body were turning into snakes. Each night it was a larger portion. I knew I was dying each time. When I awaken from

176

dreaming it has taken as long as an hour for me to convince myself my hands and feet were not snakes. . . .

Last night I dreamed I was in the hospital. They were serving dinner. It appeared to be bowls of rice, but when I looked down at my tray I suddenly realized I was eating decayed teeth instead of rice. It seemed as if everyone felt much contempt for me—even Dr. Cleckley; but not Dr. Thigpen. . . .

I seem to be losing my bearings. I can make it through the day; but when night comes it is almost as if I am transported to another realm where I lose contact with the present world. The dreams are really frightening. How much longer?

A few weeks later, during an interview in the office one bright autumn afternoon, Jane wss discussing a recent trip Eve White had made to her parents' home where she saw Bonnie. While the mother was with her little girl outside the house, Jane emerged. Bonnie, who had been bouncing and tossing about a small rubber ball, now threw it to Jane. After several exchanges of the ball back and forth, the child missed her aim. The ball rolled under the house. The building stood relatively high off the ground on separate pillars without a complete curtain wall. Latticework with thick vines and some detached shrubbery partly screened but did not entirely close off the space between floor and ground. A ... by stooping, could make his way under the sup... with little difficulty. Though the light dimin... siderable obscurity far within the area, Jane ... would be able to find the ball.

...ng a few steps she became sharply aware of ... t scent given off by earth in such places where ... nlight nor rain ever falls. Bonnie had remained outsia... nd she felt surprisingly alone, as if she had unintentionally traversed a great distance. Something about this odor seemed curious. Or should one say meaningful? Not locating the ball at once and finding herself unable to see distinctly in the fractional illumination, Jane felt her way slowly past a broken wheelbarrow, a pile of rotting boards, and several empty barrels that had accumulated over the years in a place near the central brick supports. Beyond this it was difficult to see at all. In her stooped position she turned to look back, hoping that the ball, if she had passed it, might from her present position be visible against the background of light outside.

As she looked intently, the thought came to her that this place was probably familiar to Eve White. Perhaps she had played here as a child and knew every nook and corner of its strange dark expanse. She herself, mused Jane, had never before been under a house. Perhaps it was for this reason that these surroundings pressed upon her senses as something unique and novel, something obscurely stirring. Suddenly she seemed to be losing her balance, not precisely falling, but she was swept by a sensation as if she were drifting free of gravity. Her head felt light. It was not really the feeling of one who was beginning to faint, but somehow this comparison came to mind. It was not just this place that seemed to change, but something in *her* changed that gave to the whole world an indescribable freshness. Yes, Jane said, it was somewhat like the feelings she had when she first came to life, or awareness, almost a year earlier in this office. It was a similar sensation but not the same.

She was frightened by the odd sensations, but an illogical exhilaration almost drowned her fear. Then it became clear that she was disproportionately large in her surroundings. Stooped under the floor of the house, she felt herself as a gigantic being. Before this reaction could be fully assimilated there was a quick reversal of orientation. As if a telescope had been thrust to her eye, and then after a fleeting glimpse she found herself looking through the other end, she now felt overwhelmed by a realization of her smallness. The floor and the beams still prevented her from standing erect. Her sudden sense of diminutiveness fell against a broader background than the immediate environment.

Jane, unlike the two Eves, had often spoken freely about subjective matters, about the incommunicable nuances of personal emotion. Though she was immeasureably more articulate than the others, her discourse on such subjects had, in comparison with what she now said, seemed almost academic. It had not been false or artificial, but it had lacked the depth and specificity of what she now seemed trying to convey. In a sense this nameless bit of experience under the house was almost like the filling in of a new dimension.

CHAPTER 22

As she continued to discuss the ostensibly trivial episode, it became ever more plain that Jane found in it an enthralling interest, that to her it contained the breath of hint of an essence that still eluded direct contact. Soon after speaking of the unexpected and utter strangeness that, for no discernible reason, seemed to drench her senses, she mentioned a peculiar and unrecognizable familiarity that began to permeate the whole scope of her awareness. There was an inexplicable stillness as if time paused—for how long, one would never know.

Familiarity is perhaps a misleading term for the element of experience Jane was trying to convey. Some yet unborn synonym might better suggest it. It seemed, however, to be something akin to this element that, self-contradictory as it may appear, contributed so much to the arcane flavor of the moment. It was not a feeling of rapture or of terror that she was seeking to express. The sensations were not extraordinary because of extreme goodness or badness, but because of qualities in another scale. Though her words were by no means those of a poet, or even reasonably adequate to convey the substance of her feeling, they made the hearer remember other efforts by gifted spokesmen to express what is intensely personal.

Wordsworth has commented on certain moments when, as a solitary observer, he contemplated ordinary sights and found in them qualities that led him

> To look on nature, not as in the hour
> Of thoughtless youth; but hearing often times
> The still, sad music of humanity,
> Nor harsh, nor grating, though of ample power
> To chasten and subdue. And I have felt
> A presence that disturbs me with the joy
> Of elevated thought; a sense sublime
> Of something far more deeply interfused,
> Whose dwelling is the light of setting suns,
> And the round ocean, and the living air,
> And the blue sky, and in the mind of man;
> A motion and a spirit that impels
> All thinking things, all objects of all thought,
> And rolls through all things....

Jane did not find in the incident any basis for philosophical speculation. She made no attempt to interpret the feelings she reported in transcendental terms, or to seek in them broad religious or metaphysical significance. She was concerned only with the personal sensations and her inability to state them satisfactorily. She did not take them as an omen or seem to feel that through them matters of great importance might be elucidated. She had encountered a bit of experience that surprised her and that she could not account for, and she kept on talking about it, trying to convey its specific quality.

After a few moments the intensity of Jane's unusual feeling had diminished greatly. She found Bonnie's ball and came out from the area under the house into the clear afternoon sunlight. To her surprise, all of what she had experienced so vividly only a minute before had vanished. She could remember it, of course; but it seemed much farther away than anything so recent could be. She could not by thinking bring back even a little of the sensation itself.

The therapist asked Jane to seek for some association with other events in her own memory, and, in what she knew indirectly of the two Eves, for some link that might suggest a relation between her feelings under the house and earlier happenings. She tried for some time but met with no success. Eve White was then summoned to consciousness and questioned in detail about the past, particularly her childhood, but nothing could be obtained that threw light on what Jane had described. In her turn Eve Black was questioned. She, too, could bring forth no pertinent recollection.

Later during the interview Eve White was hypnotized and in this state another attempt was made to search her memory of early years for some incident that might be connected with Jane's recent experience under the house. Various associations were followed out at length. Nothing of interest emerged over a considerable period. And then Eve White spoke of a blue cup. She had mentioned this blue cup before when she first discussed Flo's china doll. Her voice took on unusual animation and she spontaneously pursued this subject. Numerous incidents were brought up and set aside but, at first slowly, then more rapidly, bits of detail accumulated. It was, she felt, in very early childhood that she had been playing with this blue china cup. The cup itself was etched sharp in memory before any surrounding material could be brought into focus. Soon she was absorbed in recalling details of the scene in which she and her cousin Flo had been playing with the blue cup.

She was now showing considerable emotion. Whether this was chiefly fear or exhilaration, it was difficult to judge. She spoke very rapidly, spontaneously pursuing various threads of memory, many of which she found irrelevant and abandoned. She promptly picked up a new clue and proceeded. Someone else seemed to be with her and Flo. She could not recall who this might be. No; it seemed now that the presence of this third child was only a bit of fantasy. She herself (how vivid this was becoming) had on a red dress when she and her cousin as small children were playing with the cup. A red corduroy jumper, it was. Now, as if her eyes had magically opened, Eve White announced that this place where they were playing was under the house. Visibly disturbed she began now to speak almost chaotically. Among many disconnected phrases and fragmentary gropings, the therapist made out something about chairs ... a great crowd of people ... flowers. ... She abruptly fell silent, as if the zigzag path of association down which she was racing had suddenly ended.

A moment later she awoke spontaneously from hypnosis. Then, with a quick transformation of her countenance, a shudder of her body, she changed. Eve White was no longer present. Eve Black had emerged unbidden and without warning. She said at once that she wanted the therapist to tell her why he had been asking these questions, to explain what was the purpose of this interview. For the first time there was a note in her tone that suggested seriousness. Could it be that she was thoughtfully concerned about such matters? Then, almost wistfully, she asked, "Doc, do you think we're ever going to get well?"

At last her invincible confidence seemed to waver. The limitless tides of brash vitality upon which she had always so buoyantly and callously been borne were for the moment subdued. When the therapist asked her if she could remember anything about the blue cup, or about Eve White as a young child playing under the house with Flo, she shook her head.

"I feel funny [peculiar]," she said slowly. "'I don't like this business. I guess ... I'm scared."

She spoke for a moment about the many good times she had enjoyed, then surprisingly said she "didn't seem to have real fun any more." And she complained again of "feeling funny."

If she was indeed, and for the first time, sad or serious, there was nothing about her that suggested it was the sadness or seriousness of Eve White, or that it was any of

Jane's feelings she had acquired. If new attitudes or experiences were emerging in this hitherto irrepressible female entity, they seemed specifically her own. Though for the moment deprived of her bounce and sparkle, she was, as distinctly as ever before, Eve Black. As if musing half aloud over something now gone, she made a halting statement (not completely understood by the therapist) to the effect that it, or something (good times? life in general?) was perhaps not so much fun after all. Her gesture and expression, her idiom and her posture were unmistakably her own, despite the apparent alteration in her outlook. She was not showing anything she had learned from Eve White or modifying her disagreement with the other's viewpoint.

She now seemed more of a child than ever. Her eyes no longer sparkled and flashed with the familiar challenge; they sought out the eyes of the physician in an unguarded directness that Eve White's reserve had never permitted. But there was still a hint of robust frolic, an afterglow of the full vitality. She smiled, and instead of the inevitable play of coquetry, there seemed to be the trace of an affection as warm and simple as that of a puppy.

"I was just thinking about the first time I was in this office. . . . You know, Doc, I hardly know how to say it . . . but you've treated me right good. . . . Remember my red dress?"

Here her words became unclear. She began to sob. The physician could no longer be sure how much her speech was confused or how much his astonishment distorted his observations. For more than two years he had found her always the same. Tears were not a part of her world. He kept asking himself if he was not mistaken about which one of the personalities he was confronting. Looking at her again, however, he concluded that there could be no question about it. This was Eve Black, despite the fact that she wept. Eve White, in all her self-contained sorrow and distress, never shed tears except under the relaxing effect of hypnosis. Jane had not even once given the impression that she might cry, though she described in her diary experiences so terrifying one would think she might give way to unrestrained emotion. But of all things unimaginable to the therapist was the reality of Eve Black softly, pitifully sobbing. Accustomed as he was over the hundreds of hours of contact with each of the three diverse manifestations, he now felt shaken, disoriented, and wondered if his feelings had anything in common with what Jane had tried to tell him about her inexplicable sensations under the house. Eve Black, the capricious, invulnerable symbol of mischief had, it seemed, somehow found at least a hint of sorrow, a glimpse of the suffering those who are not abstainers from life are bound to discover. But she showed no sign of being at last involved in Eve White's unhappiness; nothing reflected Jane's orthodox but relatively detached comments on human affairs. Her feelings were her own.

He could make out only part of what she was saying. The change in this inimitable figure was so sudden that he felt for the moment off balance, too busy with his own confusion to perceive clearly. His senses warned him vaguely that something extraordinary was, or might be, going on, but he could not determine its nature. She spoke in brief, rapid spurts with intervals of silence. Her words did not quite complete what they set out to convey. Her manner filled the ellipses with connotations the physician could not decipher. She was looking at him intently with large soft eyes. These eyes, though changed, were no more like the eyes of Eve White or of Jane than when they first opened upon him in the office more than two years ago. He distinguished phrases now and then that he could not fully clarify or logically connect with other scattered fragments. There was something again about the red dress . . . she smiled.

"Oh, Doc," she said very softly, "I feel so funny . . . I—oh, well. . . . Maybe you'll be able to figure it out about me. I don't know at all. . . . I want you to have it. Please take it and keep it to remember me by. Only you and I know why I wanted it so bad. . . . Yes, Doc . . . , the red dress. . . ."

There were a few more unclear words. Then in silence all expression left her face. Her eyes closed. When they opened he found that he was talking with Eve White, who knew nothing at all of what had just occurred. For a few minutes her present situation was discussed. Her parents, she said, had been kinder to her than ever before, and more cooperative, during the months that followed her divorce. She showed no signs of perturbation. In fact she seemed under less than her habitual strain or tension. The presence of Jane was then requested.

Jane talked in her usual manner. Nothing of particular importance was brought out. Planning to terminate the inter-

183

view, the therapist asked Jane's permission to speak again with Eve White, who had come for the interview and whom he meant to restore to consciousness before the patient left.

Jane's neck stiffened abruptly and she gazed blankly at the physician. Her ordinary serene expression had been demolished. A wild light of terror glinted in her eyes. The features of this countenance had contorted to unrecognizable chaos. Staring now in glassy horror past the man who faced her, she suddenly cried out in frantic shattered tones:

"Mother...! Oh, Mother...! Don't make me....Don't. ...Don't ... I can't do it! I can't!"

Seizing her head at the temples with both hands, she began a banshee's scream that did not reach its eerie and piercing crescendo until the amazed physician had reached the office of his colleague across the hall.

CHAPTER 23

It was a remarkable scream. Wordless, primitive, sustained, it scarcely seemed more human than the midnight wail of an old steam locomotive. Neither of us had ever heard from distrubed psychotic patients so strange and impressive an outcry. Hurrying back across the hall, we were both in the therapist's office a moment after the weird shriek subsided. Still quickened by the physiologic manifestations of excitement we looked silently at the patient, then at each other. Perhaps, we thought, our reasoning processes would soon compose themselves.

"Which one is it?" one of us finally asked.

After further scrutiny and some effort at sober thought, the other, in sharp astonishment, replied, "Why...it isn't any one of the three....It isn't Jane. It isn't Eve White; and yet, it isn't Eve Black!"

So it seemed to us at that moment, and so it still seems, now more than two years later. We asked her now who she was and she could give no clear or satisfactory reply. Her terror was steadily subsiding but she was still bewildered, emotionally volatile, and actively groping for orientation and perspective. After a little while we asked again who she was.

"I'm not sure ... why, I can't tell," she finally murmured. We did not press her further at this point for specific information. We had often recorded previous interviews with each of the three personalities, having in fact by now accumulated many hours of conversation with each. The lady now before us also agreed to this procedure and we were able to transcribe by tape recorder a verbatim account of what followed. It was soon plain that, in contrast with Jane when she emerged approximately a year ago, this manifestation was by no means unequipped with memory. She knew a great deal about the experiences of Eve White, and also of Jane and Eve Black. Unlike the newborn Jane, she did not have to face the problem of finding her bearings in a world hitherto unknown. This young woman's immediate problem seemed to lie in identifying herself, in clearly recognizing the subjective substance and the bounds of her own personal entity, of discovering and realizing just what and who she was.

It is indeed doubtful if there can be any substructure or cornerstone of human consciousness more fundamental than the infinitely familiar, axiomatic, but utterly inexpressible sense of self in which we deal with all experience. Jane, though without memory of any antecedent life on her initial appearance, had a firm and clear sense of her own identity. The world she first looked upon must indeed have been strange and peculiarly captivating. The inner obscurity and uncertainty now experienced by our patient, though less obvious to ordinary imagination, was, no doubt, far more bizarre and mysteriously disturbing. As she talked with us, we both felt that this person was very much like Jane, far more like Jane than like either of the other two. Yes, she was like Jane in many respects; still neither of us could quite feel that this *was* Jane. On into the evening many points of great interest to us were discussed.

"When you asked me to let you speak with Eve White," she said, referring to the therapists's last request before the startling scream emerged, "when you asked for her, I suddenly realized, *I am Eve White!*"

It must have been a realization of dismaying intensity. For a moment it bleached her thought of content. Shaken deep within, as if by a subjective earthquake, there came now an opposite realization, a subsequent tidal wave of feeling.

"She isn't there. . . . There isn't an Eve White any more. . . . She's not there . . . Why, she's gone . . . gone . . . Dead . . . ? Yes, she's dead . . . no more. . . . They're both gone forever!"

The sense of death now pressed upon her with sudden and fearful immensity. With this sense there flashed in sharp clarity before her the incident from long ago, when she and Flo had been playing under the house with the blue cup. It was *there*, and *then*, that her mother had called her, telling her to come into the house and change her dress. Her grandmother's funeral.... Every detail of the scene now drenched her awareness. The lost memory stood forth in almost the freshness of immediate perception. The sad and solemn group of adults... the weeping... the uncanny stillness everywhere... the flowers, and the specific odor of those flowers....

For her it now became that very moment again. Her mother was holding her up high off the floor, and telling her she must touch her dead grandmother's face. Appalled by aspects of this situation that she did not fully comprehend, the young child shrank from this demanded contact. Fragmentary ideas of death and desolation, which she had heard spoken of by adults during the grandmother's terminal illness and since her death, fears that had stirred for the moment and then been evaded by the little girl, all now coalesced into a horrible and incomprehensible immediate reality. Her mother kept insisting that she must touch this immobile face in the coffin. She burst into tears, squirmed and struggled to pull away. Her mother, embarrassed and unnerved by the conspicuous display, intensified her insistence. She was desperate now to terminate the situation.

The force upon the young child seemed inexorable. Despite her horror she put her head against the face of the corpse. Hemmed in and frantic, she felt herself in some respects like the trapped wolf who chews off his own leg. She would plunge toward any promise of escape however dangerous and painful it might be. When her small warm hand felt the cold flesh of this dead face, recognizable as the waxlike image of the grandmother she remembered alive, a devastating innuendo of mortality shook her senses. All her old horror of the ditch with the slimy water and of the drowned man who had been dragged from its noisome depths joined synergistically into her reaction to the present perception. The monster, scaly and murderous and inexorable, the monster which her imagination and that of other children had created as a symbol of death and horror and putrefaction, and as the ever-threatening inhabitant of those fearful waters of the ditch, became palpably real in the cold touch of her grandmother's corpse. She had cried out, as her hand moved forward:

"No, no...! Oh, no, Mother.... I can't.... Don't make me do it." As her hand left the clammy cheek, all those fragmentary terrors fused into an unbearable reality. It was then that she had screamed.

Who was it that screamed again this afternoon in the doctor's office? A few days later our patient said, "It seems to me I can remember hearing someone scream. After I got home I could not be sure whether it was I or not."

After this full-voiced outpouring of terror, the memory of the grandmother's funeral remained quite clear. The acute fear that had been stirred by the incident soon passed. It was Jane, despite her lack of ability to recall any early life at all before this, in whom the lost item of experience recurred. Our new patient was unable to tell us whether or not the realization of it was also experienced simultaneously by the dormant ones, Eve White and Eve Black. In the searing intensity of the moment, a new unit had apparently been welded. What was this unit? It was difficult at this point to estimate her. In her background was the great cry of anguish and terror that in a sense marked her birth.

As she tried to tell what she had experienced, her reactions brought to mind other complex and inexpressible subjective events that other men and women have marveled at and tried by various means to convey. She discussed with us at length, on this occasion and on many others, the sensations that had possessed her. She impressed us as having undergone an experience strange and profound and difficult to communicate. After the terror of the moment subsided, however, she seemed to acquire an increasing confidence, to reflect qualities and capacities we had not seen before in any of the three manifestations.

> And as I looked a quickening gust
> Of wind blew up to me and thrust
> Into my face a miracle
> Of orchard-breath, and with the smell
> I know not how such things can be!
> I breathed my soul back into me.*

* From "Renascence" in *Renascence and Other Poems* by Edna St. Vincent Millay. Harper & Brothers. Copyright, 1912, 1940, by Edna St. Vincent Millay.

Had she, we wondered, really done something of this sort? Had a great and basic change come about? Or were we merely dealing with another peculiar facet of a patient still as disordered as before? Unlike the three other manifestations, who had always felt and known their own experiences and themselves as apart and sharply distinct from one another, our patient now reacted as if she did not regard herself as altogether separate from the previous personalities. She did not find or seem to seek a new name for herself, as Jane had immediately done a year earlier.

As her initial bewilderment lessened that first afternoon and she became better able to mobilize her efforts toward orientation or, one might say, toward finding herself, she showed an increasing tendency to identify herself with Jane. This began spontaneously and automatically, apparently on the basis of instinctive feeling rather than of deliberate thought. The identificaton did not seem to be sure or complete, nor did she simply reject all the past experiences of the two Eves as alien. She found herself accepting some of these experiences as her own. Others remained as thoroughly isolated from her sense of self as they had been to the earlier Jane. After considerable discussion and deliberation, she decided to call herself Mrs. Evelyn White, our original patient's full legal name. Any other choice would invite unnecessary attention to her personal affairs.

Later she reported that she had wept a great part of the day following the dramatic event in the office.

"I felt lonely, empty," she said. "There are so many ways to describe it."

What was she crying about?

"Eve Black chiefly, I believe. Doctor, I missed her so much. I was confused. I can't describe it. The shock of it was strange. They just weren't there any more. It made me feel awfully sad. At the time I wasn't missing Eve White. I was just missing Eve Black.... I wouldn't have thought anyone could miss her in such a way.... I knew something had to happen one way or the other.... But then, you're going to miss them, too—aren't you?"

When asked about Bonnie, she said, as if quite surprised, "Why, I feel that she is my own little girl. Before, she was Eve White's child. Now she seems to be mine. I loved her, but not the way I do now."

We asked if it were possible for her to think of Eve White and Eve Black as not really lost but in a sense regained.

"I don't think so," she said, "at least not now. I feel I have really lost something. To other people it might seem another way. Suppose a screen had been put up in front of you. Now for a year you have two sisters. They are behind this screen but you know they are there. You are aware of them working, playing, living, though all the time the screen hides them. You know where they go and in a sense you go with them, though you are then behind the screen. All the time I knew they were there. All of a sudden the screen is not there. And they are nowhere. I feel so depressed—something is missing. It is amazing how suddenly it came to me that they weren't there any longer. I knew clearly that they were gone. You can't help being lonely for them. I just wish I had known that it was the last time I would be with them. . . . Looking back I have the feeling that Eve Black may have known she would never see you again. I don't understand how she could have known. . . . When she started crying I began to realize something drastic was happening."

Referring to the last motion pictures made of the three personalities about two weeks before, she said:

"Doctor, you almost didn't get your movies. There was a difference in Eve Black even then, wasn't there? She didn't quite have the buoyance. That is the first time I've ever seen her challenged and not take it up. Singing or dancing or teasing—ordinarily she'd just come right out with it under any circumstances. I was surprised that she didn't. I am awfully sorry she didn't take that red dress [to Atlanta where the sound-movies were made]. She seemed very sorry she didn't have it. I told the family it was her request that you have it now. If you want it, I will bring it to you."

"I think you should have it made over," the physician suggested, "so you can wear it."

"No," she replied, "it's a dress you've never seen. It's real silk and bright red. It's slick and very shiny—a cocktail dress. There is no possible way to redesign it. I'd never want to wear it. Not so much because of the color—the dress itself. There's not enough material to alter it substantially. No woman outside of show business could wear it except Eve Black. No other woman would go outside the house with it on."

CHAPTER 24

As several weeks passed the new, or different, Evelyn White showed no discernible change in the outline or general features of her identity. There was change, a progressive change, it seemed, but this was a process of settling more firmly, solidifying, so to speak, into the specific personal form in which she had found herself after the resolution of the separate entities. Like wet concrete cast into its mold, she seemed to become more firmly the new, single personality. The resemblance to Jane persisted but did not increase. A sense of inaccuracy obtruded into our own feelings if we tried to think of her actually, or simply, as Jane. Her appearance, her gestures, gait, tone of voice, posture, idiom, tastes, and outlook, all brought strongly to mind the concept of some close relative of Jane, a twin sister, a daughter, or a very similar cousin in whom the likeness is extensive and remarkably close, yet who is not the same.

She showed no distinct traits that indicated specifically the original Eve White in so far as she differed superficially from the other two manifestations. We felt here, however, what might be called a dimensional difference from Jane, as if this were a more substantial and complete woman than the separate Jane. At times we wondered if in this quality, or imagined quality, she subtly revealed her family tie with the timid, unhappy, and meticulously proper little patient who had first come for treatment.

She never lapsed into the flagrant manner of Eve Black, never flashed her eyes in the inimitably bold and idiosyncratic epigram of erotic challenge. Nor did we find in her conduct any indications of capriciousness or irresponsibility. Yet there were moments when her glance sparkled with hints of vitality and of potential mirth more striking than anything of that sort we could remember in Jane alone. Long-suffering resignation, so prominent a feature in our original patient, was not outstanding in the present Evelyn White. She did not lose the earlier determination of Eve White to be firm in waiting until she was capable of looking after her daughter safely before trying to take the little girl to live with her. In making long-range plans that might eventually result in her fully regaining Bonnie, she was, however, more active and decisive.

She retained the interest Jane had found in Earl Lancaster.

Through Jane this pleasant relation had always impressed us as a little theoretical and academic, something not altogether unreal but, perhaps, with a bit more of form than of substance. Though neither of us felt that Jane had been the Lady of Shallot, she seemed now, in comparison with Evelyn, to have shared some intangible features with this symbolic figure. No sign of undue impetuousness or impatient haste toward what Jane had thought of as a goal, however fanciful, appeared in our patient. The change in her relations with the young man whom Jane had discovered seemed to us chiefly a reification of the same attitudes and hopes. There seemed now to be also a better or more deeply felt appraisal of practical difficulties that might stand in the way of the improbable eventualities with which Jane's thought had often played.

It has been noted that the semantic differential tests run on the three manifestations gave results that suggested Jane as the original personality, the presumed earlier integer of human functioning which had become dissociated. The interpretation of the tests was not known to us at the period now under discussion. This interpretation derives a particular interest from the fact that it was Jane's consciousness, the one that had never before established contact with memory of childhood, through which the incident at the funeral was suddenly recalled. Does this indicate that our patient, as an infant and young child prior to that experience, was Jane? —or chiefly Jane?—or more fundamentally Jane than either of the Eves?—or, perhaps, the potential core of what we encountered in the personality, who called herself by this name?

One can speculate at length over such questions. It is difficult to produce convincing evidence for the various opinions that might be given. It is important to bear in mind that the language we use in discussing these matters can be deeply misleading. In a verbal exercise of thought we can take "personalities," divide them, add them, subtract from them, or coalesce them in neatly logical procedures. Words such as *consciousness* or *mind* can be treated in thought as well-defined objective entities and manipulated freely in graceful sprees in theoretical reasoning. It is well for us to remember that we have not yet discovered any clear-cut tangible referent for the term *personality*, any distinct subject for investigation that can be isolated, accurately assessed, and about which various assumptions may be proved or disproved.[14]

So, too, we must not forget that (familiar as it is to us in subjective experience) little is known about the nature of what we call *consciousness*. What are its causes? What is its purpose? How are we to explain its intensifications and its contractions? What is it that dissociates during an amnesic fugue? What becomes impervious to such compelling sensations as pain from fire in the exquisitely selective withdrawals of awareness sometimes seen in hysterical anesthesia?

Let us not lose ourselves in facile speculation about things still too inadequately defined to be proved one way or another. More important still, let us avoid misidentifying our speculation (with largely abstract verbal constructs) as genuine evidence, and so coming to believe we have thereby validly explained or successfully demonstrated whatever theory we may have in mind as we consider such questions.[16]

It is interesting to ask ourselves if the small child who was terrified by the funeral and the cold touch of the corpse was actually closer to a hypothetical Jane at that age than to such a predecessor of Eve White. Could the shock and fright of this experience have played a part in such a child's undergoing alteration and becoming the little girl Eve White remembered herself as being? Perhaps this incident alone seems insufficient to account for a personality change, a dissociation, or a deep repression of its memory. If it is too trivial or too isolated, might it have served as a sharp and final stimulus to trigger, or set off, the effect of deeper and broader conflicts? Could poorly understood fears of parental rejection, childish and superstitious dreads of death (and of the dead), have mobilized at the funeral and brought into action destructive emotional forces, a great variety of conflicts, that had been accumulating perhaps since birth? The twin sisters had been born only five or six months before the grandmother died. It is possible that Eve at this time felt herself replaced by them. Perhaps the emotions aroused at the funeral served as a last straw that, added to the burden of problems she had borne up to that time, might have broken the final supports of her adjustment.

After the memory of attending her grandmother's funeral had been regained, the patient was able to fill in a good deal of detail about her feelings at that time. Her mother had insisted that she put her hand to the face of the corpse because of a belief that if one touches a dead person it becomes possible to give up the departed more peacefully, that one will thus be spared some of the inevitable sorrow and grieve less painfully. Behind these points there was also in the mother's attitude a feeling that religion demanded the believer not to fear death, that children should be taught not to shrink from it as an annihilation but to see in it the passing of the soul to immortality. The mother's insistence was firm because she was in this act of gently touching the dead face without fear or repugnance a test of faith. Pre-occupied with her own bereavement, and finally confused by the conspicuous protest little Eve made at the coffin, she perhaps lost sight of how seriously frightened the child had become.

Our patient strongly emphasized the connection she had felt between the cold, clammy feeling of her dead grand-mother's flesh and her ideas and fears about the imaginary but vividly conceived monster she had so long believed to exist beneath the stagnant water of the deep ditch by the bridge. The threat and horror of this chimera, which had at times seemed formidable even in the distance, now came down upon her directly. The fantasied creature in the slimy water (where a man had actually drowned) perhaps stood as a symbol of her unclear and imperfect concepts of death itself. The mystery and threat of death was a vague but terrible focal point toward which all feelings of guilt, all fears and sorrows seemed to lead. Our patient felt that the huge reptiles by which Jane was tormented in her nightmares just before the coalescence of personalities were, at least in part, reflections of this cold-blooded and cruel saurian phan-tom of the ditch.

The fright and horror now recalled by our patient as an adult led us to feel that the funeral episode probably em-bodied a great deal more than one can reasonably ascribe to the isolated events of that particular day. Insecurities and inner problems that she had accumulated during the time she was nursing at the breast, when she was struggling with the difficulties of toilet training may also have contrib-uted their part, directly or indirectly, to the emotional shock that, once remembered, stood out disproportionately prom-inent above all the other incidents of her early years. What were these possible or probable earlier influences and con-flicts? We must ask the reader's permission to defer our at-tempt to answer this extremely interesting question.

The degree of terror experienced by Jane when she sud

denly acquired memory of her grandmother's funeral surprised us. Indeed, it severely startled us. The incident itself had already been described to us by the patient's mother almost two years earlier. Soon after Eve Black's first appearance in the office, we made extensive tape recordings of all that the parents could tell us of their daughter's history. The details of the funeral given by the mother coincided well with the memory finally regained by the patient. Both of the parents had realized their little girl was acutely upset. They told us that her strange moods and occasional tantrum spells began shortly afterward. They also remembered that she woke up repeatedly during the night after the funeral, crying out and screaming as if in a wild nightmare.

She had not before then suffered from nightmares. Soon afterward she walked in her sleep for the first time. For several years this sleepwalking persisted as a frequent habit. It still recurred occasionally during her early teens, then subsided. What we have recorded of the parents' account of their little girl's reaction to the grandmother's funeral amply confirms what our patient now remembers of it.

During the several hundred hours of interview, the therapist had frequently tried to lead Eve White, Eve Black, and also Jane toward a memory of this experience. Eve White was familiar with many incidents at approximately the same period of her life. In discussing these with her, the therapist had tried to approach the funeral from many directions, to bring up material that might by logic or by contiguity be associated with it and so stimulate its recollection.

From time to time he had asked Eve White about events that occurred near the time of the funeral. He had also questioned her about her grandparents and tried to learn as much as possible about the child's relations with them. Death was, of course, discussed, and though Eve White told many things about her early ideas on this subject, she did not come to the funeral of her paternal grandmother. After inquiries about the maternal grandparents, the therapist asked, "What was your father's mother like? Was she playful and lively?"

"I'm not sure," Eve White had replied. "I don't seem to remember her well. You see, she died when I was very small."

The incident at the funeral was not a solitary point that stood out with overwhelming prominence in the history of childhood as given by the parents. They told us of dozens of other matters that had also seemed important. These, too, we did not bring up directly but, during interviews with the patient, led her to recall spontaneously and to discuss. We dealt with the grandmother's funeral similarly, but did not succeed in getting her to bring it up as she had so many other events that the parents had emphasized.

It appeared to be deeply forgotten, well-guarded or actively repressed from the awareness of Eve White. No trace of it was ever elicited during similar attempts with Eve Black. Jane always denied all memory of personal experience prior to her first appearance in the office. Through the bits of the others' memories, she continued to accumulate we had searched for some link that might lead to the funeral, but without success.

The parents had told us of so many other reactions and happenings during their daughter's early life that impressed us as deserving careful investigation that the grandmother's funeral seemed only one of numerous major incidents in the long and detailed story. We found little difficulty in leading our patient to recall through association many of these items that seemed to hold promise of significance in her development. It seemed to us advisable to encourage her to recall or discover all potentially influential material from early life spontaneously rather than to thrust it upon her ourselves. If we confront her with what her mother has told us about the funeral, we asked ourselves, will she, even if this helps her regain memory of the bare events, be helped to recapture the emotion, the inner significance of her personal experience? If the experience was painful and serious, and if its nature caused her to forget or repress it, might not such an effort on our part stimulate and strengthen the processes in her that had caused the evasion and perhaps were still active in maintaining it? Even if we could force her to recall and reenact emotionally all that she had felt, was she prepared for this? Might it not be harmful rather than helpful? Not being confident of our knowledge about these points, we deemed it better to proceed as we did.

CHAPTER 25

We have already expressed an opinion that no single incident of fright or stress, such as our patient's experience as a child at her grandmother's funeral, can plausibly be assumed to account in full for the disorder she developed. As a working hypothesis let us consider it likely that many adverse influences had already contributed to a serious conflict, induced an abnormal susceptibility, or had somehow worked against a healthy development of sound integration. If this is true, it is conceivable that the funeral, as a final incident, revitalized and focused intensely into the present numerous old problems and so provoked the onset of a disorder it did not solely, or even chiefly, produce.

It is widely believed today that psychiatric illness is often pathologic and unsuccessful but nevertheless a purposeful effort toward adaptation, and that it may constitute a sacrifice of health or a limitation of the patient's scope, in order to insure his survival. Did the small child Eve White suddenly find herself confronted by the terror of death in a particularly devasting form, or in a new degree of intentsity, at this funeral? If so, how might this have contributed to the subsequent developments we have followed? Death to many children seems a form of punishment. In law the ultimate penalty for the wrongdoer is execution. In civilized as well as in savage and animal life, serious errors and grossly inept behavior sometimes lead to quick extinction. The boy who disobediently scoots out on his bicycle into the swift traffic of the highway may be killed. So, too, may the squirrel who neglects to be on guard against the predatory cat. In the religious concepts of many, death is embellished with threats of violent and eternal punishment, from which only extreme goodness supplemented by the grace of God offers a possibility of escape. Proverbially, the wages of sin is death. Though the child is not likely to be told he will be slain by the parent's own hand for any act, however evil, he is aware of fatal agencies beyond the parent's control.

Often a badly frightened adult turns to the church, tries to put aside his evil ways and to lead a new life less deserving of severe punishment. The disciplinary measures by which adults gradually prepare their children from the earliest years for civilized and socially acceptable living usually embody the threat of some pain or deprivation, or of temporary banishment, to enforce more than academic realization of the basic rules. Many of the rules of conduct that the very young child must first learn are those that will preserve his life. Often physical pain (the bruise from a fall

196

down the steps) and fright (from the sense of falling), reinforce the verbal warning. As a final and fearful consequence of misbehavior looms the hideous threat of death itself. This may be conceived by a child as the sum of all imaginable pains magnified to the level of unbearable agony and at the same time as irreversible banishment so desolate that the heart shrinks from contemplating it. Whatever the small child's conception may be, it is often vaguely outlined, and full of mysterious aspects or areas more unnerving than what he can more clearly visualize. The child, and indeed the adult also, sometimes evades contemplating or even accepting unbearably distressing eventualities.

If the experience at her grandmother's funeral brought upon five-year-old Eve a new and terrifying reaction to death, it is quite possible that this might have motivated her special and extraordinary efforts to be good and to avoid what she had been taught was bad or evil. This may have been the beginning of a pattern of unusually meticulous conformity and restraint. Impulses that are regularly denied and subdued may, it seems, become more insistent of expression, just as a starved animal or man becomes more ravenous and more desperate. Most observers today probably agree that the efforts to control impulses regarded as evil or unacceptable can become so thorough that the impulses may be denied conscious recognition. Repressed or dissociated, they seem to be shut off from awareness. It is widely believed that such impulses do not necessarily atrophy and at length become extinguished, but that as penned up and invisible forces, they may retain strength indefinitely and continue to seek expression.

According to currently popular psychologic theory, drives or impulses so repressed may gain partial, or indirect, or distorted, or disguised expression in common psychiatric symptoms such as phobic anxiety, obsession, compulsive acts, or hysterical paralysis. If they are sufficiently powerful, or if the controlling functional organization lacks adequate cohesion and strength, they may disrupt or shatter the personality, producing a schizophrenic psychosis.

It has been said also that the banished and blocked tendencies may, so to speak, coalesce, unite, and organize in their underground region beneath the level of consciousness. Instead of various isolated or fragmentary impulses seeking

197

indirect outlet and distorted expression through something like compulsive handwashing or temporary hysterical blindness, they may accumulate in such quantity and eventually join in such integration as to become the nuclear potential of another personality within themselves. With recruitment con-concealed forces may become strong enough to challenge the conscious personality and, if successful in this conflict, replace it in command.

When this occurs we are dealing with the manifestation of what is said to be *another* and *different personality*. Having gained access to the mechanisms of perception and control of the complex means of human expression and function hitherto beyond its reach, the new entity employs them for its own purposes at the behest of its own tastes and intentions. Since we have assumed that the banished or repressed impulses were unacceptable, or at least foreign, to the formerly dominant consciousness, it will not be surprising if the new personality differs strikingly from the first.

Let us compare the minor and isolated symptoms of neurosis to the various disturbances of the peace that occur continually throughout a nation but are kept in check by the police. So, too, we might find an analogy between the schizophrenic psychosis and a violent rebellion by anarchists who without definite purpose destroy a civilization and leave it in chaos. Let us consider another sort of revolt, that of an organized conspiracy by a vast secret party with carefully devised aims and plans of its own. If such a party becomes strong enough before its existence is even suspected, and suddenly rises and overthrows the existing government, we may find here a good analogy to the development of dual personality. This new party does not destroy the agencies and facilities of the nation. It seizes control of them to carry out its purposes. These may be at great variance with those of the old government, but they have a design of their own. Let us assume that the defeated government is displaced but not destroyed, that it goes into exile, or underground. There, for the time being latent and invisible, it gathers its strength or waits for a weakness to develop in the currently dominant counterpart; and at an opportune moment displaces the other and again assumes control of the still intact apparatus of government and of national life.

198

Perhaps the recent political history of France may furnish the reader additional details to round out this analogy.

If little Eve, under the stimulus of influences that fell upon her with focal intensity at or after her grandmother's funeral, set herself to resist many natural impulses with great and consistent severity, we have a plausible prototype, a possible progenitor of the restrained, restricted, and invariably conforming woman who first came to us as a patient. If the tendencies denied expression did, indeed, remain unconscious but alive and gradually organized into a disparate purposive unit which finally became able to overthrow at times the prevalent consciousness, we have a theoretical explanation of the origin of Eve Black.

Such an entity organizing in rebellion against the painful conformity of Eve White might be expected to act more or less in accordance with the feelings reflected in these lines:

> The laws of God, the laws of man,
> He may keep that will and can;
> Not I: let God and man decree
> Laws for themselves and not for me;
> And if my ways are not as theirs
> Let them mind their own affairs.
> Their deeds I judge and much condemn,
> Yet when did I make laws for them?
> Please yourselves, say I, and they
> Need only look the other way.
> But no, they will not; they must still
> Wrest their neighbor to their will,
> And make me dance as they desire
> With jail and gallows and hell-fire.
> And how am I to face the odds
> Of man's bedevilment and God's?

One may, if he likes, and with some justification, think of Jane as the representative of a broader and more balanced human viewpoint or way of life. Was she a manifestation of some mere compromise between the two Eves? Or was she the shadowing forth of still other things, once potential in the little child before she became so sharply divided in her aims, but which could find no secure habitation in either of the two organized extremes? Was the final Evelyn who emerged a combination of all three manifestations?—or, perhaps, a functional entity more complex than this, some new creation born through their dramatic coalescence but including also elements never conscious or actively operational in any of them as they had appeared to us?

We do not know. It would be a gross mistake for us to consider this as an explanation derived from evidence, and a grosser folly to present it as a scientifically established analysis of our patient's disorder. We are merely offering some of our thoughts, some of the items about which we wondered while dealing clinically with the manifestations that often astonished us.

We have expressed the opinion that a better definition and understanding of *consciousness* and of *personality* must be found before any reliable explanation can be offered of such a patient as the one presented here. Since working with her for so long, we have wondered with increasing interest if the study of such disorders as the one we observed in her may eventually afford a clue to some genuine knowledge of matters that, despite confident and dogmatic claims, is sadly lacking at this time. Though McDougall's work has attracted little attention recently, we feel that some of his concepts are of interest here. In a discussion of consciousness and its disintegration, with particular reference to multiple personality, he says:

It is the evidences of coconscious activities that are of critical importance and offer extreme difficulty to any attempt at interpretation. The monist may say (and this is the line taken by Dr. Morton Prince) that he sees no special difficulty—the individual is a co-operative system of dispositions which may be regarded equally validly as mental dispositions or neural dispositions, neurograms, engrams, or what-not; and, when division of the whole system takes place, each part functions as an independent whole, enjoying its own psychical activities, pursuing its own purposes, and retaining its own memories. But there is a difficulty which Prince seems to overlook in all his discussions. If to remember were nothing more than to have an idea recur to consciousness, to think again of an object previously thought of, the monistic interpretations might seem acceptable. But it is not so. To remember is to think again of an object, and to be aware at the same time that I have thought of it before, or that I have so perceived or thought of or acted. And this self-awareness and this recognition of the past experience as one's own is the fundamental and most troublesome fact of memory. The cases of multiple personality, and of coconsciousness especially, do but accentuate and bring out more vividly this fundamental fact. For we find repeatedly that, when one personality obtains command of the memories of another, he distinguishes between his own memories and those of that other. And, when a coconscious personality is aware of the thoughts and feelings of the other, it is not that for the time being the two personalities become merged in one common stream of thinking. Rather the coconscious personality reports the experiences of the other as something of which he becomes aware as experiences foreign to himself; he knows what the other thinks and feels, but he has also his own thoughts and feelings about the same object or topic.[19]

In just such a way was Eve Black coconscious with Eve White and Jane with both Eves. Eve White enjoyed no coconsciousness with either of the other two. Eve Black, it will be recalled, never gained access to Jane's consciousness.

The dualist maintains that self-consciousness and true memory are functions that imply the true unity and continuity of a real being, a psychic being, self, or soul; and that such a self-conscious entity cannot in any sense be identified with the physical organism, or brain, or with any part of it; for the physical organism is a multiplicity of elements which appears more multitudinous and complex the further physical science progresses in its analysis of matter.

Now this reasoning cannot lightly be set aside. On really impartial and unprejudiced consideration of the problem, it does appear that no aggregation of elements or bits of conscious stuff, or of conscious processes, call them sensations or ideas or what you will, can produce a self-conscious Ego, a self-directing being aware of itself and its continuing identity over against other similar selves and the physical world. And, though the various forms of division of the personality may seem to imply a shattering or fragmentation of the self, more careful inspection of the facts seems to show that this implication is a false reading of the facts. The evidence of fragmentation may seem strongest in the case of those minor dissociations that result in such disabilities as an anaesthesia of a limb. But, when we obtain evidence of secondary consciousness in such cases, we seem to encounter, not a mere aggregate of sensations but a thinking purposive agent, a self which, though it may be rudimentary, undeveloped, and greatly

201

restricted in the modes of its activity, has yet the fundamental attributes of a self-conscious entity exercising the function of true memory.[19]

After comparing the monistic and dualistic views of human personality, McDougall asks us to join him in a consideration of the problem from a monistic hypothesis:

Without stopping to ask whether a monad can be perceived as a material object, whether it is capable of phenomenal representation as some part or feature of the bodily organism as it appears to us in sense perception, or to the anatomist or histologist, let us assume that a monad is an ultimate reality, a being that exists and is active in its own right; that the normal human personality is essentially a society of such monads, living in harmonious co-operation in virtue of the integration of them all in one system. Let us also assume that a monad is, potentially at least, a thinking striving self, endowed with the faculty or power of true memory; and that different monads are of very different degrees of development: some, being relatively undeveloped, exercise the powers common to all in a relatively simple and rudimentary fashion; others, being highly developed, exercise the same powers in a developed fashion.

We regard, then, the normal human personality as an integrated system of such monads; and the integrated system takes the form of a converging hierarchy. At the head of the hierarchy is the supreme monad which each of us calls "myself." And the integration of the system consists in the subordination of the monads of each level of the hierarchy to those of the next higher level. Complete integration according to this plan gives to the supreme monad control over the whole system. A close analogy obtains between such a system as I am sketching and such a social hierarchy as the Roman Church or an army in the field. And it is noteworthy that many psychologists who do not accept this monadic view of human nature, nevertheless, point out the analogy between the human organism and a social hierarchy. Dr. Morton Prince is only the most outstanding of such instances.

The commander-in-chief of the army sits at the centre where all lines of communication converge; but the items of intelligence, the messages gathered in all parts of the field, are not transmitted directly to him; rather they are transmitted through a hierarchy of officers who select and digest all such messages into condensed reports. And much of the detail of incoming information never reaches him, but is used only by subordinate operations of a routine nature. Such are the perceptual items of information that serve to guide the minor and routine operations of the human organism, in which operations only a limited intelligence and a special but restricted knowledge are displayed.

In a similar way, the commander-in-chief does not issue detailed instructions for all operations; he issues only general orders to his immediate subordinates, and these work them out in more detail and transmit the more detailed orders to their subordinates. The commander-in-chief could not, if he would, issue detailed orders, because he is ignorant of the details of the whole organisation. In a similar way the chief monad, ignorant of the details of the organisation over which he presides, issues only general orders, commands that the whole organisation shall move in this direction or in that, or that certain parts such as the limbs shall execute certain movements; whereupon the movements, involving the nice co-operation of a multitude of subordinate members of the system, are executed in a way that conforms to the general order. This is literally what happens when the ordinary man sees a certain situation and takes intelligent voluntary action to meet it. His appreciation of the situation requires the co-operation of a multitude of facts and processes of which he knows nothing, facts of perspective, of disparation of retinal images, of accomodation and convergence, of light and shade, and so forth. And in a similar way the execution of his intention requires the co-operation of a multitude of processes of adjustment of which also he knows nothing. He merely becomes aware of the general nature of the situation, conceives and wills the general nature of his response to it; and all the rest is left to his subordinates. If any of them do not know their job, or are in any way inadequate to their tasks, the supreme command can only very imperfectly compensate for their defects by concentrating his attention upon the neglected details.

Hence, as I said in the address mentioned above, the obvious and, I believe, inevitable inference from the facts is that I who consciously address you am only one among several selves or Egos which my organism, my person, comprises. I am only the dominant member of a society, an association, of similar members. There are many purposive activities within my organism of which I am not aware, which are not my activities but those of my associates. I am conscious at any moment only of those processes within the organism, and of those impressions from without, which it is most necessary that I should take cognisance of. And I consciously control and adjust only a few of the executive processes of my organism, those only which are of primary importance for my purposes. But I and my associates are all members of one body; and, so long as the whole organism is healthy, we work harmoniously together, for we are a well-organised society, the members of which strive for a common good, the good of the whole society. My subordinates serve me faithfully in the main, provided always that I continue to be resolute and strong. But, when I relax my control, in states of sleep, hypnosis, relaxation, and abstraction, my subordinates, or some of them, may continue to work and then are apt to manifest their activities in the forms we have learned to call sensory and motor automatisms. And if I am weak and irresolute, if I do not face the problems of life and take the necessary decisions for dealing with them, then conflict arises within our system, one or more of my subordinates gets out of hand, I lose my control, and division of the personality into conflicting systems replaces the normal and harmonious co-operation of all members in one system. And in extreme cases such a revolted subordinate, escaped from the control of the dominant member or monad, may continue his career of insubordination indefinitely, acquiring increased influence over other members of the society and becoming a serious rival to the normal ruler or dominant.[20]

After a discussion in which he applies his hypothesis to dreams, hypnosis, hallucinations, and compulsions, McDougall makes an interesting comment on Sally Beauchamp. Sally was one of the several personality manifestations of the famous Miss Beauchamp studied so thoroughly by Morton Prince. The description of her temperament and tastes, of her frivolity, prankishness, and irresponsibility make her seem, in many respects, a twin sister of the Eve Black we knew. Sally's persistent attitude of mockery toward the staid and overconventional Miss Christine Beauchamp who consulted Dr. Prince was also almost identical with Eve Black's attitude toward Eve White. Of this rebellious manifestation observed by Prince over fifty years ago, McDougall says:

This view enables us to account satisfactorily for such extreme examples of independent secondary personalities as Sally Beauchamp [and others of this type]. Sally is a monad who has become dissociated, has escaped from the

204

control of the dominant monad, or has been displaced from her place in the developing hierarchy at a very early age, and then has undergone independent development, securing control of a limited system of subordinates. Thus she remained, until the induction of deep hypnosis rendered the chief monad more completely passive and unresistant than hitherto and so gave Sally the opportunity to control the organs of expression more completely than she had previously been able to do. Further, Sally's long course of independent development had rendered her insusceptible to control by the chief monad, or incapable of fitting into the system that constituted the main personality of Miss Beauchamp. Hence, when Miss B. was restored to health by the synthesis of B_1 and B_4, Sally continued to remain outside the system, but "squeezed" as she said, i.e., denied all control over the subordinate parts of the hierarchy.

I suggest that Ireland affords a parallel to Sally. The organisation which is the British Empire may be likened to the organisation of a normal personality: Ireland has never been brought into willing subordination to the whole system; like Sally, she has remained rebellious from an early date in the development, when she was estranged by an act of violence; like Sally, she has struggled for her independence; and, during the shocks and distractions of the Great War, she has been able to assert herself successfully. Sally was the Ireland of Miss Beauchamp's body politic.[21]

Morton Prince in describing the synthesis which finally occurred in his patient seemed to feel that Sally was permanently banished in the process, that she was left entirely out of the union and did not contribute even a part or an element to the recovered patient. He speaks of her as if she remained banished at a subconscious level, existing immobilized and with no means at all of expression for the impulses that had vigorously asserted themselves through her during the years when she was able at times to emerge. Of this matter he writes thus:

And Sally, what became of her? With the resurrection of the real self, she "goes back to where she came from," imprisoned, "squeezed," unable either to "come" at will or be brought by command. Automatic writing, speech, and such phenomena cease, and it has not been possible as yet to communicate with her, and determine what part if

205

any she plays in Miss Beauchamp's subconsciousness, or whether as a subpersonality she exists at all. When, however, as a result of some mental catastrophe, she appeared again as an alternating personality, her language implied a persistent existence as a subconsciousness like that of her early youth and as described in the autobiography. Nevertheless the resurrection of the Real Miss Beauchamp is through the death of Sally.[22]

After the synthetic change took place we found nothing in our patient that suggested the presence or the activity of Eve Black as an entity. Nothing has occurred since that would lead us to think she may occasionally have emerged to consciousness or to control. One might think of her, as Morton Prince did of Sally, as continuing to exist beneath the awareness of the new Evelyn. We have mentioned that in the latter there appears to be an energy, a capacity for vivacity and humor, an occasional and appropriate flash of high spirits that we never saw in Eve White or even in Jane. Jane was not without the generic qualities these words indicate, but in Evelyn they have always been not quite the same as in Jane. It has often seemed as if some emotional element of Eve Black might be sparkling through patterns of behavior quite unlike her own. In a well-controlled and responsible person some of her very own flash and fire still appeared to reside, or at least some touch of a vivid spontaneity quite similar, a distinct characteristic that we had not detected in Jane before the synthesis.

One may regard this as an indirect expression of a still organized but no longer openly active Eve Black who, dissociated or repressed, is, so to speak, imprisoned in the unconscious of subconscious. On the other hand, one may think of Eve Black as having participated in the synthesis, as having contributed some real elements to the conscious and active personality we now call Evelyn. If so, one need not assume that the Eve Black so familiar to us is still an entity, an integrated set of forces in the unconscious, out of our view but still opposing the patient as she is now constituted. Perhaps, through a more mature character, a more versatile personality organization, the original impulses that we have conceived of as uniting in rebellion long ago against Eve White may find true and appropriate fulfillment. Such a fulfillment in socially desirable and constructive channels might be far more real and satisfying to the human needs represented than the irresponsible and fruitless antics of the Eve Black we knew so well. Perhaps, instead of being extinguished or banished to some melancholy and lifeless limbo, the charming and childlike vitality that flowed audaciously toward no serious end through our mischievous little friend may find meaningful consummation, and possibly even make a contributin not altogether unlike a redemption.

CHAPTER 26

What were the specific experiences preceding the grandmother's funeral that may have caused feelings of guilt and the conflict that we assumed in the hypothesis we have been discussing? We raised this question earlier, promising to return to it in time.

There are a number of items that suggest problems in Eve's early years. Eve White as an adult maintained the constant and determined effort to preserve a charitable Christian attitude at all times toward those who might do, or seem to do, her wrong. Despite this, it was not difficult to surmise that behind or beneath her uncritical sweetness she was aware of hurt and of impulses toward resentment. She was able to tell us directly about such feelings toward Ralph and toward her parents and other close relatives. Eve Black not only expressed open antagonism and contempt, but often expressed the opinion that Eve White also actually had stronger negative feelings than she could admit to herself. Her desperate effort to eschew hatefulness, to be fair and entirely forgiving, to follow, come what may, Christ's admonition about turning the other cheek were apparently maintained despite these feelings. Finding all bitterness and resentment unworthy, she did her best to disown and set them aside. It is so easy to see in Eve Black an outlet for such feelings that one might say she must have been born for this purpose.

We have not only Eve Black's unreliable word, but also evidence from the parents that she probably originated in early childhood. Did Eve prior to that time have unusual hostility to control because of objective factors that warranted it?—or did such a difficulty, perhaps, lie in her becoming committed to so high and unrealistic a standard of flawless benignity that even the mildest of imperfections aroused serious feelings of guilt? Such questions are indeed difficult to answer except on the basis of surmise. It is generally believed that during early years a child's chief problems arise in its relations with parents and siblings. Eve White pictured her parents as good. By Eve Black they were not regarded as parents at all; she always expressed hostility and distaste for them, particularly for the mother. From the story of early childhood furnished by the parents and from our impression of them, it would seem likely that prior to her grandmother's funeral Eve enjoyed reasonably good relations with her father, but that a good many conflicts occurred between the little girl and her mother. None of these incidents appeared to be spectacular or extreme, but they furnish some grounds for believing that negative or hostile feelings toward the mother were probably fairly frequent and sometimes strong.

During the first five years of her life Eve was an only child. Her father's work kept him away from home most of the day and it was her mother who usually maintained discipline and administered punishment. the father, apparently a genial and unauthoritative person, often played with his little girl when he returned from work. To the child he probably seemed the more approachable and permissive of the two parents.

The adult Eve White thought of her younger twin sisters with affection and recalled no serious difficulty in her relations with them in childhood. Their birth occurred a few months before the grandmother's funeral. Eve Black disliked them, and felt no regret in having bitten their toes and otherwise mistreated them when they were helpless infants. According to the parents Eve was on the whole good to the twins, seemed proud of them, and appeared to love them. They could still recall, however, that even before the funeral, when the babies were only a few months old, she occasionally showed some indications of jealousy, of feeling herself neglected because of them, or to some degree displaced. But after all this is a very common reaction in children who do not develop psychiatric disorder.

In connection with this a point made in the interpretation of the Rorschach and other projective tests is of interest.

Winter, the clinical psychologist who worked with us locally, reported:

... Actually the problem started at a much earlier period of life, with a strong feeling of rejection by her parents, especially after the birth of her twin sisters. Mrs. White loves them dearly; Miss Black despises them. In this connection an episode is related by Miss Black. After quitting school to help support the family, she (that is to say Mrs. White) sent home money to be used for overcoats for her twin sisters, denying herself a badly wanted wrist watch. When the money was used to buy them two wrist watches instead of overcoats, she reacted with strong, but repressed, hostility. Significantly, she removed her wrist watch, while examined as Mrs. White, stating that she doesn't like jewelry. There are several illustrations of her strong sense of rejection as well as sibling rivalry in her records.[14]

The two investigators, Osgood and Luria of Illinois, who studied this case only through the interpretations of the semantic differential, also make a pertinent comment. After reporting their results in two tests (run approximately two months apart) on each of the three separate personalities, and completing three more tests on the single Evelyn since the synthesis occurred, Osgood, in a recent communication with us, says:

You people have never commented on our suggestions about the dynamics of this case—split identifications of the young "Jane" with both father and mother, the model of younger *twin* sisters, break into two personalities, "Eve White" (mother-identifying, super-ego) and "Eve Black" (father-identifying, masculine, Id). Have you explored deeply into the childhood relations with parents? I suggested, if not in the paper then subsequently in talks, that such explorations would reveal that the mother was the main determiner of rewards and punishments, the representative of society, if you will, and that the daughter (Jane) was extremely ambivalent toward her mother. My main reason for doubting that this is a really successful case (forgive me my brashness) is that there is no evidence (in our data of any changes in the meaning of MOTHER or of the relationship between MOTHER and ME (except, of course, in "Eve Black").[23]

What we have been able to learn from Evelyn since the

synthesis occurred does suggest that her relation with her father in early childhood was not remarkable, but that with her mother she had considerable conflict from time to time. Whether or not she developed from this and from a hostility of really extraordinary proportions toward the twins, disastrously pathologic feelings of guilt and rejection, we are unable to say positively. Valid evidence is not easy to obtain in an adult about the detail and the degree of feelings during the first few years of life. We think it likely that these were sources of serious difficulty, but we do not assume they were the only ones or that they necessarily explain the development of the disparate personalities. We feel, nevertheless, that there is a remarkable relation between Osgood's interpretation and the facts of early childhood in so far as we could obtain them.

The Eve White we knew as a patient impressed us as lacking in ordinary tendencies to show resentment or to make it known to another when she felt hurt or wrongly judged. It is not difficult for us to see her as a child who would be likely to accept censure without protest, who, if she thought she had lost the approval of a parent, would withdraw emotionally and make no complaint about the isolation she might feel. Human beings vary greatly in their capacity to explain themselves, to offer or accept apology, to proceed actively into the painful conflict of vulnerability, pride, need, and longing that can arise when dangerous misunderstanding occurs between parent and child, or between husband and wife.

Sometimes the very intensity of one's need for acceptance and for love seals the lips against any word of appeal to the other. There were qualities in Eve White that strongly suggested she would understand Cordelia's silence after Lear had heard the extravagant protestations of devotion from Regan and Goneril. In her unhappy life with Ralph White she had seemed unable to achieve an articulateness or closeness that made it possible for them to resolve in warmth and adequate intimacy the hurts and estrangements that are perhaps inevitable in all marriages. Though undemanding and able to forgive a hurt or a wrong, it seemed impossible for her to reveal openly an inner wound, to work nakedly through a complex misunderstanding until no pain or obstacle remained. Without such a full and open resolution it is possible for small difficulties to accumulate and finally to become an imposing obstacle in human relations. If these traits began their development in Eve's early childhood, it is not difficult to see how outwardly ordinary confusions and stresses might have led to progressive conflict and serious withdrawal.

If one approaches this case, perhaps any case, rigidly committed to one of the many psychologic theories that (some feel) have profoundly clarified mental disorder and finally revealed the inner processes of human life, it is not likely to be difficult for him to find confirmation of the theory of our patient. So, too, it will be easy for him to expound much more confidently than we can what he believes to be the real causes and the meaning of her disorder.

Though Jung and Adler seem to have little influence today on American psychiatry, the concepts of either could be used to give an elaborate explanation of what we have reported. If convinced that neurosis always develops from a basic conflict about feeling inferior, one can readily see Eve as an infant beginning her efforts to compensate for her helplessness. This drive soon takes a neurotic course toward a fictive goal, *the Adlerian investigator might say*, toward one that is only ostensibly superior. In one direction she tries to excel by being good. Her overcompensation causes her to set impossible standards. Meanwhile she feels the inevitable masculine protest against her femininity which she neurotically regards as biologic inferiority. Eve Black is devised to follow this guiding line and create a fictional but impressive symbol of rebellious virility. Eventually the patient uses her illness to dominate her husband and to escape the responsibility of her child.[24]

What could seem more plain *to a devout Jungian* than the basic conflict of extroversion and introversion in the two Eves? Instead of a harmonious balance, a healthy enantiadromia, between inner realization and objective strivings, we see here a pathologically unreconciled division. The conscious life of Eve White shrinks impoverished to little more than the *persona*. Eve Black in many respects represents, or reflects, the *animus*, no longer deeply hidden behind the ego, but brashly confronting the outer world with which it is not equipped to deal directly. In her, too, we may find something of the *shadow*. Surely the fearful nightmares Jane experienced before the synthesis are big cosmic dreams. Their teleologic meaning seems

211

plain. In her drawing she represents her legs uniting and becoming transformed into a single reptilian whole, thus symbolizing the coalescence of the personalities that is to occur. The snakes which terrify her in dreams, the snakes into which her limbs are often changing, have a distinctly archetypal air. The snake of the caduceus, the snake's place in ancient mystic rites (and in some church services even today) testify to immemorial connections with magic, suggest its association with the *Wise Old Man* of the racial unconscious. The hypnopompic features of these dreams and the persistence of their effect through long periods of semi-wakefulness further underline their importance. Is Jane a reflection of the *shadow?* Was it possible that through her some reorientation toward the inmost *self* finally occurred and with this some new balance between the four personality functions, thinking and feeling, sensation and intuition? One could continue this sort of interpretation indefinitely.[25]

We do not wish to imply that the feeling of inferiority and inharmonious balances between inner interests and objective interests are not sometimes very important factors in maladjustment. But we do believe that *error is likely to arise from enthusiastic efforts to account entirely for complex disorders in such terms.* Any reader conversant with current psychiatric literature will realize that the concepts mentioned above have little to do with what is popularly called the *dynamics*, or the *psychodynamics*, little or nothing in common with the basic assumptions and the invariable manipulation of analogies and symbols whereby many enthusiastic psychopathologists are able to arrive at easy and almost identical explanations for all cases.

In the psychiatric literature we find confident interpretations of illness in which all sorts of significant material is detected in the unconscious and accepted as valid evidence for actual events which are presumed to have occurred in childhood, early infancy, or even prenatally. It is popular today to regard such discoveries, even when assumed purely on the basis of symbolism, as well established by the methods of science. Many who expound the *dynamics* of psychiatric disorder and of human life are apparently convinced that "discoveries" so made are satisfactorily proved whether or not any objective evidence is ever adduced to support them.[16]

212

By such methods we could indeed devise a detailed and elaborate explanation of our patient's illness, an account so dynamic and so orthodox that the uncritical believer in popular psychologic assumptions could scarcely fail to accept it with enthusiasm. For such an exposition we need not bring up all the details of her life which were revealed during the hundreds of hours she spent with us. Let us confine ourselves to only a few items of the limited material that has already been given about her case.

What about those huge snakes that repeatedly threatened Jane in her gruesome nightmares? According to widely practiced rules of interpretation, any snake in a dream stands for the male genital organ.[26,27] The immense size of these snakes as well as their number (*the method we now follow insists*) point to an extreme concern with the phallus. Does this not, in both man and woman, clearly demonstrate castration fear? There are many today who maintain that this is a logical conclusion. It has been thoroughly proved, we are repeatedly told, that all little girls from three to five years of age believe they have been gentially mutilated.[28,29] Whether or not the child ever becomes conscious of such a fantasy is considered of little importance in its alleged demonstration. Is not Jane in this dream still trying to reassure herself, despite obvious anatomical facts, that she does have a penis like that of a man? The continuing significance of her castration fear, some would say, is thus clearly revealed.

The dimensions of the serpents about which she dreams, their prominence, their recurrence in each scene, as well as the fright and horror they inspire, all, the rules say, indicate that this fear is of prodigious intensity. Her childhood dread of the reptilian monster she imagined in the ditch confirms this and affords support to the assumption that this awful sense of deprivation was strong during the oedipal years. The picture drawn to represent a dream in which her legs are uniting to form a gigantic snake offers evidence as impressive as any ever presented purely in terms of dream symbolism of her intense desire to grow a penis, hence of the severity of her castration fears. The remarkable size of the snakes can be said to represent a concern, in the unconscious, with a *very large* male organ. Does this not point very clearly to her specific choice as a little girl for intercourse with her father? His bigness as compared to herself as a small child must have been a prominent feature. This choice is, of course, postulated, *according to popular dynamic doctrine*, as being universal at age five,[30] but the dream indicates that Jane has not satisfactorily resolved her oedipal situation, that in the unconscious she is still overwhelmed by the old and terrible problem.

Let us consider also the drawings that show strong masculine hands tightly grasping two hooded cobras at the neck in an effort to strangle the venomous offenders. Here we see again vivid and irrefutable evidence, that is, *if we faithfully follow this method*, that the horror of genital mutilation dominated her unconscious life during a particularly dreadful oedipal difficulty. The hands, no doubt, represent not only the castrating parent but also the superego's negative reaction to incest as expressed by ego defenses through the mechanisms of repression and distortion.

In the dreams, to be sure, not sexual excitement but terror and loathing were caused by the snakes. This, *if we interpret it by the familiar pattern as a reversal of affect by the dream censorship*, points to passionate and consuming positive desire for the father's organ, disguised here behind the manifest content. Reversal of affect, we are told, is one of the most common ruses adopted by the unconscious forces of repression to conceal from the conscious ego the true nature of unacceptable libidinal strivings. The fear and horror in the dream also reveal guilt and dread of retaliation for her wishes as a child to kill and do away with her mother. These emotions, some would say, have been displaced from their real sources to the snakes.

So, too, if we rely on symbolism to produce evidence, when Eve Black bit the twins' toes she revealed the unconscious aim to castrate them. Did she not believe that these younger rivals for her father's sexual favors might have male organs and that she must reduce them to her own state of deprivation in order not to be supplanted? Serious anal fixations could be similarly demonstrated (for the next fifty pages) through Eve White's neatness, her meticulous restraint, and her very orderly habits. Eve Black's lively and profuse talk, her singing in night clubs and her passive acceptance of support from Eve White—do not all these and scores of other points, clearly demonstrate her orality? According to the rules by which the dynamics of a patient's illness are so often discovered, they reveal this unmistakably.

And of course both the frigidity of Eve White with her husband and the regular refusal by the boldly flirtatious Eve Black to have sexual relations with any man may be used to show that such relations are, in the dynamic unconscious, regarded as incestuous because of the still unresolved oedipal problems. Here is plainly demonstrated the fact that her sexual object in the unconscious was still the paternal imago. This caused her to reject all other men.

If anyone still has doubt about the seriousness of this patient's castration fears, let him recall that severe headaches suffered first by Eve White and finally by Jane. Who can deny that, *according to dynamic rules*, the human head may exquisitely represent the glans penis? This severe pain, it could be said, unmistakably points to the pain of the male organ, which every little girl is sure she once possessed, being severed in the bloody act of vengeful dismemberment that she is unconsciously convinced has already occurred. The distortion achieved here by displacement is very transparent, indicating a weak ego structure that is giving way as the forces of repression progressively fail to cope with the instinctual drives of the id. And let us not forget that Eve White once in desperation made an effort to cut her own wrist. Does this not clearly symbolize a phallic amputation and, at the same time, convincingly demonstrate an expression of thanatos, the death instinct? Confirmation is piled upon confirmation if we deal dynamically enough with the material. Even the most unimaginative of men could surely go on to produce a thick volume of discoveries about our patient *through the faithful application of these methods*.

CHAPTER 27

The sort of reasoning briefly demonstrated above is, we believe, a fair sample of methods often used to explore the unconscious as they are reported in our journals today. We offer no argument here against the opinion that experiences of early childhood and of infancy may play a crucial part in psychiatric disorder. Nor do we doubt that the emotional relations of a child with his parents are regularly and profoundly influential in the origin and development of love and hate, or that they are of paramount importance to every human being. We have no wish to minimize the significance of sexual impulses and of sexual confusion in personal growth and adjustment. Our objection is to some of the methods by which a number of the postulates and principles confidently referred to as *dynamic* were discovered and now are being "proved" over and over in precisely the way we have just demonstrated. Let us here emphasize the fact that this term *dynamic* is also used by many excellent psychiatrists for sound and wise inquiries into the causes and possible causes of emotional disorder. Some of our most respected and admired colleagues and friends depend upon it to indicate their reliable investigative procedures and their plausible and factually corroborated conclusions.

We do not contend that men and women are clearly aware of all their motives, nor do we deny that incestuous, murderous, and perhaps even more spectacular, impulses and fantasies may be seething in every human being. It is not our opinion that dreams are meaningless. There seems good reason to believe that they portray, in chaotic, primitive imagery, important reactions of the dreamer, that they may reflect experiences, recent and remote, not readily accessible to ordinary memory, or not compatible with the dreamers conscious concepts of himself and his attitudes. We have no objections to symbolic interpretation and the use of analogy, however fanciful, in efforts to explore, to explain, or to theorize.

We do maintain, nevertheless, that conclusions reached by such processes require the support of objective evidence before they can be accepted as anything more than conjecture. Our point is that the methods we refer to and will proceed to illustrate from the literature cannot be relied upon to furnish real evidence about such matters.[16]

The reader unfamiliar with what is sometimes presented today as the *dynamics* or the *psychodynamics* of psychiatric disorder is likely to feel we have unfairly caricatured the subject in our demonstration. Let us see.

It would not be difficult to fill a large volume with pertinent examples from our best-known psychiatric journals whose extravagance makes our little illustration seem in comparison inspidly sober. For several decades these responsible publications have carried such reports of dream interpretation as these:

He then related the following dream: Dream 2. He is

in a hospital and is examined by an assistant, who discussed his case with the professor. The professor asks the assistant to explain. The assistant could only explain the second part of the examination but not the third.

Interpretation: A homosexual dream. The symbol 3 written ∽ equals vagina. The 2 represents the labia. . . .

• • • •

Dream 4: Part 1. He is in a book store and buys four volumes. When he looked at the first volume he found that it was not the latest edition.

Part 2. He is at college, in the same room with his colleagues. Several colleagues come in and tell him it is eight o'clock.

Interpretation: Both parts represent his homosexual component. He is looking for the first edition. The numeral 1 is a phallic symbol. That leaves three books. Three is a symbol of the vagina. (See dream 2.) He does not care for the female, but what he desires in the female is the clitoris (male element). In part 2 we see the homosexual component, telling him it is time to act—it is eight o'clock.

• • • •

Dream 7. He is in a house in Rome. There are a woman and a child. The woman is teaching the child history.

Interpretation: The woman and child are himself. The woman is his feminine component and the child represents his genitals.[31]

It is not our intention to imply that the few hundred officially qualified psychoanalysts in our country approve of the methods we refer to. Some in this group of highly trained specialists have expressed in their writings an admirable skepticism toward the popular usages and concepts we are now briefly discussing.[32,33,34] There is nevertheless a strong tendency among some physicians not so qualified, and among the laity, to accept everything attributed to Freud as scientific fact. One prominent psychiatrist writes:

Now it must be admitted that the enemies of Freud must be careful not to admit any single part of his discoveries to be valid, since one part is interlocked with the other part, and if one admits that one thing is correct one is forced to admit the validity of the whole edifice . . .[35]

Is it true that the unconscious contains valid evidence of the chief articles of popular psychodynamic creed? And has this evidence, as many claim, been adequately demonstrated? Perhaps it will be worth our while to reexamine briefly the methods by which many of these discoveries are said to have been made. If we grant that all psychiatrists have read the major articles in Freud's *Collected Papers*, it is perhaps reasonable to assume that some who have accepted his conclusions early in their careers have not lately examined the evidence in detail. Ernest Jones, editor of the papers, writes:

All Professor Freud's other work and theories are essentially founded on the clinical investigations of which these papers are the only published record.[36]

Let us consider as a typical and representative example of this work the long report entitled *From the History of an Infantile Neurosis.*

The conclusions reached about this case rest chiefly and fundamentally on the interpretation of a dream recalled by the 26-year-old male Russian patient as having occurred at the age of four years. The entire dream is thus described:

I dreamt that it was night and that I was lying in my bed. (My bed stood with its foot towards the window; in front of the window there was a row of old walnut trees. I know it was winter when I had the dream, and nighttime.) Suddenly the window opened of its own accord, and I was terrified to see that some white wolves were sitting on the big walnut tree in front of the window. There were six or seven of them. The wolves were quite white, and looked more like foxes or sheep-dogs, for they had big tails like foxes and they had their ears pricked like dogs when they are attending to something. In great terror, evidently of being eaten up by the wolves, I screamed and woke up. . . .
The only piece of action in the dream was the opening of the window, for the wolves sat quite still and without any movement on the branches of the tree, to the right

218

and left of the trunk, and looked at me. It seemed as though they had riveted their whole attention upon me.[37]

From this dream and its associations with a number of rather ordinary childhood memories and several fairy tales familiar to the patient during his early years, some remarkable conclusions are derived. We are told that the dream reveals events experienced by the patient two and a half years earlier when he was precisely eighteen months of age. Details of the dream are offered as proof that the infant at that time avidly watched his parents indulge in sexual intercourse three times in succession and that, furthermore, the relations were carried out *a tergo*. Freud is equally positive that the baby, in reaction to this scene, contrived to have a bowel movement as an excuse to cry and interrupt the still active pair. The stationary dream scene (the stillness of the wolves) is offered as evidence for lively coital activity by the parents. The number of wolves (six or seven) is taken as an effort by the dreamer to disguise what he had actually seen (the two parents) and therefore is counted as additional evidence. The attentive look on the faces of the animals in the tree is offered as a confirmation of the voyeuristic intensity attributed to the eavesdropping infant. His fear of the wolves in the dream and the assumed reaction of the infant to his (assumed) sight of his mother's genitals at eighteen months convinced Freud that the boy at four was laboring under an overwhelming dread that his father would castrate him. The long tails of the wolves are confidently accepted by the interpreter as evidence of taillessness (through contrast); and therefore as additional proof of this unhappy preoccupation. This hypothetical fear is offered as the restraining influence on the boy's dominant passion, which is assumed to be for his father to carry out the sexual act upon him *per anum*. No objective evidence is offered anywhere in the paper to support these interpretations.[37]

Freud expresses the most positive convictions in this explanation, insisting that his entire study "is all a piece of nonsense from start to finish, or everything took place just as I have described it above."*[37] Many years later when revising

---

* In material added after original publication of the paper, Freud discusses the possibility that the dramatic experience attributed to the infant might have been a fantasy. After considerable equivocation he seems to decide again that it was an actuality. He insists,

some of his concepts, Freud still proclaimed absolute faith in his proof of castration fear from the interpretation of this dream. *In The Problem of Anxiety* he says:

> The Russian's fear of being eaten by a wolf contains no suggestion of castration, it is true; through oral regression the idea has been removed too far from the phallic stage; but the analysis of his dream makes any other proof superfluous.[38]

Are these conclusions better supported by evidence than the ones we devised above in a modest attempt at irony from the dreams of our patient? If one finds difficulty today in accepting such discoveries as plausible and such methods as scientific, is it to be assumed that his judgment must necessarily be distorted by an unconscious pathologic resistance which prevents his accepting adequately demonstrated facts? Or are we confronted with a scheme so elastic that it can be used to arrive at almost *any* conclusion that comes to mind? Is real evidence adduced merely by appeal to symbolism or analogy and by free assumptions about what is in the unconscious but what is never made conscious, demonstrated, or otherwise corroborated? Do not such methods serve ideally to create a *dynamics of illusion?*[16]

When symbolism and reasoning by analogy are accepted as proof without support of objective evidence there seems no limit to the discoveries that can be produced. In one of our best psychiatric journals an observer reported recently on the effect of parental intercourse on the embryo:

> In the matter of pre-natal traumata the author experienced some resistance against accepting the possibility the unborn child could react to pre-natal sexual intercourse. This resistance, however, had to pass when a female patient told this dream: "I am in a church, all is good. But then Christ enters. He had a wooden leg and I become extremely afraid of the rhythmical clashing of His foot on the floor."[39]

The interpreter admits that "the wooden leg may be associated to the swollen foot of Oedipus"* but finds that it really

furthermore, that even if the experience had not occurred, all the conclusions he derived from it (the four-year-old boy's desire for sodomy with the father and his overwhelming fear of castration) are still proved valid.

is only a transparent disguise for the erect penis of the dreamer's father which terrified and traumatized her as an embryo by its intrusion into her mother's vagina. He expresses no doubt at all that "the extreme anxiety and the disturbance of silence and security (in the dream) indicate a pre-natal experience in this case." For the investigator proof is apparently clinched when "interpretations of this dream in this way caused the anxiety to disappear at once."[39]

Another investigator had reported the demonstration by similar methods of dream interpretation of a bodiless, immaterial self or *double* of the opposite sex, a sort of immaterial twin which, we are told, all people possess. Though without anatomical habitat this interesting twin is said to be quite active and to exert a remarkable influence on her biologically real brother all his life. According to the investigator the *double* has a dream life all her own that can be dynamically interpreted.[40]

In April, 1953, the *Journal of Mental Science*, official organ of the British Psychiatric Association, carried the report of discoveries no less remarkable through the use of hypnosis. The investigator's seriousness and sincerity we do not question. Let us quote him as he describes what emerges dynamically from his patient's unconscious:

Eventually he reached his conception, in which he saw himself as the ovum being raped, rather than wooed, by the over anxious sperm of his over-anxious father. Though I have phrased this rather jocularly, I am in fact in earnest about its significance, though time does not permit me to go into this topic at length. Suffice it to say that following this session still more improvement was noticeable. . . . In short since we recovered this material he has turned from an apparently hopeless therapeutic prospect into a promising one.[41]

In the light of such revelations as these let us now reconsider the first dream reported by Eve White. She finds herself immersed in a pool of stagnant water (the amniotic fluid) and enclosed in a tremendous room (the uterus). By the methods just illustrated, one can immediately demonstrate that Eve White's basic difficulty lies much deeper than

* Surely one needs no more than a modest imagination to associate it, by similarity, or by contrast, with several thousand other things.

oedipal, or even oral levels. How readily one could show by this dream that her original trauma occurred when she was a *foetus in utero!* The fanciful monster of the ditch, also, may symbolize not only the male organ as conceived during oedipal years but, just as accurately, the father's penis which during intercourse long ago disturbed the embryonic daughter. Is Eve Black a manifestation of the ordinarily unconscious *double?* If we follow these methods with confidence *and without a demand for further evidence,* we shall find no difficulty at all in proving these things to our complete satisfaction.

Since no confirmatory objective evidence was obtained in our case to support the various symbolic interpretations suggested above, we must refrain from offering them as a satisfactory explanation for her peculiar difficulties. For all its polysyllabic jargon the reigning scheme of popular dynamics narrows down in the end to an amazingly rigid and stereotyped process by which the same stilted and tiresome answers are always ground out. However rich, complex, marvelous, or profound the material of human experience may be, it is at last mechanically reduced by this rule of thumb to unvarying banal and implausible little equations. Anyone so inclined could, by manipulation of the trite and essentially simple syllogisms of the prevailing method, construct whatever paradigm his creed demands out of the assumed contents of preverbal memory, the septet of baby fears, various pre-oedipal countercathexes, gelatinizations of the libido, interrelations of orality and psychic masochism, embryonic intrauterine emotional traumatra, and anally incoporated parental imagos, as well as out of assumed unconscious fantasies of incest and castration (umbilical as well as penile). It is our opinion that such an exercise would not be likely to contribute valid understanding to the complex realities of this patient's illness or of her life.

CHAPTER 28

Only a few days ago we had the pleasure of talking again with Mrs. Evelyn Lancaster. It was a delightful and gratifying experience. We had kept in touch with her by correspondence and her letters had informed us that she remained in good health and was happy. But to see her again at first hand and to review her story almost two years after the integration or coalescence which had so dramatically occurred, was an experience we had long anticipated with particular interest.

It was about six months after she was granted a divorce from Ralph White that the manifestations of multiple personality ceased. From that time on she had not been seriously troubled by headaches. There had been no blackout spells. The distressing nightmares that had afflicted Jane never recurred. We had no way of knowing whether or not this unitary and, so far as one could determine, healthy status would be maintained. She was able to work regularly and successfully, and without the frustrations and interruptions of the pranks that the former Eve Black had played on Eve White. After her divorce was obtained the seriousness of her interest in Earl Lancaster became more obvious to us.

Though we could only hope without knowing that further serious dissociations would not occur, she felt all the conviction of certainty that the disparate Eve White and Eve Black and the separate Jane of the past were gone forever in all the finality of death. Her problems now were not in the ordinary sense psychiatric symptoms. She had no complaints, only the wish and the need to discuss plans for her future, to orient herself in a world still in many subtle ways strange and unexplored. Freed from the ties of her former marriage, and in this new unity, she was able to find in the steadily increasing devotion of the young man who had been attentive to Jane something hitherto unknown and something at which she marveled. Within a few months she had no doubt at all about her desire to marry him. Her judgment told her that she should not decide impulsively about such a matter. She was determined to proceed as carefully and as wisely as she could. Though she did not, like Jane, feel totally without a past, a great deal of Eve White's life and almost all of Eve Black's was apprehended by her as not quite fully personal experience. She seemed to feel a need in her present situation to consolidate herself, a need for time to gain self-assurance and a more direct familiarity with the surrounding world and all its ways.

Though much of Eve White's past still seemed not quite her own, she never wavered in the sense of motherhood toward Bonnie. As far as we could judge, this was not the identical attitude shown by the tense and troubled Eve

White we had known so well. Though genuinely devoted, she was less anxiously, less desperately absorbed in her little girl. At the basis of all her planning was a longing to have the child with her. She had seen the reasonableness of her former husband's wish that Bonnie remain with the grandparents until sufficient time had passed for some more reliable estimate to be made of her future health. She accepted these stipulations which Eve White had agreed to in the divorce procedures, and showed herself willing to abide by them. There was at first some difficulty in her recognizing Eve White's parents as her own and reacting to them without reservation as a daughter. They did not, however, even at first seem entirely foreign to her in this role, as they had to Eve Black and to the original Jane. Through a slow progressive emotional realization she gradually oriented herself emotionally to her status as their daughter.

Eve White had maintained an attitude of affection and loyalty to both her parents. In relations with her mother she often seemed to be hurt and confused by attitudes and traits that she did not criticize and apparently did not understand. Evelyn impressed us as having a more realistic appraisal of the mother, as being able to recognize and accept in her elements that Eve White had reacted to with unprotesting emotional withdrawal. None of Eve Black's careless scorn appeared in this daughter's feeling toward her parents. Despite certain differences and disagreements she seemed able to regard them both with warmth and respect, to see them as human beings, necessarily with imperfections, but thoroughly deserving of her love.

After the coalescence out of which she emerged, she often discussed with us the problems concerning her steadily increasing wish to marry. Earl Lancaster had come to the city to work in the construction of large and complicated chemical plants that were part of the hydrogen-bomb project. Within less than a year his task here would be completed. His profession would probably require that he move about the United States through the next fifteen or twenty years, going to various cities where the construction of chemical plants was in progress. This nomadic life which he had accepted probably played an important part in his having remained single. He was in his early thirties and had been long accustomed to the freedom of a bachelor's life.

Would it be detrimental to Bonnie's chances for happiness

if she had to grow up moving from place to place, never knowing the stability and continuity of a home in the ordinary sense? Our patient had frankly and fully discussed her strange illness with Earl, and he had assured her it made no difference to him. Yet, was it possible for this extraordinary past not to thrust itself somehow into their relations? Perhaps it would insinuate itself between them in the transient breach of some minor quarrel and, taking root, grow malignantly. Lacking some part, or, to a degree, some dimension of the experience most women of her age had acquired, would she be able to fill the role of a wife adequately? She was convinced that Earl wanted Bonnie with them, that he would do his best to raise her as his own child. Having lived so long in the full independence of a single man, would he be able, in the multitudinous small stresses of daily living, to accept this little girl without reservation? With her own medical history and with all that had happened to confuse Bonnie and make her insecure and distort her growth, would it be too big and too difficult a responsibility to let any man take, even one whom she regarded as so wise and admirable?

These were questions to which reasoning alone could furnish no certain and no altogether satisfactory answers. She knew she must feel along these questions into the future, hoping for assurance at last that what she most desired was possible and right. Finding herself, at least for the time being, with the whole of a life instead of the fractional existence led by Jane and the two Eves, she reached out with keen interest, and usually in the company of Earl, toward all the normal and ordinary little satisfactions of daily existence.

Almost a year after her divorce, Earl found that he was to be transferred sooner than he had foreseen, that he must leave within a week for a distant city. Evelyn's new existence had grown about him as ivy finds its way about a supporting tree. The prospect of his absence filled her with sadness and empty dread.

Prompted more by the intensification of their emotional relation than by any new facts or reasons, they decided to wait no longer but to marry without delay. She deferred the step only long enough to visit her parents in order to inform them and ask their blessing; and she felt she must talk over her decision with Bonnie. The little girl would remain for the present with her grandparents. After they were settled in the distant city ... if she could maintain her health ... if she did not fail in her marriage—she dared not say it to herself as if she were counting on it to come true.

Now after almost a year and a half of marriage she sat talking with us. Her voice, her face, and general appearance, her personal mannerisms and her posture were clearly those of the Evelyn we had first known after the sudden disappearance of Eve White, Eve Black, and Jane. When she stood and walked it was not with quite the identical stateliness that had so clearly distinguished Jane. She looked stronger, in far better health, than when we last saw her. She had in fact gained twelve pounds. This, and her greater animation and energy lent to her figure and her movements something that recalled a little more definitely than before her marriage the memory of Eve Black's exuberant physical appearance. Actually she had not changed in such a way as to become more like any *one* of the preceding three in thought, gesture, or outlook, than she was before she left our city. She was unquestionably a better-looking, a far more attractive woman than we had ever seen before.

She did not wear stockings when she came back to see us. Neither Eve White nor Jane had complained of any irritation from nylon; but Eve Black, as we have noted, scratched her legs and complained that the stockings Eve White put on caused itching. Before the resolution occurred, we had all three personalities tested for allergy to nylon. No objective sensitivity was found in any one of them. But, after her marriage and long after the resolution or coalescence, Evelyn developed a severe rash. She consulted her local physician and he found in her a specific and serious allergic sensitivity to nylon. From then on, she wore cotton underclothes and stockings of some material that contained no nylon.

We learned from her letters that she and Earl had not immediately reacted according to the old formula by which people are said to marry and, in uncomplicated simplicity, live happily thereafter. She had written to us often during the first troubled months after the marriage, and twice during that time had traveled hundreds of miles for conferences with the therapist. Mrs. Lancaster's difficulties seemed to have little or no relation to the old problems of Eve White and Eve Black. They were for the most part reactions to the inevitably subtle, paradoxical, and scarcely less than magic process through which man and woman either achieve the valid goal of love as sexual mates or fail miserably and find disillusion in what had seemed so rich and bright a promise.

Aside from overt marital disasters there are less obvious failures, of great concern to the psychiatrist, that are regarded by both husband and wife as reasonably successful unions. Perhaps a brief illustration of such a marriage will convey some realization of the complexities and obstacles that our patient found it necessary to avoid in order to feel the security of love.

Let us consider a relation in which a good deal of basic affection and reciprocal respect persists. The man provides well for his family and remains technically true to his wife. The couple feel they have much in common through their interest in the children. Such a husband may even say he has the finest wife in the world and take pride in the fact that she does not object to frequent "nights out with the boys." He avoids illicit entanglements with other women and confines himself in his pleasure to stag barbecues, class reunions, the poker club, and Saturday afternoon golf with male friends. Amiably he agrees to stay at home with the children when the wife goes out on Thursday night to play bridge with seven other wives, or when she attends meetings of The Circle, a group of fifteen women who gather regularly to discuss politics, literature, mental health, or sociology. When friends call during the evening highballs are served and enjoyed. It has been years, however, since either he or his wife has felt it would be appropriate for them to have even one drink just with each other, or otherwise to expend resources of intimacy or festivity when only the two of them are together.

There are times when such a man and woman put on evening clothes and attend a party together. If they go in the car with another couple, the two husbands sit together on the front seat. The wives find nothing unnatural in this and welcome the chance to share the back seat and chatter freely to each other about who was at the supermarket this morning and how hard Junior is on shoes. It is during the hours when her husband is at home with her that she applies face packs and chin straps to maintain the fresh beauty that indeed is hers. This, no doubt, is logical, for her husband is desultorily reading the newspaper or, for the want of something better to do, trying out various channels on the television set. It has been years since he looked at her steadily with the mute yearning and delight that was habitual while they were engaged.

Having accepted the popular opinion that a man and woman who have been married for some years may love each other, but that for them to *be in love* is impossible and ridiculous, she does not grieve particularly over the change. She takes pride in her looks and at the dance is reassured by the appreciative glances of various men. Her real sense of triumph comes, however, from the realization that her uncommonly voluptuous figure, her hair-do and her becoming and expensive gown have passed the critical scrutiny of other women and have even excited among them admiration not entirely free of envy. She is very careful to make the most of her lustrous hair and always sleeps with it done up in pin curls on the nights before she attends meetings of her garden club or the League of Women Voters. The last time she and her husband had sexual relations she felt pleased that she was able to conceal her irritation when he inadvertently tore the tight net she wore over these carefully guarded ringlets.

This husband and wife quarrel very little. He is devoted to her very much as an eighteen-year-old boy is devoted to the mother who sees that his clothes are pressed and that his steak is tender. Such a devoted son is likely to seek what he finds most delightful and exciting away from home and not in the company of his mother, who has her own domestic preoccupations. So, too, such a husband regards the woman he married as a fine and necessary figure in the background of his more personal life and his more stirring interests. They nearly always call each other *Daddy* and *Mother* but without any undertone or overtone of playfulness to convey that there is between them an important direct relation in addition to the pleasantly matter-of-fact relation they maintain chiefly through a vivid interest in their children.

In such a marriage as this the primary deficiency lies not in a localized sexual inadequacy on the part of husband or wife, but rather in the failure of originally strong satisfactions to be accompanied or followed by a more general development of intimacy and joy in the sharing of self and of life. Poets have written of *love's sad satiety*, and many have assumed that the glowing promise a normal and imaginative boy reads in the eyes of his sweetheart must, after varying periods of illusion, prove in the end to be false.

Often syndicated columnists in the newspapers who give advice on personal problems warn their readers against the foolish idea that marriage holds any prospect at all for genuine fulfillment of the bright hopes of love. Wives are often advised to consider themselves fortunate if their husbands are sober, peaceable, and industrious, and are gently reprimanded for hoping to find in them anything like a sweetheart or a genuinely stirred admirer. These commentators are undoubtedly correct in the opinion that no life can maintain a summit of breathless and uninterrupted rapture. But they seem to forget that, despite this, love can be real, that it can grow to proportions never dreamed of by those who know only the spectacular features of its onset.

Both Evelyn and Earl Lancaster had hope and need of something from each other that is lacking in such a relation as that of the husband and wife mentioned above. He did not decide to marry because it was the usual thing for a man to do, or primarily to find himself some day with a home and children. Now several years past thirty, he had grown accustomed to the life he had led for over a decade.

He had vaguely hoped to encounter some day a girl he would want to marry; but as the years passed he became more discriminating, more wary about the risks of disillusionment. He had grown to accept his solitary life as a bachelor and regard it as preferable to many of the marriages he had seen. The unhappiness or the incompleteness of a relation between husband and wife is often demonstrated to the bystander, whereas the most genuine and deep fulfillment of those in love can never be conveyed to another. Perhaps without ever formulating it precisely, he had come to the firm conclusion that he must be on guard against any attachment that might lead him into such relations as we have tried to illustrate fragmentarily in the hypothetical husband and wife mentioned above.

Evelyn also found herself truly in need of something that she could not accurately define. Probably no one can put into precise words exactly what she hoped for. People appear to vary immensely in the degree to which they must

229

share the central privacy of being with the sexual mate, the degree to which they commit what is most centrally the self into the keeping of another. Those doomed to spend their lives in extreme isolation have occasionally in fragmentary emotional utterance hit upon inexact and literally inarticulate language that may reflect illogically a glimmer or hint of the needs that love can evoke.

Many men and women seem reasonably contented in marriage with a level of intimacy that to another would seem scarcely more than what might be expected in a casual acquaintance. Though often warm-hearted, jovial, and free in talking about their more external feelings and affairs, it would seem to such people distasteful, absurdly unnatural, perhaps even psychotic to offer or accept the sort of emotional closeness, the total and open commitment of nuclear self, that another, otherwise similar, person would be lost and desolate if he did not attain.

What our patient needed to find in her marriage probably cannot ever be obtained ready-made. Apparently it must be developed out of an interaction of lives, out of sorrow, misunderstanding, and despair no less than out of pleasure. There is no need to describe or enumerate the many incidents during which hurt and misunderstanding arose. Nor could we say how these troubles might have been avoided. Perhaps it was necessary that they be suffered in order for the growth of understanding and of love to be possible.

When Earl Lancaster talked with us at the time we last interviewed Evelyn a few days ago, he said that it made him feel very foolish to remember the attitude he had held about many small matters during the first months after the marriage.

"It wasn't until about a year ago," Evelyn told us the last time we saw her in the office, "that I found I was sure he really wanted me. And it wasn't until then that I could understand what had been the matter before. It's something there isn't any way of explaining. I suppose I just had to learn something from inside of me that you can't get to know in a hurry. And no matter what anybody might do, there's no way for it to come except by growing."

No, Mrs. Lancaster told us, sexual relations had not been really satisfactory during the first months of her marriage. She had tried to let Earl feel it was better for her than she found it. She had tried also to make herself think this. She had hoped so much that she could be all that he longed for in this respect. She found herself unable to do anything directly to make this better. The change did not occur until a broader change all through their personal relations had come. But for a year now this had been exactly right for them both. In our discussion with Earl we found that he had realized his wife's inability at first to fully enjoy their physical love relations. He had no doubt at all that this had changed, and felt confident the happiness they had worked out in this was secure and would now continue.

Bonnie had come to stay with them for visits a few times after they had been settled for a month or two. After six months she came to remain for two weeks. When the time came for the child to return to her grandparents she seemed more reluctant than before to part with her mother. Earl, whose business required a trip into that section, drove her in the car to the grandparents' home. She seemed entirely reconciled to the fact that she must go back. After her suitcase had been brought into the house and he had visited a while with Evelyn's mother and father, he said good-by and went toward the car.

The little girl now, to his astonishment, broke into a run toward him, "Daddy," she cried, "oh, Daddy, I want to go back with you. Please . . . please Daddy, take me too."

Her feelings impressed the grandparents. They profoundly moved Earl Lancaster. He swept her up in his arms and held her very close. He had not realized until that moment that she had been able to accept him in the role he hoped some day to win. Since then Bonnie has remained with her mother and her new father.

After long discussions with the patient and with her husband, separately and together, we felt that, particularly during the past year, she must have made admirable progress. We cannot of course say that this progress will continue; but after being with her again, we felt that the happiness she expressed was genuine. We are convinced that she has been able to make a happy life for her husband and her child. Will all this endure?

Three testings with the semantic differential have been made, since, instead of three personalities, only one remained for observation. The first of these showed changes that definitely suggested improvement, that were more in keeping with the responses of a normal and healthy person. But one test administered almost a year after marriage was far from encouraging. Its results were consistent with an increasing degree of emotional disorder. It is of particular interest to note that some of the responses on this occasion showed considerable resemblance to those of Eve Black when she was active. Our co-workers point out, however, that in this second test of Evelyn Lancaster "the *concepts* are still placed in the socially approved regions of the space, unlike Eve Black."[23] The last test was administered at approximately the time of our recent interview with Evelyn. The changes this time, though not conclusive, indicated improvement. There was nothing, however, that paralleled the encouraging gains reported by Mrs. Lancaster and her husband and which seemed to us so impressive clinically. Is this improvement deep and quite real, or is it more superficial than it seemed to the patient and her husband, and to us? Only time can give us this answer.

Osgood, who has so generously and effectively contributed to our work with this patient by conducting the investigation with the semantic differential tests, still finds in the most recent material some points that suggest a doubtful prognosis. Though the last test was in many respects better, there were responses that might indicate "a kind of rigidly controlled normalcy—meeting the external requirements but not internalizing them."[23] Pointing out that he is considering this patient he has never seen from a point approximately a thousand miles away and without information about what life-history events precede, coincide with, or follow the changes in the tests, he has to conclude that, judging by the tests alone, one cannot feel entirely confident about her future. What Osgood and Luria were able to estimate by their blind analysis of the responses of Eve White, Eve Black, and Jane impressed us as so remarkable that we cannot fail to consider very seriously this recent appraisal of our patient by their methods.

Whether or not Evelyn Lancaster will continue to enjoy a happy life we are unable to predict. Whatever may come, there seems to us little doubt that she has already won her way to a kind of victory against unusual odds that, however long it may be held, is truly remarkable. No life lasts forever. If the integration she somehow achieved breaks and she becomes unable to fill her present role, we shall nevertheless remember that she reached a goal of love and fulfillment that many people, even without the strange and formidable handicaps that beset her, never know. Be it win, lose, or draw—can we withhold from her our admiration? Though we cannot predict, we can prayerfully wish her well and hope the love she at last forged from what she found in herself and in another can sustain her against whatever destructive forces may still threaten her now beautiful integration.

BIBLIOGRAPHY

1. Walker, Kenneth: "The Strange Case of Miss Beauchamp," *London Courier*, May, 1955, pp. 67-72
2. Taylor, W. S., and M. F. Martin: "Multiple Personality," *Journal of Abnormal and Social Psychology*, 39: 281-300 (1944)
3. Prince, Morton: *The Dissociation of a Personality*, Longmans, Green and Company, Inc., New York, 1906
4. Barrett, W. F.: *Psychical Research*, Williams and Norgate, Ltd., London, 1921
5. Salter, W. H.: "Psychical Research," *Encyclopaedia Britannica*, 18:668-672, Chicago, 1949
6. McDougall, William: *An Outline of Abnormal Psychology*, Methuen and Company, Ltd., London, 1926, p. 497
7. Muncie, Wendell: *Psychobiology and Psychiatry*, 2d ed., The C. V. Mosby Company, St. Louis, 1948
8. Strecker, E. A., F. G. Ebaugh, and J. R. Ewalt: *Practical Clinical Psychiatry*, 7th ed., P. Blakiston's Son & Company, Philadelphia, 1951
9. Henderson, D. K., and R. D. Gillespie: *A Textbook of Psychiatry*, 6th ed., Oxford University Press, London, 1947
10. Noyes, A. P.: *Modern Clinical Psychiatry*, 3d ed., W. B. Saunders Company, Philadelphia, 1948
11. Erickson, M. H., and L. S. Kubie: "The Permanent Relief of an Obsessional Phobia by Means of Communication with an Unsuspected Dual Personality," *Psychoanalytic Quarterly*, 8:471-509 (1939)
12. Masserman, J. H.: *The Practice of Dynamic Psychiatry*, W. B. Saunders Company, Philadelphia, 1955, p. 386
13. *Ibid.*, p. 592
14. Thigpen, C. H., and H. Cleckley: "A Case of Multiple Personality," *Journal of Abnormal and Social Psychology*, 49:135-151 (1954)
15. Hubbard, Ron L.: *Dianetics*, Hermitage House, Inc., New York, 1950
16. Cleckley, Hervey M., and Corbett H. Thigpen: "The Dynamics of Illusion," *American Journal of Psychiatry*, 112:334-342 (1955)
17. Prince, Morton: *Clinical and Experimental Studies in Personality*, Sci-Art Publishers, Cambridge, Mass., 1929

18. Osgood, C. E., and Z. Luria: "A Blind Analysis of a Case of Multiple Personality Using the Semantic Differential," *Journal of Abnormal and Social Psychology*, 49:579-591 (1954)
19. McDougall, Wm.: *An Outline of Abnormal Psychology*, pp. 541-543
20. *Ibid.*, pp. 546-548
21. *Ibid.*, p. 552
22. Prince, Morton: *The Dissociation of a Personality*, p. 524
23. Osgood, C. E.: Personal communication
24. Adler, Alfred: *The Neurotic Constitution*, Kegan Paul, Trench, Trubner & Company, Ltd., London, 1921
25. Clark, R. A.: *Six Talks on Jung's Psychology*, The Boxwood Press, Pittsburgh, Pennsylvania, 1953
26. Freud, S.: *The Interpretations of Dreams*, The Macmillan Company, New York, 1932, pp. 336-342
27. Brown, J. F.: *The Psychodynamics of Abnormal Behavior*, McGraw-Hill Book Company, Inc., New York, 1940, pp. 224-228
28. Brunswick, Ruth M.: "The Preoedipal Phase of the Libido Development," in Robert Fliess (ed.), *The Psychoanalytic Reader*, International Universities Press, Inc., New York, 1948, pp. 261-284
29. Healey, W., A. F. Bronner, and A. M. Bowers: *The Structure and Meaning of Psychoanalysis*, Alfred A. Knopf, Inc., New York, 1938, pp. 151-155
30. Baruch, Dorothy: *One Little Boy*, Julian Press, Inc., New York, 1952
31. London, L. S.: "Mechanisms in Paranoia," *Psychoanalytic Quarterly*, 18:394-412 (1931)
32. Masserman, J. H.: "Faith and Delusion in Psychotherapy, The Ur-Defenses of Man," *American Journal of Psychiatry*, 110:324-333 (1953)
33. Masserman, J. H.: *Principles of Dynamic Psychiatry*, W. B. Saunders Company, Philadelphia, 1946, pp. 92-97
34. Thompson, Clara: *Psychoanalysis: Evolution and Development*, Hermitage House, Inc., New York, 1950
35. Allen, Clifford: *Modern Discoveries in Medical Psychology*, Macmillan and Company, Ltd., London, 1937, p. 113
36. Jones, Ernest: Editorial Preface, Freud's *Collected Papers*, Hogarth Press, Ltd., London, 1940
37. Freud, Sigmund: "From the History of an Infantile Neurosis," *Collected Papers*, Hogarth Press, Ltd., London, 1943, vol. 3, pp. 473-605
38. ——: *The Problem of Anxiety*, W. W. Norton & Company, Inc., New York, 1936, p. 38

39. Peerbolte, M. L.: "Psychotherapeutic Evaluations of Birth-Trauma Analysis," *Psychiatric Quarterly*, 25:589-603 (1951)
40. Fodor, Nandor: "The Search for the Beloved," *Psychiatric Quarterly*, 20:549-602 (1946)
41. Kelsey, D. E. R.: "Phantasies of Birth and Prenatal Experiences Recovered from Patients Undergoing Hypnoanalysis," *The Journal of Mental Science*, 99:216-223 (1953)

ADDENDUM

Since the original report of this case at the American Psychiatric Association meeting in Los Angeles in May, 1953, we have been asked many times by psychiatrists and psychologists what type of therapy we employed. In general what these people want to know is what psychological theory was followed—whether we treated this patient by Freudian, neo-Freudian, Jungian, or other methods of depth psychology; whether we adhered in principles of ego psychology or perhaps proceeded along Meyerian, Adlerian, nondirective, or Stekelian lines. When we answered that we did not deliberately follow any of these specific schools of thought or theories of practice, many of our questioners were bewildered.

It has for so long been customary to cloak what is not yet known about emotional illness in profuse polysyllabic or neologistic verbiage that many seem to feel it is unprogressive or unscientific to do otherwise. Much of what occurred in the relations between this patient and her therapist probably differed little in essential quality from what often occurred between the country doctor of former days and some of his patients. It is unlikely that many of these general practitioners were able to spend so many hours with a single patient, to be sure; but the inadequately defined relation between them and their emotionally troubled patients probably represents the therapy employed in this case better than the rigidly schematized and overformulated verbalizations often used in the current literature to account for still imperfectly understood processes. One prominent psychoanalyst said, "Though you fellows didn't know just what you were doing, you were really practicing ego psychology." Perhaps we were.

Over the years we have followed with interest the various schools of thought in psychiatry and psychology. Almost all these systems make some sense theoretically. Most of them have some wise principles. Unfortunately, in most theories there are also many unrealistic concepts that must be accepted on the basis of faith rather than evidence. More unfortunately, some of the most strongly held articles of belief often prove to be of little use in helping the actual patient. And to all physicians this must remain the major objective.

In retrospect is seems to us that several factors played a

part in the relief of our patient, in the termination of her unusual dissociation:

(1) All three of the personality manifestations established a relation with the therapist that was apparently utilized to diminish the basic conflict of tendencies represented by Mrs. White and Eve Black.

(2) Jane, as a newly organized entity without ordinary experience, probably felt toward the therapist in some important respects as a young child feels toward her parents. She found in him uncritical acceptance and understanding as she worked to orient herself adequately to her surroundings and discover more practical patterns of behavior and more realistic goals than those pursued by the other two contrasting functional units.

(3) During many months of contact with the therapist the rebellious Eve Black encountered no active condemnation or punitive opposition to furnish stimulus toward the continuation of her revolt. It seems likely that inner changes in the patient never discernible in Eve Black herself may have sapped the originally strong incentives toward a shallow and irresponsible pursuit of amusement at the cost of all other objectives.

(4) The persistent attempt by the therapist to offer understanding seemed to help Eve White continue to work despite her difficulties.

(5) The painstaking review of Mrs. White's past, in which she explored the events and emotional experiences of her early years, accompanied so to speak by the therapist, perhaps contributed to gradual diminution of the severity of repression or dissociation.

(6) When Jane fell in love, a very strong incentive toward progress came into play. A goal more promising and more appealing than any goal clearly discernible to Mrs. White or Eve Black gradually shaped itself in her awareness.

(7) The passage of time with the influence of intrinsic biologic factors toward repair, reintegration, and growth may have played an important part in the outcome.

Many other factors, some of them never clearly discernible to us, may have contributed to this patient's recovery. We say again that we do not know if Mrs. Lancaster will stay well. We do not believe that any psychiatrist could accurately make such a statement about any patient. At this date our patient appears to be happy, not merely at superficial levels but in a meaningful experiencing of love, and of life.

APPENDIX A

CASE REPORT*

*A blind analysis of a case of multiple personality
using the sematic differential*

CHARLES E. OSGOOD *and* ZELLA LURIA
University of Illinois

For more than a year the writers have been collecting semantic data from patients undergoing psychotherapy. This
has been feasible through the cooperation of psychotherapists in various parts of the country. When the manuscript
of "A Case of Multiple Personality"[3] arrived, the editor of
this journal, without our knowledge, suggested to Thigpen
and Cleckley that it would be interesting to have semantic
data from each of the "personalities" in their patient. Thigpen and Cleckley accepted the suggestion and administered
a form of the differential we have been using for this purpose to their patient in each of her three personalities. The
editor also suggested that we might see how much these
semantic data would allow us to infer about the patient
without our having any knowledge of the case history,
protocol, or prognisis.† This appeared to be a useful and
rather intriguing way to estimate the validity and sensitivity
of this instrument. If we could infer descriptions of the three
personalities which correspond with clinical observations,
and if we could make reasonably accurate interpretations
and predictions, we would be encouraged to continue our
efforts to improve the semantic differential as a clinical tool.

* Reprinted from *The Journal of Abnormal and Social Psychology*, Vol. 49, No. 4, October, 1954. Copyright 1954 by American
Psychological Association. Printed in U.S.A.

† We wish to thank Dr. J. McV. Hunt, editor of this journal, for
utilizing the opportunity presented by the work of Thigpen and
Cleckley to arrange for the data in this study, for suggesting the
blind analysis, and for his general encouragement. We are also
very grateful to Drs. Thigpen and Cleckley for giving the semantic
differential to their patient and for their interest in the instrument.

THE SEMANTIC DIFFERENTIAL

The semantic differential is a combination of association and scaling procedures designed to give an objective measure of the connotative meaning of concepts. The underlying logic[1] can be summarized as follows: (*a*) The process of description or judgment can be conceived as the allocation of a concept to a set of experimental continua defined by pairs of polar terms. Thus the connotative meaning of a linguistically complex assertion, such as "My father has always been a rather submissive person," can be at least partially represented as

MY FATHER active——:——:——:——$\overset{X}{:——}$:——:——passive

MY FATHER soft——:$\overset{X}{——}$:——:——:——:——:——hard

The greater the strength of association, e.g., ". . . . extremely submissive, a regular doormat," the more polarized, toward 1 or 7, the allocation.[2] Since may scales of judgment are highly intercorrelated (e.g., *good-bad, fair-unfair, honest-dishonest, kind-cruel*, and so forth all reflect mainly the single "evaluative" factor in judgments), a limited number of such continua can be used to define a semantic space within which the connotative meaning of any concept can be specified. This clearly indicates some variant of factor analysis as the basic methodology in developing such an instrument. Two such analyses have been completed both providing evidence for three general factors, "evaluation," "potency," and "activity," and some unknown number of specific factors that are probably denotative in nature.

The form of semantic differential we have been using in studying psychotherapy is based on this factor analytic work. In the 10 scales used, it gives approximately equal weight to the first three factors isolated. These scales and their factor loadings are given in Table 1. The 15 concepts used in this form of the differential were selected after consultation with clinicians and pretesting for their differentiating power. Ideally, they should sample the major persons and problems involved in therapy-in-general; we are not entirely satisfied with the present set, however, and more work should be done here. The concepts used are also shown in Table 1. In the test form itself, concepts are rotated against scales in such a way that each concept appears once with each scale, but with a maximum interval between successive appearances of both. The subject is instructed to do his checking rapidly, without struggling over particular items, to give his "immediate impressions." A 150-item form such as this usually takes less than 10 minutes to complete.

Recording the raw data for a single subject on a single testing yields a matrix of N columns (here, 15 concepts) and i rows (here, 10 scales). The *meaning* of a particular concept to the subject, as defined by the operations of measurement here, is the profile of numbers in its column (or, more efficiently, the position in the n-dimensional space defined by the projection of these numbers onto the factors). *Difference in meaning* for two concepts is defined by the distance between their positions in this space, as computed

TABLE 1: *Concepts and scales used in this analysis*

Concepts		
LOVE	MENTAL	SELF-CON-
CHILD	SICKNESS	TROL
MY DOCTOR	MY MOTHER	HATRED
ME	PEACE OF	MY FATHER
MY JOB	MIND	CONFUSION
	FRAUD	SEX
	MY SPOUSE	

Scales and Their Factor Loadings			
Scales	Evaluation	Activity	Potency
valuable-worthless	.79	.13	.04
clean-dirty	.82	.03	−.05
tasty-distasteful	.77	−.11	.05
fast-slow	.01	.70	.00
active-passive	.14	.59	.04
hot-cold	−.04	.49	−.06
large-small	.06	.34	.62
strong-weak	.19	.20	.62
deep-shallow	.27	.14	.46
tense-relaxed	−.55	.37	−.12

by the generalized distance formula, $D = \sqrt{\Sigma d^2}$, in which d is the difference in allocation of the two concepts on a single scale.[2] The more similar any two concepts are in connotative meaning, the smaller will be the value of D. *Change in meaning* (of the same concept at different times during therapy, or in different "personalities") can be defined by the same operation, except that d here refers to the difference in allocation of the same concept on the same scale at different testings. The mathematical properties of this formula also allow us to represent the semantic structure of an individual in a concise form; computation of the distance, D, of every concept from every other concept yields an N/N matrix (here, 15/15) of distances which have the property of plotting within a space having dimensionability equal to the number of factors. To the extent that the individual subject being studied uses the same three factors isolated in our general factor work, his data will plot accurately in three dimensions.

THE SEMANTIC DATA

At this point we should state exactly what information we have about this case. We know that we are dealing with a case of triple personality, and these have been labeled for us (presumably by the therapists who collected the semantic data) "Eve White," "Eve Black," and "Jane." We suppose the "White" and "Black" have some connotative significance —certainly, as will be seen, the quantitative semantic data distinguish sharply between them. We also know, of course, that the patient is a woman, presumably participating in some kind of therapy; we do not know the stage of therapy or whether or not she is hospitalized. We considered it also fair to ask (from J. McV. Hunt) about the following items of sociological status, because they contribute to the meaningful interpretation of certain concepts: Concept CHILD—does this woman have a child? Yes, she does. Concept SPOUSE-is this woman married? Yes, she is. Concepts FATHER and MOTHER—are her parents alive? The mother is, but Hunt doesn't know about the father. Concept MY JOB—has this woman had a job outside of homekeeping? Yes, she has. This is the sum total of our external information about the case.

The semantic differential was given to this woman twice while "in" each of her three personalities; a period of about 2 moments intervened between the two testings. The raw semantic data for each of the three personalities are given in Tables 2-4. The roman numerals I and II refer to first and second testings respectively.* We take the space to give these raw data in full so that anyone who is interested may study them and test any particular "hypotheses" about the case he wishes. Low values in these tables indicate judgments toward the polar term on the left and high values judgments toward the polar term on the right. The data in these tables show the semantic profiles, or meanings, of each concept at each testing and while "in" each personality. Since the form given at each testing was actually a double form (each item repeated once), we were able to estimate the reliability of these data. The immediate test-retest reliability coefficients for each of the testings are as follows: Eve White I, .82; Eve

* These values are actually averages of two check marks, a double form of the semantic differential having been used for reliability purposes. In this double form, each item appears twice.

	LOVE		MY CHILD		MY DOCTOR		ME		MY JOB		MENTAL SICKNESS		MY MOTHER		PEACE OF MIND		FRAUD		MY SPOUSE		SELF-CONTROL		HATRED		MY FATHER		CONFUSION		SEX		
	I	II	I	II	I	II	I	II	I	II	I	II	I	II	I	II	I	II	I	II	I	II	I	II	I	II	I	II	I	II	
cold	5.0	5.5	4.0	6.0	6.0	5.0	5.0	4.0	4.0	3.5	5.0	4.0	5.5	4.0	1.5	6.0	5.5	4.0	1.0	2.5	4.0	5.0	1.0	1.0	6.0	5.0	1.0	4.0	3.5	2.0	hot
valuable	1.0	1.0	4.0	3.5	1.0	1.6	4.0	6.0	1.0	1.0	4.0	1.0	1.0	1.0	4.0	7.0	7.0	1.0	1.0	7.0	1.0	1.0	7.0	1.0	1.0	6.0	3.0	5.5	2.5	4.5	worthless
tense	4.0	2.5	4.0	7.0	7.0	7.0	1.0	1.0	4.0	6.0	1.0	2.0	1.0	1.0	5.3	3.5	7.0	6.5	1.0	1.0	4.0	5.5	5.0	3.0	1.0	1.5	1.0	1.0	3.0	5.5	relaxed
small	7.0	6.0	1.0	7.0	7.0	7.0	1.0	2.0	5.5	6.5	7.0	6.5	5.5	7.0	7.0	6.0	1.0	1.0	1.0	1.0	5.0	3.0	1.0	1.5	6.0	1.0	4.5	2.5			large
fast	7.0	4.5	3.5	2.0	3.0	2.0	5.5	6.0	7.0	6.0	7.0	6.0	1.0	2.0	7.0	7.0	1.0	2.0	7.0	3.0	4.0	2.0	2.0	7.0	5.0	6.0	2.5				slow
dirty	7.0	7.0	7.0	7.0	5.5	6.0	7.0	7.0	5.5	6.5	7.0	2.0	5.5	6.5	7.0	6.5	1.0	1.0	4.0	4.0	7.0	3.0	1.0	1.0	5.0	4.0	4.0				clean
weak	7.0	5.0	7.0	7.0	7.0	1.0	5.5	6.0	7.0	0.5	7.0	2.0	7.0	6.5	7.0	7.0	1.0	1.0	5.0	4.5	6.5	7.0	1.0	1.0	7.0	7.0	1.5	6.0	5.5	3.0	strong
tasty	1.0	2.0	1.0	1.0	3.0	5.5	1.0	1.5	7.0	5.0	1.0	1.0	5.5	1.5	7.0	6.5	7.0	1.0	5.0	4.5	1.0	1.0	1.5	1.0	7.0	7.0	1.5	6.0	4.0	2.5	distasteful
deep	1.0	2.0	1.0	1.0	1.0	1.5	7.0	0.5	1.0	1.0	3.0	5.5	1.0	1.5	7.0	7.0	1.0	1.0	5.0	3.5	1.0	2.0	4.0	1.0	7.0	7.0	1.0	1.5	4.5	5.5	shallow
active	1.0	2.5	1.0	1.0	1.0	1.5	4.0	5.0	3.5	4.0	1.0	1.0	7.0	6.5	4.0	2.0	4.5	4.5	1.0	2.0	2.5	3.5	1.0	2.0	2.5	1.0	1.0	1.5	4.0	5.0	passive

	LOVE		MY CHILD		MY DOCTOR		ME		MY JOB		MENTAL SICKNESS		MY MOTHER		PEACE OF MIND		FRAUD		MY SPOUSE		SELF-CONTROL		HATRED		MY FATHER		CONFUSION		SEX		
	I	II	I	II	I	II	I	II	I	II	I	II	I	II	I	II	I	II	I	II	I	II	I	II	I	II	I	II	I	II	
cold	4.0	1.0	7.0	7.0	7.0	1.0	1.0	1.0	1.0	1.5	6.5	6.0	2.5	1.0	3.5	2.0	6.0	6.0	7.0	6.5	4.0	1.0	1.0	1.0	hot
valuable	7.0	7.0	7.0	6.0	1.0	1.0	1.0	1.0	4.5	2.5	1.0	3.0	2.0	2.0	7.0	1.0	4.5	4.5	1.5	2.0	1.0	7.0	7.0	7.0	worthless
tense	1.0	1.0	1.5	7.0	7.0	7.0	4.0	1.0	2.5	1.0	7.0	6.5	6.0	6.0	4.0	2.0	2.0	6.5	5.0	1.0	1.0	2.0	1.5	1.0	relaxed
small	1.0	1.0	7.0	1.0	7.0	7.0	4.0	3.5	1.0	4.0	4.5	7.0	5.5	5.5	2.5	1.0	6.0	4.5	6.5	6.0	1.0	2.0	1.5	1.0	large
fast	7.0	1.0	7.0	7.0	4.0	7.0	5.5	1.0	4.0	1.0	7.0	5.5	5.6	6.5	2.5	1.0	6.0	4.5	6.5	6.6	4.0	1.5	1.0	1.0	slow
tense	7.0	1.0	4.0	3.5	1.0	1.0	7.0	7.0	1.0	1.0	1.0	1.5	1.5	7.0	6.5	2.0	1.5	4.0	1.5	4.5	1.5	4.0	5.5	slow
dirty	2.0	2.0	1.0	3.0	7.0	7.0	4.0	1.0	7.0	6.0	5.0	6.0	4.0	1.0	4.5	4.5	6.0	6.5	7.0	7.0	1.5	1.0	4.0	1.0	clean

weak	1.0 1.0	7.0 1.5	7.0 7.0	1.0 1.0	4.0 7.0	7.0 1.0	1.0 4.0	7.0 7.0	6.0 6.0	6.0 4.0	5.0 5.0	1.0 4.0	1.0 1.0	1.0 1.0	strong
tasty	7.0 7.0	7.0 6.0	1.5 1.0	1.0 1.0	7.0 7.0	7.0 5.5	2.0 2.0	5.5 7.0	1.0 1.5	2.0 4.0	7.0 2.0	4.0 4.0	7.0 7.0		distasteful
deep	7.0 7.0	7.0 2.5	1.0 1.0	1.0 1.0	7.0 7.0	7.0 1.0	1.0 1.0	1.5 2.0	4.0 7.0	2.0 1.5	1.5 1.5	4.0 1.0	7.0 7.0		shallow
active	7.0 7.0	7.0 1.0	1.0 1.0	1.0 1.0	7.0 7.0	7.0 1.0	1.0 1.0	1.5 1.5	7.0 4.5	4.0 1.5	1.5 1.0	4.0 1.5	1.5 7.0	7.0	passive

Table 4: Raw data for Jane

	LOVE	CHILD	MY DOCTOR	ME	MY JOB	MENTAL SICK-NESS	MY MOTHER	PEACE OF MIND	FRAUD	MY SPOUSE	SELF-CONTROL	HATRED	MY FATHER	CON-FUSION	SEX	
	I II	I II	I II	I II	I II	I II	I II	I II	I II	I II	I II	I II	I II	I II	I II	
cold	4.0 6.0	4.0 6.5	4.0 6.5	4.0 5.5	4.0 6.0	4.0 4.0	4.5 4.5	4.0 6.5	1.0 2.0	4.0 6.0	4.0 6.0	1.0 1.5	6.0 6.5	4.0 4.5	4.0 6.5	hot
valuable	1.0 1.0	1.0 1.0	1.0 1.0	4.0 2.0	1.0 1.0	2.0 1.0	1.0 1.0	1.0 1.0	7.0 7.0	1.0 1.0	1.0 1.0	6.0 7.0	1.0 1.0	2.5 4.0	1.0 1.0	worthless
tense	7.0 7.0	5.0 5.0	7.0 7.0	2.0 1.0	1.5 2.0	1.0 1.0	1.5 2.0	7.0 7.0	1.5 2.0	7.0 7.0	7.0 6.5	1.0 1.5	1.5 2.0	7.0 7.0	1.0 1.5	relaxed
small	7.0 7.0	7.0 7.0	4.0 4.5	7.0 6.5	7.0 6.5	1.5 2.0	5.5 6.5	7.0 7.0	4.5 1.5	7.0 7.0	7.0 7.0	4.5 2.0	7.0 7.0	6.0 4.0	6.5 7.0	large
fast	7.0 6.5	3.0 1.5	1.0 2.0	4.5 2.0	7.0 6.5	7.0 6.5	5.5 6.5	7.0 7.0	1.5 2.0	3.0 2.5	7.0 6.0	7.0 4.0	2.0 2.0	1.5 2.0	4.0 4.0	slow
dirty	7.0 7.0	7.0 7.0	7.0 7.0	7.0 7.0	7.0 7.0	7.0 7.0	7.0 7.0	7.0 7.0	1.0 2.0	7.0 7.0	7.0 7.0	2.0 2.0	7.0 4.0	7.0 4.0	7.0 7.0	clean
weak	7.0 7.0	4.0 6.0	7.0 7.0	4.5 4.0	6.5 6.5	4.0 5.0	2.0 6.0	7.0 7.0	1.0 2.0	7.0 7.0	7.0 7.0	1.0 2.0	7.0 7.0	4.0 4.0	7.0 6.5	strong
tasty	1.0 1.0	1.0 1.0	3.5 2.0	1.0 1.0	2.0 1.0	5.0 4.0	2.0 1.0	1.0 1.0	1.0 1.0	1.0 1.0	1.0 1.0	7.0 7.0	1.0 1.0	7.0 5.5	1.0 1.5	distasteful
deep	1.0 1.0	1.0 1.5	2.0 3.0	1.0 1.5	1.0 1.5	1.0 2.0	1.0 1.5	1.0 2.0	1.0 2.0	2.0 2.0	1.0 1.5	1.0 2.0	1.0 1.5	1.0 1.5	4.0 1.0	shallow
active	2.5 1.5	1.0 1.0	2.0 1.5	4.5 2.0	1.0 1.0	1.0 1.0	1.0 1.0	5.5 2.5	6.0 4.5	4.0 1.0	2.5 2.0	2.5 2.0	4.0 1.0	1.5 2.5	4.0 1.5	passive

White II, .90; Eve Black I, .65; Eve Black II, .89; Jane I, .89; Jane II, .94. These coefficients indicate (*a*) a generally satisfactory level of reliability, (*b*) a consistent trend in all three personalities toward greater stability through time, and (*c*) that Jane is the most consistent or stable personality over short intervals of time and Eve Black is the least.

To obtain measures of semantic similarity and structure, we computed the matrices of D for each concept with every other concept, for each personality and testing. With an ordinary desk calculator and a table of square roots, these operations are very simple and rapid. In order to conserve space, the six matrices of D are not given here. These "distances" are based on application of the formula given earlier across all 10 scales. For convenience in plotting the models which appear as Fig. 1-6, the data for scales contributing to each of the three factors were averaged and new D's computed. This, in effect, forces those data into three dimensions and hence, into solid models that have no error. The very slight amount of distortion, or loss of information, resulting from this averaging process and restriction to three dimensions can be seen from the following correlations between original (10 scale) and "factor" D matrices (3 average scales): Eve White I, .91; Eve White II, .93, Eve Black I, .96; Eve Black II, .98; Jane I, .86; Jane II, .92. In other words, nearly all the variance in this woman's judgments can be accounted for in terms of three factors. Figures 1-6, then, provide quite accurate representations of the ways various concepts are related in each of the personalities; the smaller the distance between any two concepts the more similar in connotative meaning they are.

THE THREE PERSONALITIES AND THEIR CHANGES THROUGH TIME

The general assumption we are following is that "mental illness" is essentially a disordering of meanings or ways of perceiving from those characteristic of people judged "normal" in our society, and that the process of psychotherapy from the patient's point of view is essentially a reordering and changing of these meanings. Within the limitations of our type of measurement and our sampling of concepts, the locations and relations among concepts shown in Fig. 1-6 can be thought of as pictures of how this woman perceives herself, the significant people about her, and certain modes of action—when functioning "in" her several personalities.* We assume that this woman is receiving some kind of treatment

* The authors wish to thank Professor Jozef Cohen for his help in preparing these figures.

through the period covered by our two samplings, I and II, and therefore look particularly for the types of changes in meaning that are taking place in the three personalities, as well as at the general nature of their organization. For purposes of ready comparison, all of the models are oriented in respect to the concept MY DOCTOR, which stays practically con-

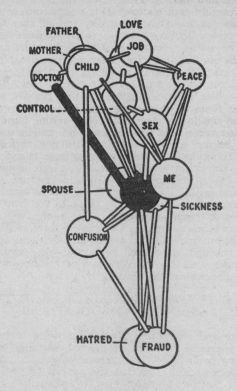

FIG. 1. Eve White I

stant in meaning (*good, strong,* and *quite active*) through both time and personalities; spatially, in the figures, *good* is up and *bad* down, *active* to the left and *passive* to the right, and *strong* is away from the viewer while *weak* is near to or toward the viewer; the solid ball represents the origin of the space, e.g., a hypothetical "meaningless" concept that would result from checking all 4's.

Semantic structures for Eve White I and II are shown in Fig. 1 and 2. The most general characterization would be that *Eve White perceives "the world" in an essentially normal fashion, is well socialized, but has an unsatisfactory attitude toward herself.* Here the usual societal "goods" are seen favorably—MY DOCTOR, MY FATHER, LOVE, SELF-CONTROL, PEACE OF MIND, and MY MOTHER are all *good* and *strong* whereas FRAUD, HATRED, and to some extent CONFUSION are *bad.* The chief evidence of disturbance in the peronality is the fact that ME (the self concept) is considered a little *bad,* a little *passive,* and definitely *weak.* Substantiating evidence is the *weakness* of her CHILD, as she sees him (or her), and the essential meaninglessness to her of MY SPOUSE and SEX. Note also the wide evaluative separation between LOVE and SEX. In the interval between testing I and II ME and SEX become more *bad* and *passive* and simultaneously become almost identical in meaning to her—and note that her conceptions of LOVE (a good, strong thing) and SEX (a bad, weak thing like herself) have moved still further apart.

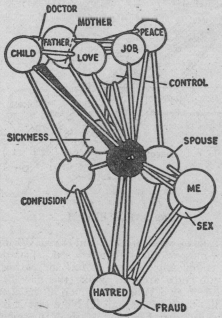

FIG. 2. Eve White II

Semantic structures for Eve Black I and II are shown in Fig. 3 and 4. The most general characterization here would be that *Eve Black has achieved a violent kind of adjustment in which she perceives herself as literally perfect, but to accomplish this break, her way of perceiving "the world" becomes completely disoriented from the norm.* The only exceptions to this dictum are MY DOCTOR and PEACE OF MIND, which maintain their *good* and *strong* characteristics, the latter, interestingly enough, also becoming *active* on II. But if Eve Black perceives herself as being *good*, then she also has to accept HATRED and FRAUD as positive values, since (we assume) she has strong hatred and is socially fraudulent. So we find a tight, but very un-normal, favorable cluster of ME,

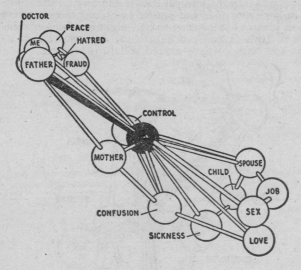

FIG. 3. Eve Black I

MY DOCTOR, PEACE OF MIND, HATRED, and FRAUD. What are positive values for most people —CHILD, MY SPOUSE, MY JOB, LOVE, and SEX—are completely rejected as *bad* and *passive*, and all of these except CHILD are also weak (this may be because CHILD was weak in Eve White and much of the change here is a simple "flip-flop" of meanings). Note that it is MOTHER in this personality that becomes relatively meaningless; FATHER, on the other hand, stays *good* but shifts completely

248

from *strong* (in Eve White) to *weak*—possible implications of these familial identific tions will be considered later. Note also that in this personality LOVE and SEX are closely identified, both as *bad, weak, passive* things.

Jane

Semantic structures for Jane I and II are shown in Fig. 5 and 6. The general characterization is that *Jane displays the most "healthy" meaning pattern, in which she accepts the usual evaluations of concepts by her society yet still maintains a satisfactory evaluation of herself.* MY FATHER, MY MOTHER, MY CHILD, and MY DOCTOR—most of the significant persons in her life—are seen as *good, strong,* and *active.* The major modes of behavior, PEACE OF MIND, LOVE, SELF-CONTROL, and MY JOB, are seen as equally *good* and *strong,* but *somewhat passive*—as if these ways of behaving and thinking were simply accepted without stress. The two socially agreed-

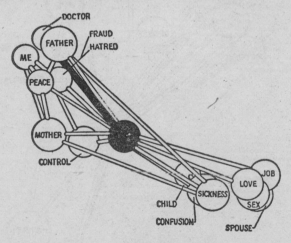

Fig. 4. Eve Black II

upon evils, HATRED and FRAUD, are put in their proper places. The most significant characteristics of Jane's meaning system, however, are these: The self concept, ME, while still not *strong* (but not *weak,* either) is nearer the *good* and *active* directions of the semantic space; note also the close identification of ME and MENTAL SICKNESS, which here is *not* an unfavorable concept to her. Her attitude toward her husband, MY SPOUSE, is for the first time meaningful (unlike Eve White) and tending toward the *good, strong, active* directions, like the other significant persons (unlike Eve Black). And LOVE and SEX (quite unlike Eve White) are both favorable and quite closely identified. The changes from testings I to II are simply such as to strengthen the "healthy" pattern evident in the first view. ME becomes considerably more *good* and *active;* MY SPOUSE for the first time becomes completely identified connotatively with MY DOCTOR and MY FATHER (and loses its tie with CONFUSION); and LOVE and SEX becomes intimately identified with each other and close in meaning to SELF-CONTROL, and PEACE OF MIND.

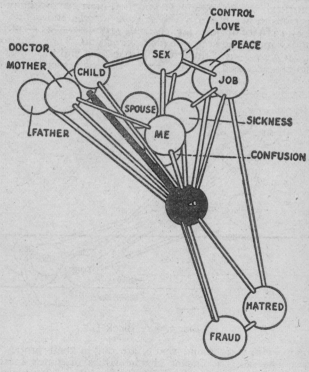

FIG. 5. Jane I

The thumbnail semantic sketches of each personality just given make it intuitively evident that the semantic differential does draw sharp distinctions between the three personalities inhabiting one nervous system. It is possible to demonstrate these distinctions quantitatively by intercorrelating D matrices between personalities and over time. If two of our models are generally similar in structure, such that large and small distances between concepts in one are reflected also in the other, then the r will be high. Table 5 gives these cor-

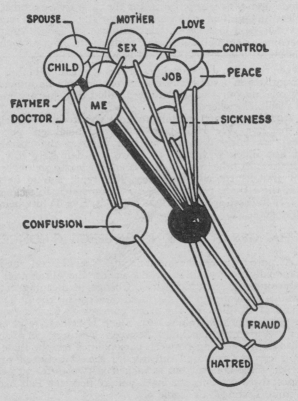

FIG. 6. Jane II

relations. The first thing to note is that the correlation of each personality with itself (e.g., testings I and II) is regularly much higher than the correlation of that personality with any other personality (with the single exception of Eve White I and Jane I). This is quantitative justification for the statement that the semantic differential does differentiate be-

251

Table 5: Correlations of D-matrices between personalities and over time

	White I	White II	Black I	Black II	Jane I	Janc II
White I	—					
White II	.73	—				
Black I	−.06	—	—			
Black II	—	−.02	.86	—		
Jane I	.73	—	−.26	—	—	
Jane II	—	.53	—	−.08	.92	—

tween the several personalities of this woman. Whether it differentiates in a valid way is a matter that can be judged only by relating our analysis to the detailed case history material available elsewhere.[3]

Another important thing to note about these correlations is that Eve White and Jane (the two "socialized" personalities) are fairly highly correlated whereas the correlations of Eve Black with the other two are definitely low, even negative. In other words, Eve Black is clearly the most deviant and disordered personality. Finally, it should be noted that these three personalities differ somewhat in their stability, as indexed by the I/II correlations, Eve White being the least stable and Jane the most.

CHANGES IN MEANING OF SPECIFIC CONCEPTS

As noted earlier, the meaning of a specific concept is operationally defined as its profile against the differential (e.g., its position in semantic space). Change in meaning between testings I and II can be measured directly by the D between I and II profiles for the same concept (e.g., between the paired columns in Tables 2-4). These D values are given under "Within Personalities, Between Testings" in Table 6. Changes in meaning between personalities for the same concepts can be measured directly by the D between profiles for the same concept but as judged in two different personalities; these D values are given under "Between Personalities, Within Testings" in Table 6.

Semantic Stability Through Time

In general, although the differences are not great, Eve Black is the least stable personality through time and Jane the most stable (cf., columns 2-4 in Table 6). The concept-by-concept data thus confirm the stability of Jane as shown in the structural data given above. For Eve White the

252

Table 6: Changes in meaning of specific concepts

Concept	Di-ii Eve White	Di-ii Eve Black	Di-ii Jane	Dw-b I	Dw-b II	Dw-j I	Dw-j II	Db-j I	Db-j II
LOVE	.42	.67	.23	1.58	1.44	.35	.57	1.62	1.81
CHILD	.71	.96	.37	1.65	1.40	.68	.54	1.47	1.41
MY DOCTOR	.15	.05	.27	.23	.23	.28	.25	.30	.12
ME	.36	.32	.42	1.21	1.40	.60	.88	.83	.77
MY JOB	.27	.62	.42	1.30	1.43	.49	.43	1.19	1.54
MENTAL SICKNESS	.45	.45	.19	1.24	1.38	.40	.32	1.30	1.47
MY MOTHER	.54	.78	.46	.71	.78	.66	.23	1.02	.68
PEACE OF MIND	.40	.35	.41	.86	.66	.21	.28	.81	.61
FRAUD	.64	.12	.40	1.46	1.35	.73	.34	1.29	1.22
MY SPOUSE	.30	.62	.47	.67	.96	.61	.89	1.04	1.75
SELF-CONTROL	.32	.25	.24	.78	.80	.34	.39	.92	1.01
HATRED	.51	.19	.44	1.54	1.31	.51	.23	1.37	1.19
MY FATHER	.53	.71	.09	1.06	.60	.25	.43	1.06	.43
CONFUSION	.64	.67	.44	.86	.96	.71	.42	.98	.88
SEX	.62	.34	.47	1.10	.62	.63	1.20	1.45	1.76

Note.—Numbers in italics indicate concepts that serve best to characterize differences between Eve White and Jane.

most unstable or labile concepts are CHILD, MY MOTHER, FRAUD, HATRED, MY FATHER, CONFUSION, and SEX. For Eve Black the most labile concepts are LOVE, CHILD, MY JOB, MY MOTHER, MY SPOUSE, MY FATHER and CONFUSION. For Jane the most unstable notions are ME, MY JOB, MY MOTHER, MY SPOUSE, HATRED, CONFUSION, and SEX. We note that the family constellation—mother, father, spouse, child—tend to be more susceptible to change through time within these personalities, but that the self concept stays relatively constant within personalities (e.g., the location of the self concept, in a sense, defines these three personalities). HATRED, SEX, and CONFUSION also seem to be points of stress.

Semantic Stability Between Personalities

The data given in columns 5-10 in Table 6 make it clear that concept meanings in general shift more between Eve

Black and the other two than between Jane and Eve White, this again substantiating the over-all correlations between total structures. The only concept that remains strictly constant in meaning through the personality changes in this woman is MY DOCTOR, although PEACE OF MIND and CONFUSION show greater stability than most others. It is interesting to note which concepts serve best to characterize the differences between Eve White and Jane (Eve Black shows gross differences on almost all concepts). These two "socialized" personalities differ from one another chiefly on ME, MY SPOUSE and SEX, and these differences are increasing in magnitude through time. This clearly suggests this woman's sexual life as a core problem, Eve White being highly critical of all three concepts and Jane accepting them as positive values. It is also interesting to note in this connection that semantic differences between Eve White and Jane on CHILD, MY MOTHER, FRAUD, HATRED, and CONFUSION are decreasing through time.

INTERPRETATIONS OF THESE SEMANTIC DATA

The analyses of these personalities and their changes given so far have been descriptive rather than interpretive for the most part. In a sense, we have merely put into words what this woman herself, in her several personalities, has indicated by her check marks. The treatment of semantic differential data, from the patterns of check marks to construction of the models shown in Fig. 1-6, is completely objective, and any investigator starting from the same data and following the rules would have to end up with the same pictures we have.

Making interpretations and predictions about this case on a "blind" basis is another matter entirely. In this section we go far beyond the objective data, and we are consequently much less confident about our statements. For one thing, neither of the writers is an experienced clinician—certainly not experienced with respect to the dynamics and characteristics of multiple personality. For another thing, we do not know at what stage in therapy our two testings were made, and interpretation would certainly vary greatly in terms of such information. It should also be pointed out that in the ordinary use of the semantic differential as a clinical tool (as compared with a blind analysis) many other sources of information would be available to support certain alternative interpretations and render other farcical. Let it be understood, then, that what follows is a flight into conjecture, in contrast with the preceding, factual reporting of semantic data.

Eve White is the woman who is simultaneously most in contact with social reality and under the greatest emotional stress. She is aware of both the demands of society and her own inadequacies in meeting them. She sees herself as a passive weakling and is also consciously aware of the discord in her sexual life, drawing increasingly sharp distinctions between LOVE as an idealized notion and SEX as a crude reality. She maintains the greatest diversity among the meanings of various concepts. She is concerned and ambivalent about her CHILD, but apparently is *not* aware of her own ambivalent attitudes toward her MOTHER—and seems to become more resistant to this by testing II. Those psychoanalytically inclined may wish to identify Eve White with dominance of the *superego*: certainly, the superego seems to view the world through the eyes of Eve White, accepting the mores or values of others (particularly her mother) but continuously criticizing and punishing herself. If this case came to the psychotherapists with a voluntary, self-initiated plea for help, then it seems likely that Eve White was dominant at the time.

Eve Black is clearly the most out of contact with social reality and simultaneously the most self-assured. To rhapsodize, Eve Black finds PEACE OF MIND through close identification with a God-like therapist (MY DOCTOR, probably a father symbol for her), accepting her HATRED and FRAUD as perfectly legitimate aspects of the God-like role. Naturally, she sees herself as a dominant, active wonderwoman and is in no way self-critical. She is probably unaware of her family situation. Those psychoanalytically inclined could say that the *id* looks out at the world through the eyes of Eve Black. Like a completely selfish infant, this personality is entirely oriented around the assumption of its own perfection. Actually, Eve Black seems to be more harmonious with the Adlerian than with the Freudian model, since personal perfection is apparently the demand acceded to rather than sexuality. If the case was committed to an institution, it seems likely that this personality was the reason for commitment.

Jane is the most puzzling of the three personalities, and our interpretation will have to depend upon assumptions about the stage of treatment (see below). Superficially, Jane is a very healthy personality: "all's well with the world, and day by day I'm getting better and better." Thus we find all the people in her life perceived as *good* and *strong* and *active* and all the socially approved modes of action perceived as *good* and *strong* and *passive*, SEX is LOVE-ly, her SPOUSE is becoming more like the noble DOCTOR all the time, and she is coming to perceive herself even, as a pleasant and reasonably active (if somewhat weak and submissive) person. But all this is a little too rosy, a little too pat. We note that Jane is becoming more and more "simple-minded"—all of her judgments tending to fall along a single factor of *good-strong* vs. *bad-weak*—which makes the Jane II model the most restricted and undiversified of all. Those psychoanalytically inclined may wish to view this personality as representing dominance of a self-deceptive *ego* which has woven a web of repression as to the state of reality; or, they may wish to view Jane as an essentially strong, healthy, and improving ego-dominated personality. In any case, we doubt if Jane would have either come for therapy or have been institutionalized—as such.

Possible Dynamisms Operating in the Case

Identification mechanisms. We say the patient "identifies" with some other person when her meaning of herself, ME, is semantically close to her meaning of the other person; e.g., if she sees her father as a kind, active, relaxed, etc. person and describes herself in the same terms, we infer identification. However, the pattern of identifications displayed by this patient seems unusual. Only in Eve Black, the obviously disoriented personality in terms of her values, is there clear differential identification—with her FATHER (and this may reflect the semantic tie-up between FATHER and MY DOCTOR). Jane shows some slight tendency toward closer identification with MOTHER, but it is not close. Eve White shows none with either parent. The fact that identification with FATHER (and MY DOCTOR) in Eve Black is accompanied by rejection of MOTHER to meaninglessness is suggestive of an underlying conflict in identifications. Note also, in this connection, that in Eve Black I the ascendancy of ME to the *good, strong, active* position is accompanied by making FATHER *weak*—as if she were taking over her father's role and putting her mother in her own previous place. And, interestingly enough, the concept SELF-CONTROL suffers the same fate as MOTHER. This picture of Eve Black is certainly suggestive of an *Electra complex* as the underlying dynamism. In "real" life, her MOTHER is or was the dominant, threatening figure—moralizing, demanding standards and SELF-CONTROL—and in Eve Black this woman escapes the pressure by rendering both MOTHER and SELF-CONTROL meaningless and simultaneously identifying with and taking her FATHER's place (via the therapist). Suggestive evidence may be found in Tables 2-4: MOTHER is consistently *colder* than FATHER and usually more *tense* and *fast* (e.g., Factor 3). Identification of the self with the therapist in Eve Black is perfect, of course. The concept

MY DOCTOR is the only personal concept to show perfect stability both between personalities and through time. The patient thus displays what might be called maximal *positive transference* in all three personalities; there is no sign of any negative transference at either testing, which may be indicative of the stage of therapy (e.g., early).

Significance of the patient's sexual life. Although Jane shows a rosy acceptance of normal sexual patterning—with LOVE and SEX linked and passively favorable, Eve White clearly displays awareness of a basic conflict in this area—SEX is early somewhat more distasteful than LOVE and becomes distinctly distasteful and dirty by testing II. In Eve White also we find ME and MY SPOUSE becoming linked with SEX in this unpleasant location. Eve Black, on the other hand, rejects both SEX and LOVE—but closely links them in her thinking. If we were to relate these facts with the Electra situation described above, the interpretation would be that her persisting conflict with her mother and attempts to identify with her father make it impossible for her to experience normal sexual satisfactions with her husband and to carry out the normal mother-wife-home role. Eve White is aware of this, in a sense, but Jane clearly is not. The concept MY JOB is interesting in this connection: its persistent linkages with LOVE, PEACE OF MIND, and SELF-CONTROL in the two "socialized" personalities, coupled with its linkage with SEX and MY SPOUSE in Eve Black, clearly suggests to us that this woman is interpreting MY JOB in the sense of "my job as a mother, wife, and homebuilder" rather than in terms of her outside work (which we understand she has). In any case, there is clear evidence of involvement with her sex life as a major problem, and this may have been the presenting problem when she began therapy.

Repression and amnesia. Knowing that we are dealing with a case of multiple personality—usually characterized by complete dissociation between states—it is interesting to speculate on what meanings are repressed in the several personalities. It will be recalled that, operationally, meaninglessness of a concept is defined by its closeness to the origin (the solid balls in the models). This is probably to be interpreted as "connotative deadness" or "damping of affect" with respect to the concept involved. Within the matrix of our instrument, however, there is another way in which repression or amnesia may show up, and that is via a complete shift in meaning of the concept being judged (e.g., CHILD may shift from the personal reference of "my own youngster" to "children-in-general"). Looking back at the semantic data with these points in mind, we hazard the following guesses: Eve White probably has the best contact with reality and may not be amnesic at all (except for the other personalities);

Eve Black may be amnesic for her mother and her own role as a mother and wife; Jane in Pollyanna fashion may be amnesic for her own problems, e.g., MENTAL SICKNESS and CONFUSION, and the indiscriminate way in which she lumps all socially favorable concepts at least suggests that she is judging CHILD, MOTHER, etc. in the abstract rather than MY CHILD, MY MOTHER, and so forth.

Interpretation I—Assumed Early Stage of Therapy

The "original" personality, in the sense of being most characteristic of the woman her friends and relations knew, was Jane. The first testing of this personality shows a relatively weak ME that is associated with MENTAL SICKNESS; i.e., she was dimly aware of her own inadequacies but was striving to maintain a rigid acceptance of the real world and maintain an adequate home life. The people about her, with the exception of her husband, were seen as strong and active (perhaps threatening) in relation to herself, and her love life was regarded as a sort of deliberate, controlled duty. She was completely unaware of her (repressed) emotional ambivalence toward her mother, husband, and child. The things being hidden in this personality, and providing the force behind the eventual split, were (a) her Electra complex, (b) her repugnance for sexual relations with her husband, and (c) her ambivalent attitude toward herself. We suspect that she had a position in society that demanded "good front."

We must assume strong and about equal pressures toward solving the Electra complex, (a) by identifying with FATHER and asserting the self (id?), and (b) toward solving it by identifying with MOTHER and devaluing herself (superego?). This produces a two-way split away from the Jane pattern, one into Eve Black where selfish needs for superiority and playing the father role are achieved and another into Eve White where societal needs for submission and playing the mother role are achieved. This split, and the subsequent availability of the other roles, allows Jane to shift toward the "sweetness and light" view of the world, and that is clearly demonstrated by the changes between Jane I and Jane II. Eve White continues to become more simply and rigidly self-critical and Eve Black continues to become more simply and rigidly self-satisfied.

Assuming successful therapy is possible—which seems questionable—it will involve less and less time being spent in being Jane and Eve Black and a consequent shift into Eve White, where better contact and differentiation seems to be maintained. But here it will be necessary to bring Eve White to understand the reason for her depression, the role of her ambivalence toward her mother in her problem—which shows no signs of happening yet—and thence a gradual restructuring in which ME becomes more favorable, along with SPOUSE and SEX, and identifications with FATHER and MOTHER are reassign ed. This will probably involve a period of negative transference, with MY DOCTOR and MOTHER becoming closely identified and being temporarily shifted to *bad*, *strong*, and *active* directions of the semantic space. In other words, successful treatment will mean increasing time spent in, and gradual restructuring of, Eve White to the point where it incorporates what is now Jane, but with a realignment of significant persons. On the other hand, if this woman is in a mental institution and remains there, it seems likely that Eve Black will become the dominant house she lives in. In either case, it is probable that Jane will appear less and less.

Interpretation II—Assumed Late Stage of Therapy

If we assume that we are seeing the terminal stages of therapy with a case of that sort, then a quite different interpretation is necessary. The difference in interpretations hinges upon Jane, either as a deceptive and vanishing original personality (interpretation I) or as an increasingly healthy and augmenting personality (interpretation II). In the latter case we would assume that Eve White had been the "original" personality as people knew her—a socially acceptable wife and mother, but one laden with conflicts, anxieties, and self-criticism. The split in this case—into one personality in which the self-criticism completely disappears via irrationality (Eve Black) and another in which self-criticism vanishes via rationality (Jane)—seems less sensible, however. Jane seems unnecessary at this stage and really should have developed out of Eve White rather than being contemporaneous. If we assume there was a split in any case, Jane is clearly the most healthy personality, since LOVE and SEX are identified, the world is viewed in acceptable fashion, and the self concept is becoming more favorable all the time. The prediction here would be increasing time spent in Jane and less in the others. The stumbling blocks in the way of this interpretation are (*a*) the lack of any realignment of the system of parental identifications, and (*b*) the fact that Jane is becoming *less* diversified semantically (more "simple-minded") rather than the reverse. This second interpretation was actually the one we first adopted—because of the superficial "healthiness" of Jane—but consideration of all the evidence seems to favor the first interpretation. However, it should be noted that *if* this case is near the end of successful therapy, Jane is the only personality that combines both a normal view of the world and reasonable (increasing) acceptance of the self.

It is possible to combine interpretations I and II by assuming that Jane is both the original personality which broke apart and the terminal personality which is being developed out of therapy. In this case, the early development of the case, probably in childhood, would be the same as that given under interpretation I—the conflicting parental identifications (id and superego determined respectively) were of about equal strength and finally became too intense to be contained within the self-deceptive personality organization of Jane. During the middle course of the case, when therapy was undertaken, we thus find all three personalities oscillating, temporary dominance of the mother and wife role being represented by Eve White, temporary dominance of the self-gratifying father role being represented by Eve Black, and temporary dominance of the face-saving, problem-saving ego being represented by Jane. Intentionally or unintentionally, the effect of therapy may be to strengthen the self-deceptive organization of Jane without resolving the underlying conflicts dramatized by Eve White and Eve Black. The over-simplified, Pollyanna-like ways of perceiving herself as *good* along with all the other significant persons in her life yields a superficially happy person who views the world in an acceptable, if rigidly stereotyped, fashion. If the present combined interpretation approximates the actual situation, then we feel compelled to predict another breakdown at some later period in this person's life. In other words, the effect of therapy (whatever type it may have been) seems to have been further to strengthen the self-deceptive original organization of Jane, while making this personality even more rigid and insensitive to subtle differences in meaning and without resolving the underlying conflicts which created the original disturbance.

What Price Therapy?

It is impossible to tell from our semantic data whether the increasing simplification in structure characteristic of all three personalities is due to therapy itself or is happening despite therapy. However, a number of specialists in psychotherapy have from time to time expressed concern over the "hidden" effects of therapy even in so-called successful cases—particularly reduction in initiative, creativeness, and flexibility of the patient. Certainly in the present case we are witnessing an over-all reduction in differentiation of meanings. If overt behavior is in considerable part determined by meanings, as we believe it is, then we must expect Jane (if she is the terminal personality) to be now even less capable of behaving differentially to her mother, father, spouse, and child—they are all essentially undifferentiated "strong-active-goodness" to her. This would also be true, but to a lesser extent, of Eve White, although here we would assume an earlier stage of therapy and hence a possibility of secondary elaboration of semantic diversity under sensitive therapy.

Is rigidity of this sort a necessary price of therapy? In striving to achieve the goals of societal acceptability and individual happiness, does the therapist have to sacrifice the richness, individuality, and subtler adjustiveness of the patient? These are serious questions raised by the data of this single case—but not answered by them, of course. From the larger sample of cases we are presently working on, better answers may be forthcoming, but the cases are generally less severe. One other interesting phenomenon in the present cases should be mentioned: Despite the gross changes in meaning of concepts in the several personalities, and the over-all reduction in diversity, the semantic judgmental frame of reference remains constant. In other words, all three of the personalities in this woman utilize semantic scales in the same ways—the correlations between scales are the same for all three personalities and reduction in diversity in all of them is accomplished by a coalescence of *good, strong,* and *active* into a single evaluative dimension. Thus it would appear that the level of scale meanings is below that at which concepts vary, and common to all three personalities.

REFERENCES

1. Osgood, C. E. The nature and measurement of meaning. *Psychol. Bull.*, 1952, 49, 192-237.
2. Osgood, C. E., & Suci, G. J. A measure of relation determined by both mean difference and profile information. *Psychol. Bull.*, 1952, 49, 251-262.
3. Thigpen, C. H., & Cleckley, H. A case of multiple personality. *J. abnorm. soc. Psychol.*, 1954, 49, 135-151.

Received December 1, 1953

APPENDIX B

PSYCHOLOGICAL
CONSULTATION REPORT*

This twenty-five-year-old married female patient was referred for psychological examination with a provisional diagnosis of dual personality. Two complete psychological examinations were requested, one of the predominant personality, Mrs. White, the other, ... of the secondary personality, Miss Black.

The patient is the oldest of three siblings, having twin sisters. She quit school two months before graduation from high school. She was employed as a telephone operator. She has been married six years and has a girl four years old. Patient states that she did things recently she cannot remember having done, and expresses serious concern about this condition. The following psychological tests were administered in both examinations:

> Wechsler-Bellevue Intelligence Scale
> Wechsler Memory Scale
> Drawings of Human Figures
> Rorschach

Test Behavior

Patient was neat, friendly, and cooperative. However, while Mrs. White was more serious, more conscientious, and displayed more anxiety, Miss Black appeared somewhat less anxious and was satisfied with giving more superficial responses. Still the basic behavior pattern was very similar in both personalities, indicating that inhibitory forces were not markedly abolished even in the role of the desired personality. Speech was coherent, and there were no distortions in ideation or behavior according to the assumed personality. No psychotic deviations could be observed at the present time.

Test Results

While Mrs. White is able to achieve an IQ of 110 on the Wechsler-Bellevue Intelligence Scale, Miss Black attains an

---

* Cited in the text of No. 14 of the Bibliography.

IQ of 104 only. There is evidence that the native intellectual endowment is well within the bright normal group; however, in Mrs. White's case anxiety and tenseness interfere, in Miss Black's superficiality and slight indifference as to achievement are responsible for the lower score. While Mrs. White shows more obsessional traits, Miss Black shows more hysterical tendencies in the records. It is interesting to note that the memory function in Miss Black is on the same level as her Intelligence Quotient, while Mrs. White's memory function is far above her IQ, although she complained of a disturbance of memory. The only difficulty encountered by both personalities is on recall of digits, a performance in which telephone operators usually excel! On the other hand, the Rorschach record of Miss Black is by far healthier than the one of Mrs. White. In Miss Black's record a hysterical tendency is predominant, while Mrs. White's record shows constriction, anxiety, and obsessive compulsive traits. Thus Miss Black is able to conform with the environment, while Mrs. White is rigid and not capable of dealing with her hostility.

Personality Dynamics

A comparison of the projective tests indicates repression in Mrs. White and regression in Miss Black. The dual personality appears to be the result of a strong desire to regress to an early period of life, namely the one before marriage. Miss Black is actually the maiden name of Mrs. White. Therefore, there are not two different personalities with completely dissimilar ideation, but rather one personality at two stages of her life. As is characteristic for this type of case, the predominant personality is amnesic for the existence, activities, or behavior of the secondary or subordinate system, while the secondary personality is aware and critical of the predominant personality's activities and attitudes. The latter reaction is quite similar to the ego-conflict in obsessive compulsive disturbances.

Mrs. White admits difficulty in her relation with her mother, and her performances on the Rorschach and drawings indicate conflict and resulting anxiety in her role as a wife and mother. Only with strong conscious effort can she compel herself to subject herself to these roles. The enforced subjection results in ever increasing hostility. This hostility, however, is not acceptable to her, and activates a defense mechanism of regression to avoid severe guilt feelings, by removing the entire conflictual situation from conscious awareness. At the same time, the new situation (in which she plays the role of Miss Black) permits her to discharge some of her hostility towards Mrs. White. Miss Black on the other hand has regained her previous status of freedom from marital and maternal conflicts, and thus has liberated herself from the insoluble situation in which Mrs. White found herself through her marriage. In addition, she can avert the—in her conviction—inevitable spiritual loss of her child. Thus, it is not surprising that she shows contempt for Mrs. White who permitted herself to become involved in such a situation because of her lack of foresight, as well as her lack of courage to forcefully solve the dilemma.

Actually the problem started at a much earlier period of life, with a strong feeling of rejection by her parents, especially after the birth of her twin sisters. Mrs. White loves them dearly, Miss Black despises them. In this connection an episode is related by Miss Black. After quitting school to help support the family, she (that is to say Mrs. White) sent home money to be used for overcoats for her twin sisters, denying herself a badly wanted wristwatch. When the money was used to buy them two wristwatches instead of overcoats, she reacted with strong, but repressed, hostility. Significantly, she removed her wristwatch while examined as Mrs. White, stating that she doesn't like jewelry. There are several illustrations of her strong sense of rejection as well as sibling rivalry in her records.

LEOPOLD WINTER, PH.D.
Clinical Psychologist
U. S. Veterans Administration Hospital
Augusta, Georgia
July 2, 1952